HEREFORDSHIRE FARMING THROUGH TIME

Wheat ears and grass wheat
by Alfred Watkins, 1930
(© Hereford Libraries)

HEREFORDSHIRE FARMING THROUGH TIME

Fellers, Tillers & Cider Makers

Katherine Lack

LOGASTON PRESS

FRONT COVER IMAGES, FROM TOP: Hay-making on the Lugg Meadows, by Alfred Watkins, early twentieth century (© Hereford Libraries); Oxen ploughing, from *The Luttrell Psalter*, *c*.1325–40 (© British Library Board, Add. 42130, f.170r); View south-west across Herefordshire from Munderfield, just south of Bromyard (© Paul Lack).

BACK COVER IMAGES, LEFT TO RIGHT: Modern Ryelands sheep, the Ryemeadows flock, Birtsmorton, Worcestershire (© Katie James); Cider press (© Paul Lack); Iron Age sickle found at Sutton Walls (Hereford Museum acc. no. 6747).

First published in 2021 by Logaston Press
The Holme, Church Road, Eardisley HR3 6NJ
www.logastonpress.co.uk
An imprint of Fircone Books Ltd.

ISBN 978-1-910839-51-5

Designed and typeset by Richard Wheeler in 11 on 15 Minion.
Cover design by Richard Wheeler.

Printed and bound in Poland.

Logaston Press is committed to a sustainable future for our business, our readers and our planet.
The book in your hands is made from paper certified by the Forest Stewardship Council.

British Library Catalogue in Publishing Data.
A CIP catalogue record for this book is available from the British Library.

CONTENTS

FOREWORD

It is a great pleasure to be asked to write a foreword to this fascinating history of farming in Herefordshire. Katherine has done a great job in drawing together the various sources, both from inside and outside the county, and combining them with a substantial body of primary research, to paint a vivid picture of an industry that dates back to prehistoric times.

My own predecessors as bishops are part of this story. In the days before easy transport, they held manors throughout the diocese, which were both places to lodge, and farmed to generate income. Records show Bishop John Scory was growing a substantial acreage of hops on his estate in 1577. At one time monastic estates were generating large incomes from their farming enterprises. Growing produce to sustain the episcopal household was common even at the Palace in Hereford: at one stage the gardens stretched to six acres, employing six gardeners. The produce would have supplied a substantial household with vegetables all year around. Bishop's Meadow, now gifted to the Council on the other side of the river, was, at one point, part of the bishop's estate. Horses and other livestock would have been grazed there. The lease was only granted to the city in the early twentieth century, perhaps following the tenure of Bishop John Percival (1895–1917), the last bishop to travel around the diocese on horseback!

But this book also has a personal resonance. On my paternal grandmother's side, I can trace relations back to the fifteenth century. Generations of Jones and Davies were resident in Leominster and surrounding villages. From the late eighteenth century back they become the Pyfinches and Rodds of Presteigne. Whilst many gravestones have been lost, you still pass the tomb of what I think is my great, great, great, great, great uncle as you walk into Presteigne churchyard.

Many of these were yeoman farmers – at least judging by the standard and expense of that particular tomb. Others may have been labourers or involved in agriculture in some different way. I consider myself fortunate to come from Herefordshire farming stock, albeit with a few generations' urban break. After reading agriculture and forestry at university, and before ordination, I worked as an agronomist in Wiltshire, advising on all aspects of arable crops. I also was fortunate enough to marry into a farming family.

The story of farming in the county is a story of change and development as human ingenuity, cultural change and the rich soils and clement weather combine. The soil takes its red colour from the sandstone rocks, which also creates a free draining, fertile loam suitable for many crops. Steep hillsides, unsustainable for arable, have provided coppice for extensive hop growing. At one stage Herefordshire had the second largest percentage of its land under hops after Kent.

The story is one of evolution and revolution. Settled agriculture took many years to develop from Stone Age hunter-gathering, helped by new advances on the Continent. Climate change plays its part. Mini Ice Ages; periods of dry and cold then wet and warm influenced the extent of cropping. The altitude at which cereals could be grown rose and fell by hundreds of feet over relatively short periods. Crops changed and evolved. Plants we now think of as garden weeds like fat-hen were once the equivalent of millet in the local diet. Wheat varieties were gradually bred to produce higher yields.

As recently as the late thirteenth century, wolves were still roaming the county. The last were hunted to extinction in 1281. The removal of such predators allowed for great changes in livestock farming. But the role of these animals also changed over the centuries. Beef cattle were originally valued for their ability to pull the plough. It was only in the eighteenth century that the world-famous Hereford breed came into being, pioneered by families like the Tomkins and Yeomans. Even now, few people overseas will know about Herefordshire, but our prize export of Hereford cattle is an agricultural icon around the world.

Sheep were originally kept primarily for milk. The development of the wool industry was kind to Herefordshire and there were fortunes to be made. Laurence de Ludlow was able to buy Stokesay Manor in 1281. A great friend of Edward I, he drowned on a business trip to Flanders. A fitting end, said some who resented his persuading the king to impose punitive taxation on the nascent industry. Dore Abbey wool was the gold standard against which others were judged. It was produced in lower quantities than some of the county's neighbours but was of much higher value. The Ryeland breed, only recently saved from extinction, was the mainstay of these high-quality fleeces exported all over Europe.

Over time the dominance of sheep farming declined, to be replaced by other crops. Ale slowly gave way to cider as the beverage of choice by the mid-1600s. So embedded in the culture did it become that John Wycliffe's Bible translation, now in the Hereford Cathedral Archive, came to be known as the Cider Bible. In this translation from the original languages, the phrase 'strong drink' is replaced with 'cider'! The tradition continues with the Bulmers and many other families today, and the county remains a centre for cider and perry production.

Agricultural production here has grown and developed over centuries, responding to the market, climate change and economic pressures. The next few years will bring unprecedented challenges to the industry. The replacement of headage and acreage payments with environmental land management schemes as Britain leaves the EU will cause a seismic shift in land use. It is likely that a number of those currently farming will leave the industry.

But history tells us that the landscape and people of Herefordshire are entrepreneurial and resilient. We do not know what the future holds, but the rich red soil of Herefordshire will continue to yield the high quality products beloved of generations, for many generations yet to come.

Richard Hereford, December 2020

ACKNOWLEDGEMENTS

Any book with a broad sweep is likely to rely on contributions from many people, and this one, perhaps, more so than most. It arose from a series of lectures exploring the history of farming, and a few people who could not attend asked for the 12 lectures to be 'written up into a book'. So far, so relatively simple. But then it expanded to look at why Herefordshire's farming has evolved so differently from that in other counties; and then it was 2020, and the rest is history.

So, here at last is an introduction to the farmers who made Herefordshire unique. That it is finished is thanks in large part to those who helped me to gather the material I needed, to set the scene here at a domestic level and to make wider comparisons elsewhere. Thanks go first to Noëlle Wilson, who patiently assisted with the copying of hundreds of probate documents, so the local could be rooted in real lives, hitherto unexplored. With another hat on, Noëlle was also the illustrator who drew the comparisons from tombs, tapestries, manuscripts and artefacts from far and wide.

Judy Stephenson and Ben Moule at the Hereford Museum and Resource Centre, Rhys Griffith and the staff of the Herefordshire Archive Service (HARC) and the team at the Museum and Archives of English Rural Life, University of Reading, all remained helpful and attentive throughout, and to all I am very grateful. Tim Hoverd at Herefordshire Archaeology, Laura Templeton at Worcestershire Archaeology, Michael Little from the National Archives, Keith Ray, Rosemary Firman at Hereford Cathedral Library, and the cathedral vergers, have all helped with their specialist knowledge and given access to specific images. Where Keith's pictures from his *Archaeology of Herefordshire* are used, they are credited in the captions as 'Ray 2015'.[1] Sally Mansell at the Hereford

Cider Museum's Archive of Pomology was most helpful, as was Matthew Pudge at The Hop Pocket, Bishops Frome; and Helen Nicholson, at Cardiff, generously shared her knowledge of the Templars.

Many others have helped with particular sections or details, including Sue Bayliss, Ian Blair, Elizabeth Cathie, Crunchie from Crunchie's Cobs, Olly Evans, Priscilla Flower-Smith, David Freke, Jude Harley, Geoff Holborow, Andrew and Myrtle Kneen, Edward Lewis of the Haven Hereford herd, Julia Llewellyn-Roberts, Nicholas Lowton, Will and Jan McMorran, Pete and Felicity Norman, Julia Owen, Tim Roberts, Esther Rudge, Christine Shaw at Butser Ancient Farm, Meg Thorpe's Lucton herd of Welsh Blacks, Susan Tyzack and John Walker.

Last but by no means least, Liz Kershaw has read most of the text, clarified it when possible and challenged the most egregious grammatical foibles; Bromyard and District Local History Society's Archives (BDLHS) have regularly come to the rescue, especially with their specialist hop collections and their excellent book *A Pocketful of Hops*;[2] and my husband Paul has combined the roles of editor, proofreader, chauffeur and photographer, as we supported our excellent local pubs for lunch when they were allowed to be open, and familiarised ourselves with new corners of this wonderful county. The picture copyrights are all his unless otherwise stated.

Kate Lack, 2021

Sadly Kate was not able to see this book through to its final publication, but she had completed the entire text before she fell ill, and she continued to debate key issues with the publishers as her health deteriorated. I am very grateful to Richard and Su Wheeler at Logaston Press for their very careful work on the manuscript: we believe that between us we have produced the book that Kate wanted, and would be proud of.

Paul Lack, 2021

WEIGHTS AND MEASURES

MODERN IMPERIAL TO METRIC

linear: 1 metre = 3' 3½" (3.281 feet).
area: 1 hectare = 2.47 acres = 10,000 m².
liquid volume: 1 litre = 1.76 pints;
8 pints = 1 gallon = 4.55 litres.

MONEY

*This was fixed nationally from the later
Anglo-Saxon period, and controlled
through royal mints.*
12 pennies (d.) = 1 shilling (s.);
20 shillings = 1 pound (£);
1 mark = 13s. 8d. = 2/3 of a pound;
½ mark = 6s. 4d.

*Many measurements varied both in time
and regionally, so what follows is only
an approximate guide. For example, the
Saxon perch (also called a* rod *or* pole*)
was 18 feet in Wessex but 15 feet in the
Midlands and east of England, before
being standardised in the Middle Ages at
16.5 feet.*

LENGTH

12 inches (") = 1 foot ('); 3 feet = 1 yard;
5½ yards = 1 perch; 40 perch = 1 furlong;
8 furlongs = 1 mile
*BUT, a perch is also a square measure,
i.e. one square perch: see below.*

AREA

1 rood = a quarter of an acre = 40 square
perches; (1 acre = 160 perches).
1 yardland = 1 virgate = approximately
30 acres; 120 acres (4 virgates) = 1 hide.
*Fields were measured in acres, roods and
perches.*

LIQUID VOLUME

*The capacity of different casks varied
through time, as well as according to what
they contained. The basic unit in England
was a tun, for wine, honey or oil.*
1 tun = 256 gallons (before the fifteenth
century; it was slightly reduced later).
1 hogshead = *c.*52 gallons (variable,
sometimes as much as 66 gallons).
1 quart = 2 pints; 4 quarts = 1 gallon.

DRY VOLUME

*Details varied according to the crop, but
also regionally. Each market had its own
standard bushel measure.*
1 bushel = *c.*8 gallons of grain;
8 bushels = 1 quarter;
1 quarter of wheat = 420 modern lb.
Bulky goods like hay varied locally, so
that one market might be dealing in
several different load sizes.

WEIGHT

Since 1340, 1 stone = 14 lb;
1 hundredweight = 8 stone, so henceforth
1 hundredweight = 112 lb.

WOOL

*King Edgar was the first to try to
standardise the wool trade, in about 970,
by fixing the price of a 26-stone sack
(equalling 2 weys) at 10s. By the fifteenth
century, a sack of wool was fixed at 364 lb.*
1 clove = 1 nail = 7 lb;
2 cloves = 1 stone;
2 stones = 1 todd;
13 stones to the wey;
26 stones to the sack;
1 sack = 52 cloves = 13 todds.

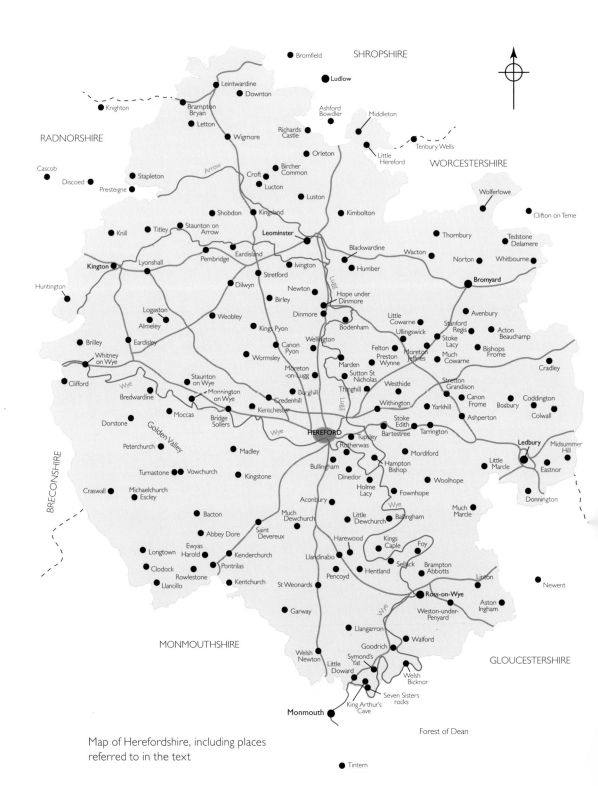

Map of Herefordshire, including places
referred to in the text

ONE

Where are we going?

THIS is a history of Herefordshire farmers. But this simple statement begs questions that need clarifying. When does the history begin? What, come to that, is a farmer, and what does farming include? And, because Herefordshire's boundaries have changed over time, what area will be covered?

HISTORY

History is assumed here to include all and any evidence for human activity shaping the landscape, whatever form that evidence takes. Written evidence, the physical evidence on and in the ground, and for the later periods the surviving built remains as well. History includes a wide range of disciplines, from place-name studies to pollen analysis, charters to crop marks.

We will, however, only look at the activities of *Homo sapiens,* true modern humans, since the last Ice Age, even though there is evidence for Neanderthal activity in this region much earlier, in the warmer periods between glaciations. Within the boundaries of Herefordshire itself, four early hand axes have been found: a flint axe from Tupsley and one from Mathon, dated to around 340,000–250,000 years ago, and two others, from Welsh Newton and Norton Canon.[1] There is also some evidence for human occupation of caves along the Wye, including both by Neanderthals and *Homo sapiens* (which were probably coexisting and merging at this time), in two warm interludes about 60,000 and 36,000 years ago.

Despite these early indications of human presence and activity across the Herefordshire area, none of these epochs yield any evidence that could be called farming. This is because in the last major flourish of the Ice Ages, about 20,000 years ago, the ice caps advanced one more time, extending down as far as Bridgnorth. For thousands of years, the Herefordshire area was uninhabitable for humans, and was on the edge of a huge ice sheet stretching north and west beyond the present shorelines of Britain. This transformed the landscape, the drainage pattern and above all the soils, which were swept away before deep new residues were deposited as the ice melted. Because of this, what went before can only be dimly surmised. Only in about 10,000 BC did the ice retreat, and with Neanderthals extinct as a discrete species, 'modern' humans could begin to use the land as we now know it.

So, this book will look at farmers in 'Herefordshire' from around 10,000 BC, with only passing glances at earlier periods.

At the other end, the survey concludes for the most part with the Victorian era, because there are already specialist books bringing at least part of the story up to date from there. Specifically, the book is mostly concerned with the years before 1871, when the railway was finally completed across north Herefordshire. This linked the county to Worcester and the east and also to the booming towns of south Wales and Merseyside, making the county, in agricultural terms, gradually less distinctive.

FARMERS

What is a farmer? Who should we include?

Is someone who has poultry and milking goats for domestic consumption a farmer? Or are they just smallholders and 'good-lifers'? How small-scale and domestic does the enterprise need to be not to constitute farming? What about growing vegetables in gardens or allotments: do crops have to be sold for the producer to count as a proper farmer, or will self-sufficiency with barter qualify? What about the recent trend towards foraging, which has evolved from the age-old practices of blackberrying, nut-collecting, even apple scrumping? Can this count as farming? And where does fishing fit in? Or culling deer and eating the resulting venison?

This is not idle speculation. As soon as we leave the safe territory of tractors, modern livestock breeds and cash crops in large fields, some boundaries need to be set. And the further back in time we go, the hazier the boundaries become, and the more vital the definitions. Should people who also earn income from a craft be included? If not, we miss out much of the rural population of the past: all those who worked their own small plots but were also the carpenters, coopers, shoemakers, blacksmiths and the others who bound together their communities.

Is there a lower size limit on the land-holding of farmers? Should we exclude all those who only cultivated their cottage garden, harvested the apples from their one small orchard, or (helped by communal grazing rights) kept a cow for milk, one sow, a few hens? If so, much of the population will be ignored, and also there is a real danger that the definition of 'farmer' will change over time, to include a different segment of the rural population in different centuries.

And what of the enterprises that can legitimately be included? What of those people who herded pigs, or drove cattle to distant markets, without owning any land of their own, or managed woodlands by coppicing for firewood, poles, acorns, beechmast or tanning bark?

Here, too, some lines have to be drawn. So, we will be looking at as many living resources of the land as possible, and as many of the people who managed them as we can. But there will be a deliberate bias towards those who leave the smallest footprints in the records. This is because much of local and social history still tends to be told through the lives of the major landowners, who have left most records and superficially had the biggest impact. But none of this would have been possible without the small farmers of both sexes, all ages and often little means who together comprise the great bulk of humanity in a given place.

This, therefore, is a book about Herefordshire farmers of many types but mainly of modest means, and their management of the land to produce goods of widely varied kinds.

HEREFORDSHIRE

How can we best define a place which has changed its boundaries over time? And how to determine what area was relevant to its farmers at different periods in its history?

The modern county, whose borders have only been modified slightly since the Middle Ages, is set between the River Teme and the Malvern Hills to the east, the Black Mountains in the south-west, and mostly lies within the Wye drainage basin. Superficially, it is a discrete area. It is almost entirely based on the Old Red Sandstone that gives the soils their distinctive colour, with the older and harder limestone of the Woolhope Dome protruding through in one small area, and more limestone in the north-west.

As far back as the evidence exists, farmers in Herefordshire have had surplus produce in some years, and have benefitted from goods from elsewhere. So, they have traded in two main directions: to the west and east by long-established roads, and north to south via the Wye and Severn routes. The story of Hereford-shire farmers, therefore, also includes their connections to markets far beyond the county, both as sellers and buyers, and their social and cultural bonds to people in these places.

The River Wye, from Kerne Bridge

This, then, is the story of a segment of our population over 12 millennia, framed and shaped by the landscape of the modern county of Herefordshire but influenced by a succession of incoming traders and settlers. The unifying thread is that these people have progressively shaped the land to provide many resources, from food to fuel, clothing and building materials, in ways that suited the needs of their time. It is a story of a continuity of needs, opportunities and experiences over the centuries, and of connectivity to apparently remote places.

TWO

Farmers or foragers: who were the earliest Herefordshire farmers?

Until recently, it was thought that farming 'arrived' with the Neolithic peoples, in about 4,000 BC. However, new research now suggests that the boundaries between Neolithic farmers and their predecessors may be less clear-cut.

It remains hard to be confident about this period, not least because Herefordshire is in a part of the British Isles with relatively little available information about early human activity. There are many reasons for this. A major factor may simply be that, although we have the Woolhope Society publications going back to 1852, for example, there is no university with a long tradition of Herefordshire research comparable to that of Oxford for the Thames Valley or Cambridge for East Anglia. Nor do we have extensive areas of peat such as are found in the south-west, the fenlands and Ireland, where structures and artefacts have lain buried and undisturbed, waiting to be rediscovered by modern archaeological techniques.

More particularly, there are three specific features of Herefordshire's location that may explain this lack of evidence. Firstly, the Welsh Marches were closer to the remnants of the last great ice cap than the rest of lowland Britain, so were less inviting to the hunter-gatherers who moved in as the climate warmed, and the region was settled later. Secondly, reconstructions of the early drainage patterns in post-glacial times show that the water from the Rhine and Thames basins flowed in a huge 'Channel River' towards the Atlantic. This must have been a barrier to movement, so post-glacial Britain is likely to have been settled initially from the east, the route that offered easiest access.

Thirdly, as the ice melted, sea levels rose and much of the evidence for early land use around the coasts and estuaries was lost. This effect was partly offset by the land rising as the pressure of the ice weighing it down was released;

Map of the British Isles c.9,000 BC, showing the area of land that once connected Great Britain to Continental Europe, and which is now submerged beneath the southern North Sea

Doggerland

since there had been more ice further north, the Scottish coasts are actually now higher relative to sea level and so they are a good source of information about early human activity. Some new finds are now being made in and near Herefordshire, but to understand how the earliest 'modern' users of the land lived we still have to draw parallels with information from elsewhere.

What was early 'Herefordshire' like?

The freezing conditions of the last phase of the Ice Ages seem to have finally ended in about 9,500 BC, as swiftly as they had begun. However, recent studies of pollens preserved in ancient soils, including at Bridge Sollers and Staunton on Arrow, show that the climate was far from constant. There were three broad climatic periods in the next 5,500 years: predominantly cold, dry and tundra-like from about 9,500–8,800 BC; milder but still relatively dry from 8,800–5,800, and then wetter from 5,800–4,000 BC. Within these periods there were some significant variations, for example from 6,200–6,000 BC there seems to have been a sudden drop in temperature of between two and five degrees centigrade. Whether of long or short duration, these changes would have forced the humans here to adapt, sometimes within a single generation. Adaptation encourages inventiveness and versatility, so the descendants of the people who did well through these centuries emerged best placed to prosper.

With more benign conditions came rapid changes in the vegetation. In most places there was a standard progression: first grasses, then shrubs and birch, with willow, aspen and alder on damper ground. Later, pine spread west and north. By 8,000 BC, hazel became common and soon after this the dominant trees were oak, elm, hazel and alder. In the upland regions to the west of Herefordshire, on the Black Mountains and beyond, tree cover was still sparse, with more juniper, birch and pine, and many of the river valley bottoms would have been marshy in places, with shallow lakes.

Birch and stunted oak on wet ground

In this new environment, the herds of reindeer which had dominated the earlier tundra and grasslands seem to have dwindled to nothing, to be replaced by red and roe deer, elk, aurochs (wild cattle), horse, boar, bear, wolf and other mammals such as wild cat, lynx and beaver. Humans, too, spread out, moving north to keep pace with the remaining reindeer or exploiting the new woodland opportunities. Soon a varied ecosystem became available, including forests, open uplands, rivers, marshes and the Severn Estuary, broadening as sea levels rose.

The people

In the closing years of the twentieth century, it was hoped that DNA studies would reveal the origins of the 'British' population which was here before the Anglo-Saxons, but this has not yet proved possible. What we do know is that of the present population, up to half have ancestors who arrived before about 4,000 BC, in the hunter-gatherer-fisher period known as the Mesolithic. So, they were not entirely swept away by later settlers.

As for the total population of the British Isles at that time, estimates vary from as few as 3,000 to over 20,000. The basic problem is that so little material has been found that gives a clear picture, and in any case this era lasted for 5,000 years and there must have been many fluctuations within it.

What we can definitely say is that the land bridge between the Low Countries and East Anglia, which gradually shrank through the Mesolithic as sea levels rose until it was finally severed in about 5,000 BC, was not the only route by which people moved into the British Isles, particularly into its western parts. Comparisons of stone tool styles (notably harpoon designs) at different times make it clear that there was considerable contact between communities along the Atlantic coast of France and that this extended up the west coast of Britain. These populations were keeping in touch and were, to some degree, in contact via the sea.

Moreover, Ireland was already cut off from mainland Britain by about 7,000 BC, when its human colonisation began. It is difficult to find much data about the earliest arrivals, because the old shore-line is now far below the Irish Sea, but the crossing here involved a significant sea voyage, even if the two shores were within sight for much of the time. This is crucial, because it means that from very early times there were boats, and navigators, which could make journeys far from land. There is no reason to suppose that this technology was lost subsequently, and indeed every reason to believe that the use of boats continued to be an important part of life for coastal- and estuary-dwellers, even though no physical remains from this early have yet been found in Britain.

As the sea level rose, coastal hills gradually became offshore islands, and the rocks of the inter-tidal zone became cut off as reefs, needing boats to access them and their valuable resources which previously could be harvested on foot. In the outer Severn Estuary, Flat Holm and Steep Holm, where Mesolithic flints have been found, as well as later remains, would have been among the first islands to become cut off.

These finds are compatible with the assumption that in the early phases of this hunter-gatherer-fisher period, before Britain became an island, long-distance migrations were already normal over both sea and land. To guide people on these journeys, navigation systems using the stars could have been a useful addition to relying on landscape features, especially once there was dense tree-cover. It is known, after all, that by about 3,000 BC knowledge of astronomy made it possible to construct megalithic monuments in many parts of the British Isles. Such knowledge would have been equally useful for coastal communities spending part of their time exploiting the sea.

As to the actual types of boats used this early, there are, not surprisingly, few surviving. Some Mesolithic log boats are however known from France, the Netherlands and Denmark, and contemporary British ones could well have been similar, requiring only fire and a stone axe or adze for their construction. The Danish examples at Tybrind Vig, for example,[1] include one boat of which a nine-metre length survives; the site is dated to 5,400–4,000 BC. Several of the Tybrind Vig boats seem to have fireplaces, so they may have been used for more than short-distance travel. Some other Continental boats have holes near the gunwales; while these may be for rowlocks, they could also have been for outriggers or to lash two or more craft together to make them more sea-worthy.

How many people lived in Herefordshire at this time?

There is no firm evidence with which to address this question, but it is possible to get an idea of how densely the landscape might have been occupied. If we use the often-quoted figure of about 25 km² per person for a migrant hunter-gatherer leaving a light trace on the land, and if we assume a population pool of 500 people to provide adequate diversity, 'marriage' partners and skills, this group (the size of a typical modern Herefordshire parish) would occupy some 13,000 km², or 114 km by 114 km – rather less if the marine environment of the Severn Estuary were also being drawn upon. This corresponds to the combined area of Herefordshire, Gloucestershire, Worcestershire, Radnorshire, Breconshire and Monmouthshire. Within this area, it is likely that the Mesolithic population was subdivided into small bands, perhaps meeting up for significant events including the migrations of salmon, eels, trout and freshwater herring at key points along the major rivers.

Map showing a possible home-territory for the Mesolithic population using 'Herefordshire'

So, rather than thinking of Herefordshire as a discrete area during this period, inhabited by a distinct group of people, it would be better to imagine these ancestral people as migrating over and making use of a swathe of dry land and seasonal marsh, on both sides of what is now the Severn Estuary and the River Wye.

Despite uncertainty over their numbers, and few definite occupation sites, we have occasional, poignant glimpses of their lives. Near Goldcliff, Monmouth-shire, over two dozen human footprints in the mud around the old marshy shore-line have been found, as well as tracks of birds and deer, and the remains of prehistoric trees. At a nearby site which may represent a temporary camp, fragments of charcoal, butchered animal bones, hazelnut shells and typically Mesolithic slim flint and chert blades were found. Precise dating of the organic materials and the peat layers which now shroud the sites fixes this activity in the period 4,940–4,000 BC.[2] A set of similar footprints, preserved in mud at Formby Point, Merseyside, has been used to suggest that the tallest of the men of these Mesolithic communities were about 1.65 metres (5'5") and the shortest adults, perhaps women, were 1.45 m. This fits well with the only near-complete skeleton yet found, that of so-called Cheddar Man (*c*.8,000 BC): he would have been about 1.66 metres tall.

Within Herefordshire itself, traces of hearths have been found at King Arthur's Cave and the Seven Sisters rocks, in the Wye gorge near Symond's Yat. As with other cave finds, this does not mean that Mesolithic people were dependent on caves for warmth and shelter, but it is here that the evidence is most likely to survive undisturbed. At Goldcliff, there are traces of at least one free-standing timber shelter, but no hearths. There are many other places where concentrations of worked flints from this period have been found: several sites just west of Bromyard, two areas north of Ledbury, in the Golden Valley, near Pembridge and west of Kington. All these show that groups of these people were using the landscape and perhaps occupying places on a regular basis, to collect plants and hunt or fish for meat.[3] They were also certainly building huts and using fire in a controlled way.

In the extreme north-west of the area within reach of our 'proto-Herefordshire' people, in the Black Mountains, there is evidence for land use of a different kind. Here, in the upper Tawe valley, there is a bog called Waun Fignen Felen, which was once a Mesolithic lake. Around its eastern shores there are large numbers of tiny flint fragments and abandoned broken projectiles, but despite very detailed surveys, no trace has been found of any shelters or hearths. All this is consistent with repeated hunting: the topography and prevailing winds mean that the flint scatters fit with approaches to the lake from a well-concealed location, downwind. Waun Fignen Felen, then, can be seen as a 'persistent place', where hunting or fishing could usually be depended on, and to which small groups made frequent but very transient visits.[4]

How did these Mesolithic people manage their landscape?

Once the land was covered with woodlands, hunting in the old ways, which worked well on grasslands, became impractical. The big herds of grazers would have split up, and individual targets were harder for their human trackers to see. A new set of weapons soon developed, many of which were made of small pieces of flint, microliths, fitted into wooden shafts. Others were heavy axes or adzes, which could have been used for digging for edible roots or perhaps ring-barking trees. There is logic in this, because ring-barking is the simplest way to kill trees, and a clearing in woodland attracts grazing animals and gives clear sight-lines, so ambushes can be set.

Three Mesolithic microliths and a micro-blade, found at Cefn Hill, Craswall. (Hereford Museum acc. no. 7172 RS Gavin Robinson Collection)

At Starr Carr in North Yorkshire, one of the best-preserved Mesolithic sites known in the British Isles, there were probably two phases of use in the 8,000s BC; shortly before both of these there is evidence for burning, presumably to clear the vegetation. The combination of ring-barking trees and clearing vegetation with fire is efficient: the resulting lush growth can greatly increase the numbers of grazing mammals drawn to the area, making hunting easier, and is also a simple means of livestock management. Wild boar would also have been attracted to these clearings, and their bones are found in many Mesolithic contexts. At one such site in the Kennet Valley, Berkshire, which is thought to have been a spring or summer camp, it has been possible to identify a large number of the bones found, and almost all were wild boar, mainly juveniles.[5] This may not appear an efficient way to obtain large quantities of meat if hunting for wild animals, but it is typical of the slaughter pattern found at later encampments when boars may have been more actively 'farmed'. For a small hunting band, of course, one piglet represents a much more manageable quantity of meat than a larger beast. Even allowing for the ferocity of adult wild boars, especially a sow with piglets, perhaps this is evidence for calculated culling, and the first stages of a gradual transition from hunting to livestock farming.

The felled or ring-barked trees were not merely a waste product of the woodland clearances. In the rare cases where sites have been preserved by water-logging, as at Starr Carr or several sites on the Danish coast, there is evidence for careful and precise timber use. At Starr Carr there was a long platform made from planks split from poplar or ash, with birch brushwood used to stabilise the lake shore, and a timber hut which was probably roofed with reeds or perhaps animal skins. At Mount Sandel, County Londonderry, there is convincing evidence for circles of stake holes cut into the rock, potentially making timber shelters about 6m across. This site dates to about 7,000 BC.[6]

Forest glades everywhere were colonised by lower-growing species, especially hazel, and hazel nut availability was probably deliberately promoted by selective removal of other species of tree. Although the evidence may well be distorted by the longevity of the shells, the nuts do have the advantage of being easy to store. Hazel seems to have remained a near-universal food source long after 'farming proper' began. It is probably no exaggeration to suggest that this Mesolithic activity was a proto-farming system, nurturing a crucial crop for the next generation, and that these hunter-fisher-gatherer communities were managing and using a high percentage of the hazel trees in their landscape.[7] Charred hazel shells are a common and clear indicator of human activity, and have been dated to as early as 7,660 BC on the Isle of Man.

As well as hazel nuts, there are many other plants which are of obvious use to people and whose pollen and other remains are found in archaeological contexts of this period. Edible plants like fat-hen, sheep's sorrel, corn spurrey, hedge mustard, blackberry, raspberry, strawberry, sloe, apple, cherry and nettle are all typical of clearings and light under-storey, with nettle famously flourishing in the nitrogen-rich soils created by human activity and waste deposition. There are also several plants of use for basket, rope- or net-making, including reeds, rushes, sedges, flax, nettles, clematis and honeysuckle, while bracken, heather and rushes are ideal for thatching, bedding or tinder. Some archaeologists now even believe that north-western European Mesolithic tools include significantly more hoeing, reaping and grinding equipment than would be expected from societies that were simply foraging for their plant foods.[8]

A different example of resource use has been proposed after a survey of the pollen-rich deposits at Oakhanger on the edge of the Weald. In addition to the expected high percentage of hazel pollen, there was also a large amount of ivy, which could have been cut while it was flowering in the late autumn, and carried to clearings to attract hungry prey. This theory fits with the tools found at the site, which bear the hallmarks of a winter camp focussed on processing meat and skins, and repairing tools.[9]

All these modifications to the natural environment, and specialised techniques to optimise its available resources, are likely to have gradually increased the number of people that could be supported on a given area of land, so that by the late Mesolithic, approaching 4,000 BC, the population may well have increased quite significantly.

USING THE COAST?

Coasts, estuaries and marshes were also probably a vital part of the food supply network. On Oronsay, the uplift of the land since the Ice Age has outstripped sea level rises by up to 30 metres, leaving valuable evidence safe above the waves.

Huge piles of shells and fish bones have produced surprisingly detailed information because some of these can be dated to specific seasons. Because of this it is possible to be confident that different camps were occupied at different seasons, either for protection from weather or to maximise access to the island's resources. The Mesolithic people of Oronsay were fishing in the shallow water, and collecting a wide variety of shellfish from or near the shore. They were also using red deer, reindeer and wild boar (all of which they may have deliberately introduced to the island), grey seal and many sea birds.[10] Much smaller shell 'middens' do survive closer to home, in Dorset, Devon and south Wales, and although they cannot match the Oronsay ones as

'Mace stone' from Dulas. It could have been used as a fishing net weight, or perhaps a thatch weight. (Hereford Museum acc. no. 7804)

a detailed source, they show that at least some of this specialist food-gathering knowledge was implemented here in the south-west.

Recent research at a series of sites on the Severn Estuary has indeed provided important hints of the value of this knowledge. At Woolaston, between Chepstow and Lydney, a few flint flakes have been found at what may have been a transient camp, and pieces of charcoal show that in the late Mesolithic there was repeated burning of the reed-swamps here. At Oldbury Flats on the eastern shore, there was also some evidence for occupation and reed burning. In both cases this was perhaps to entice prey animals onto the regrowth. At Llandevenny, on the west shore just north of Goldcliff, a combination of tools, stone waste, charcoal and pollen at a late Mesolithic occupation site indicates deliberate repeated burning of blackberry or raspberry plants after harvesting. Other seeds confirm that the site was often used from June to October, with a peak in August and September, and the charcoal spreads nearby may mean that reed beds were also being burned. These varied sites show that the estuary was probably being used in a carefully structured way, with visits to different locations through the year to optimise resource use, rather than a simple bimodal 'winter camp *versus* summer transience' pattern.[11]

FORAGERS OR FARMERS?

In summary, then, we should visualise these early inhabitants of Herefordshire as living in small groups, making deliberate use of the landscape surrounding the lower Severn and Wye, perhaps with an increasing reliance on the resources of the rivers as sea levels rose. These rivers would also have formed a major transport and communication network. Although mobile rather than settled, these groups probably had multiple known camps, which they visited more or less frequently according to need.

These people were managing and altering their environment; not merely opportunistically foraging, fishing and hunting, but shaping the land's production to increase the food, clothing, tools and shelter it could yield. In this way, we could see them as occupying the first step on a threefold ladder of intervention, changing their surroundings to a significant degree, but less than people with domesticated animals, and even less than arable farmers. One consequence of this is that they were more flexible than the farmers who came later, with far greater scope for moving on or switching to other strategies when supplies failed.

Research into the lifestyle choices of southern African Bushmen has revealed some interesting parallels here. They live in small units, but these are fluid and linked to perceptions of broad kinship in a larger unit of population, as might have been the case here when people came together to take advantage of seasonal flushes of fish, for example. Bushmen are also famous for their detailed knowledge of their environment and what it can provide. Compared with neighbouring (farming) groups, they have few possessions and are not tied to one place. Above all, this piece of research concluded that the Bushmen and their Mesolithic-like choices represent a different mode of thought, not an inherently inferior one. When given the option of adopting livestock farming, they do not always do so.[12]

This last point may be relevant to the final arrival of 'true farming' in the Marches. There is a famous mystery concerning a site in south-west Ireland, at Ferriter's Cove on the Dingle. This was a hunter-gatherer-fisher community in about 4,350 BC, largely reliant on wild boar, sea fish and limpets. But among the finds there was also a cache of domesticated cattle bones. There are three other possible examples of these caches around the Irish coast, dating to between 5,500 and 3,800 BC. Crucially, it is known that there were no wild cattle in Ireland before cows were introduced by man, so these sites demonstrate transfer of livestock or preserved meat to Ireland, *before there is evidence for 'farming' in mainland Britain*. Farming was, however, well-established in north-west France, with domestic cattle known in Brittany by 5,300–4,800 BC. Whether this early cattle trading was carried out by Bretons or Irish we do not know, although the Irish coastal communities were certainly still using maritime resources while their French farming neighbours were focusing more inland. But this surely represents contact between farming and non-farming communities for several hundred years, without the supposed advantages of the transition to farming being chosen. The presence of wild cattle in mainland Britain confuses the picture here, so we cannot be sure if comparable links existed in areas such as the Severn Estuary, but there is no inherent reason why not.[13]

THREE

The transition to full-time farming:
4,000–2,000 BC

FARMING as a way of life brings with it a whole cluster of social and cultural implications, many of which leave a significant mark on the land.

THE CONTEXT FOR CHANGE

The skills and behaviours involved in agriculture spread slowly across Europe from the Middle East over several thousand years, but when they reached the English Channel coast in about 5,000 BC, the British Isles were already cut off by rising sea levels. So, whereas the adoption of farming in mainland Europe could take place by progressive assimilation and mimicry, a more decisive step was required in order to transmit it to Britain.

It used to be assumed that this transmission would have needed large numbers of 'European farmers' with seeds and stock, to cross the Channel, probably at its narrowest point, and to invade or settle in overwhelming numbers in order to convert the British to farming's benefits. More recently, however, every part of this theory has come under scrutiny, and an alternative narrative has emerged in some quarters. In part, this is because of an increasing realisation that people in the distant past saw the world differently to the way we might assume, just as a farmer doesn't see 'grass' in a field, as a city-dweller does, but sees a crop, for grazing or hay, permanent pasture or ley. New light is also being shed by the increased accuracy of dating techniques, which have modified part of the picture.

It is almost certain that the practice of farming reached the Continental Channel coasts by degrees. There were no farmers in north-western Europe in 6,000 BC, but by 4,000 BC there were only pockets of genuine Mesolithic lifestyle left: one example seems to be the wetlands of the Rhine delta, which were perhaps more suited to maintaining the old fishing-hunting-gathering ways.[1] This relatively long transition period fits with other occasional evidence

– for example some sites in the Pyrenees and elsewhere that would be classified as Mesolithic except for scattered finds of pottery, perhaps acquired through contact with the early farming communities.

By about 4,500 BC, many southern British people (including in Herefordshire) could have heard about the changing lifestyles on the Continent, but for whatever reason it seems that they chose not to adopt them for themselves. For some 500 years (25 generations of 20 years), they would have been repeatedly making these choices, suggesting that the perceived benefits of farming were outweighed by its drawbacks, or possibly that a partial transition was underway but was so nuanced that it has left no visible trace.

Subsequently, over a further 30 generations or so, life-strategies changed significantly. People went from managing the landscape in order to maximise their use of plants and animals that had been indigenous for many centuries, to being heavily reliant on species imported from across the Channel. This transition was much quicker than the length of time it took farming to be adopted along the Continental Channel coasts, which could support the idea that, whatever the trigger for adopting farming here, the local population had already seen or understood the implications of making such changes.

Why, after resisting for 500 years, did the British population decide to adopt farming practices established on the nearby Continent? Certainly, the Severn Estuary was becoming increasingly flooded as sea levels continued to rise: by 4,000 BC the coast was approaching its modern position, making many low-lying places inaccessible. There is also evidence for an increase in the use of coastal resources where possible, and for more clearance of woodlands. These may both be signs of increasing population, which could have been a spur to adopt new food-sources.[2]

There is now evidence for a specific period of climate-stress at around this time, which could have had an even more direct impact. There were changes in rainfall, temperature, frequency of Atlantic storms, a decline in oceanic plankton and a drop in sea temperature as many more icebergs came south from the Arctic. Consequences included the death of many woodland trees over a few decades, opening up bigger clearings; rivers becoming harder to ford and changes to fish stocks; offshore islands becoming less accessible and estuaries more dangerous. All of this could have encouraged people to see that change was possible and necessary. The chalk downlands began to appear at this time, even before sheep were introduced, as trees were weakened and native grazers flourished.[3]

In Herefordshire, recent research at Wellington gravel quarry in the Lugg Valley, and also at Bromfield on the Shropshire border at the Teme-Corve confluence, has helped improve knowledge of the local environment through this time. This gives a useful impression of the way of life of those concerned, who were after all intelligent people, managing and adapting to their environment and making choices resulting in a transition to something we would classify as farming.

At Wellington, a site which was perhaps only used seasonally because it was so damp in winter, bone is poorly preserved but detailed pollen analysis has been possible. So it is known that here the woods were predominantly lime, mixed with oak, elm and hazel. In the damper valley bottom, alder were common. By about 4,500–4,000 BC, small clearings were appearing, with more elder and alder, and there is evidence that people were gathering hazelnuts; there are also some charcoal deposits. From about 3,900 BC, cereals begin to appear. In stark contrast to this early transitional phase, the period from about 3,890 to 1,920 BC showed signs of much more disturbance to the woodland. There were more low-growing trees such as hawthorn, sloe and hazel, and many more grassland species. Cereal pollen increased, and was almost continuously present from 2,000 BC. Alongside this environmental information, a group of shallow pits was discovered, containing almost 1,000 small sherds of pottery from 26 different vessels, dating to 4,000–3,000 BC. Both pottery-making and flint-working was probably happening on-site, suggesting a settlement which was in regular if not continuous use.[4]

Pieces from three Early Neolithic pots, c.3,500 BC, from Wellington Quarry.
(© Worcestershire County Council; Ray 2015, fig. 2.7)

How did the transition happen?

It is quite possible that crops and stock for farming arrived in many different ways, places and times, rather than only from the south-east or south, as was once thought. This fits with the idea of contact being maintained across the Channel, and blurs the distinction between the 'invading' Continental farmers and non-farming natives. As well as the caches of cattle bones at Ferriter's Cove and other Irish locations mentioned in Chapter 2, scatterings of pottery in Pembrokeshire, Anglesey, the Lleyn Peninsula and south-west Scotland dated to 4,300–4,000 BC represent other early examples of possible Irish Sea connections with Continental farmers and their culture.

On the other side of Britain, meanwhile, a type of pottery which is found widely in the lower Rhinelands also appears on many sites along the east coast and in the north (this pottery is rarer in the south-west). Wide-ranging trade routes associated with this kind of pottery have been traced, and the communities involved are known to have kept cattle and sheep (or perhaps goats), and to have grown wheat, barley, flax and field beans, all of which were non-British species.

There are also strong parallels between the early tomb styles of south-west Britain and north-western France. A typical example is the Broadsands passage tomb near Paignton, where the burial dates to 3,845–3,726 BC. There are similar tombs, with distinctive pottery linking them to each other, along the south-west coast and up the Severn Valley, where the earliest monuments on the Cotswold scarp date to the same period.[5] Here we have a possible route by which farming reached Herefordshire, and studies of ancient DNA may soon be able to supply more detail.

Whoever the people were who brought the earliest examples of domesticated animals and crops to our shores, it is not hard to see how word would have spread. The local population was inherently mobile and travelling over significant distances. 'Herefordshire' people must still have been using the lower reaches of the Severn for food and trade, so they would soon have come into contact with the new farming methods and spread knowledge of them to groups further inland. Polished stone axes, dating to this early farming period and made from Scandinavian, Cornish and Lake District stone, have been found in Herefordshire, pointing to some very long-distance communication routes.

The most tangible change that now marks this transition is the adoption of pottery. It was virtually unknown in pre-farming cultures but then became quite common, perhaps universal, over relatively few decades. Pottery survives

Stone axe head made from Langdale stone, Lake District, found near Symond's Yat. (Hereford Museum acc. no. 1982-37-15)

better than evidence for arable farming, and so it is a clear cultural marker; even demonstrating that animal bones are domesticated can be complex. Using and making pottery is more suited to a sedentary way of life, perhaps particularly linked to cereal growing or dairying. Indeed, in the absence of metal it is hard to imagine how dairying would be possible without pottery. It has been suggested that pottery making may have been one of the most potent or magical aspects of the package of cultural changes that went with the transition. As such, it may be that those people – men or women – with the skills to make pottery, even if it was only fired at low temperatures, could have been major players in the process, with a status akin to the metal workers of later eras.[6]

EARLY LIVESTOCK

It seems plausible that the transition from hunting and fishing to livestock farming came before the adoption of arable. As we have seen, many prehistorians now believe that far from being opportunists, Mesolithic people managed their landscape carefully: maintaining glades, selectively killing particular age-groups of prey, using dogs, maybe beginning the process of taming animals such as deer. So, having domesticated animals was not such a foreign concept. Also, wild plants including hazel nuts continued to form a significant part of the diet for a long time after dairy lipids begin to be found on early pottery, and after livestock dung beetles and the bones of domestic animals are found associated with human activity.[7]

It is not difficult to see why domestic animals would appeal to people: if a pig was introduced that was less aggressive than wild boar, it would be welcomed. Even more welcome would be sheep and goats, which had no native parallels but which are more readily controlled than pigs, far less violent and content to graze grass and small saplings and so keep glades open. The other introduction, cattle, would have been a revelation. Whereas the huge native wild aurochs could not be tamed (according to Caesar) even if captured as young calves,[8] the much smaller domestic imports were relatively tractable and, crucially, could be herded.

These early British cattle were once thought to have been bred from aurochs, but recent DNA studies on ancient cattle remains suggest that they were essentially domesticated in Anatolia (Turkey) and the Near East, before spreading gradually across Europe, reaching the Low Countries in about 5,300 BC and Brittany a little later, before eventually arriving in the British Isles.[9] Sheep and goats were imported, while early pigs may have been hybrids between Continental ones and native wild boar. Some light is shed on early attitudes to these livestock through a comparison of their body sizes: while sheep become larger, both cattle and pigs tend to become smaller with time, suggesting that they were being protected from breeding with the larger wild cattle and boars. This probably means that from the start there was careful corralling, penning and herding. Wolves and bears would also have been a considerable threat to livestock. Wild bears only became extinct after the Roman Conquest, while the last wolves in Herefordshire were not exterminated until a campaign against them in 1281, on the orders of Edward I. Interestingly, there is evidence for foxes being seen as a pest, with skeletons periodically being excavated from rubbish pits.

Sheep at Flag Fen, Cambridgeshire, showing the probable build and size of Neolithic stock

A major problem with understanding how early farming communities managed their livestock, and the proportions of each type of animal that were kept, is that much of the evidence still comes from large ceremonial sites. Here, meals would be more likely to take the form of communal feasts, whereas at domestic settlements, of which few have yet been discovered and even fewer studied, smaller meals would have been the norm. At a time when the technology for salting surplus meat was almost certainly unknown, this skews the results found. It makes sense that a preponderance of cattle bones is often found at major sites, while sheep and goat bones, coming from animals with a carcass weight a fraction of a typical prehistoric cow, are usually more common in smaller settings. Pigs are different again, of course. Not only do they have a different diet but they are far less amenable to being herded any distance. Not surprisingly, they seldom feature strongly at ceremonial sites, and when they do, it seems likely that most were local pigs moved a minimum distance. Just as we do today, we could imagine a hierarchy for consuming different types of early livestock, developed from the culinary practices of pre-farming communities: an immature pig, one of many produced by the sow each year, would provide a normal household meal, and many piglets do seem to have been eaten. A sheep, with a mature carcass weight of some 30 kg, represents a meal for an extended family (and at some sites sheep were also slaughtered when immature). A pig, weighing four times as much, would be reserved for a bigger celebration, perhaps after a communal sowing or harvest; but a cow three times larger again could have been driven to a regional ceremonial location for what would amount to a festival.[10]

There is an exceptional site in south Gloucestershire, on the inter-tidal peat and mud flats of the Severn Estuary at Oldbury. Here, cattle and human footprint trails, together with cattle bones, charcoal and worked stones, show conclusively that people were grazing cattle on these saltmarshes between 3,100 and 2,150 BC. No nearby settlements have yet been found, but we can now say with confidence that, by this date, cattle were being farmed here.[11]

Meanwhile, the use of wild animals seems to have reduced rapidly once domesticated animals were established. With the exception of deer and some fur animals, meat eating seems to have switched to favour domestic livestock, which by 2,000 BC typically comprise 90% of bones found. Wild prey may have been seen as a reserve 'hunger food', or hunting might already have begun to emerge as a status symbol. Coastal resources, too, were used less, although whether this was a positive choice or simply because farming as an activity allowed fewer opportunities to go fishing, we can only guess.

Although there is some evidence that, in northern Europe, livestock farming developed before arable, the rate and extent of woodland clearance eventually accelerated. This was presumably for grazing and to make built monuments more visible (*see below*), as well as for crops. Overall, though, it is likely that while livestock farming changed the landscape more than hunter-gathering had done, arable farming had even more effect. Exactly when this next development occurred here is unknown, because so few sites in the western West Midlands have been dated. There is little sign of widespread woodland clearance, and associated alluvial accumulation on river valley bottoms, until well after 2,000 BC. Until about 1,500 BC, even, the landscape may have remained quite heavily-wooded.[12]

Most of the new food plants were newly-imported cereals, requiring a wide range of skills to be learnt: everything from how to prepare the ground, which soils best suited the different crops, how and when to harvest and store them and how the grain could be processed. All this knowledge had to be acquired, mastered and passed on. There is no reason to doubt that local people were making their own choices, according to both preference and environment. Such evidence as there is strongly suggests that early farming developed in very different ways at different locations. Herefordshire does not, for example, seem to have developed extensive areas of grassland typical of the drier Wiltshire chalklands by 3,000 BC. Instead, the timing of build-up of alluvial deposits suggests it maintained a patchwork of woodland, perhaps linked to pig farming.

Emmer: a long-awned wheat with strong husks around the grains. One of the first cereals to be domesticated in the Middle East (© Peter J. Reynolds, Butser Ancient Farm)

Emmer wheat is the only cereal which was positively identified at the Wellington excavations. This prospers in heavy soils so would be well-suited to most of Herefordshire, particularly in areas already covered with significant layers of rich, red soil. Among the other crops known elsewhere in southern Britain, barley prefers deep loams and is sensitive to acidity but is more tolerant of frosts and damp than emmer. On the Continent, pulses and rye are widely found, but they are rare or absent at most early British sites, although quite common in a few. In general, rye and oats might have begun as weeds, and been accepted as useable so allowed to remain.[13] Poppy and flax are also found on a few early sites, but are by no means universal.

An early, probably Neolithic or Bronze Age, field clearance cairn at Woodbury Hill, Dorstone. Other stones in this picture formed a field-dividing lynchet, visible as a break of slope behind the excavators and in situ, newly exposed in the further part of the trench. (Photograph Tim Hoverd © Herefordshire Archaeology/ Herefordshire Council; Ray 2015, fig. 3.26)

SOCIAL CHANGES

Beginning to grow arable crops in any quantity brings profound societal changes. Cereals are highly calorific, but the price is that a significant percentage of the population must become sedentary, in order to cultivate the ground, to weed, control pests before and after harvest, and prepare the stored grain for eating.

This increases the number of semi-permanent settlements in a landscape and may also change the length of time for which they are used, as this is now determined by how long the soil maintains its fertility. It will also tend to alter the way in which the old 'persistent places' are used. This has been well-described as 'tethered mobility'. A gradual transition from a more mobile life to an increasingly rooted population as arable farming began to dominate over a few hundred years, seems to be a plausible way in which this transformation could have taken place.[14] Associated with this is an altering perception of land-ownership, which may have been linked to the construction of clearly-visible monuments and tombs (of which the distinctive 'Cotswold-Severn' examples in Herefordshire, for example, date to the period 4,000–3,200 BC) as ways of declaring a stake in the land, or perhaps a bond with it.[15]

Traces of a Neolithic fire at Wellington: the ultimate evidence for occupation of the land, however transitory (© Worcestershire County Council; Ray 2015, fig. 0.3)

There is a further aspect of these shifting cultural practices. At the same time as the innovations of farming changed the norms of life for the earliest farmers, so also the land was progressively changed and shaped by the many new needs of farming. This would in turn have made the old hunter-gatherer way of life harder to sustain, until over the centuries it gave way altogether.

Wherever both crops and livestock were raised, some sort of fences or corralling would have been needed. One possible Herefordshire example is near Leen Farm, Pembridge, where a near-circular stockade of posts and wattle fencing has been dated to about 2,800 to 2,500 BC.[16] The earliest known farming infrastructure in the British Isles are the Ceide Fields in Co Mayo, where stone wall systems buried under blanket peat have been dated to before 3,500 BC. In Herefordshire, however, where stone is relatively scarce, it is more likely that hazel hurdles or willow fences were used, as at Leen Farm. Where residues on pottery have been analysed, the presence of milk lipids has on several occasions confirmed there was some dairying practised from the early decades of pastoralism. This would of course have required close control of the milking flocks or herds, perhaps using crush systems and paddocks as well as pens.

Pieces of a tub-shaped Late Neolithic pot, found at Rotherwas (© Worcestershire County Council; Ray 2015, fig. 2.18)

Similarly, if a community were managing significant numbers of livestock, access to water would become more of a priority. Encouraging deer to gather at natural watering places is rather different from controlling safe access to stream or river frontages. These places might easily become cherished resources.

New sites

In some parts of southern Britain, circular monuments and traces of individual or grouped houses and some large rectangular wooden 'halls' have been found, which date from the time of the beginning of farming. On the whole, the West Midlands and particularly Herefordshire have few such remains. This is perhaps largely because the soils do not lend themselves to aerial photographic surveying, so detection rates are lower than on drier ground, such as the chalklands. As yet, the only two significant large-scale Herefordshire sites known from this period are at Dorstone Hill, where ongoing work is revealing the context of three massive 'longhouses' or 'halls', and at Hill Croft Field, Bodenham, where in the last decade an approximately circular ditch and bank structure has been dated to between 3,650 and 3,450 BC from fragments of charcoal found together with some human and cattle bone.

But if direct large-scale evidence for early farming is scarce in Herefordshire, it is more readily found in the characteristic worked flints of this period, which are widely scattered throughout the county. Almost any field walk or dig has a good chance of turning some up. In the past, these have been particularly frequently recovered in the Bromyard area and the Golden Valley, but recent investigations near Rotherwas, at Wellington Quarry and elsewhere, demonstrate that many more await discovery. These flints may prove to be the most significant evidence for farmers in these early centuries, pointing to a growing population adopting new methods to increase their food supply.

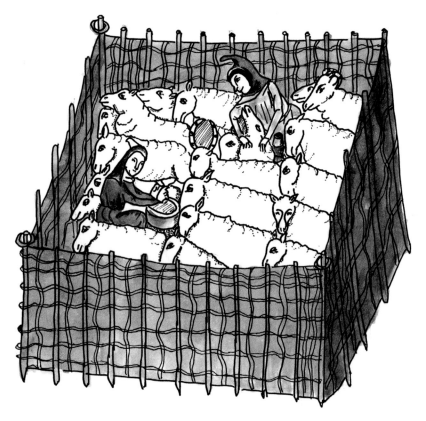

Milking sheep in hurdle pen; based on an illustration in the Luttrell Psalter, c.1325–1340, but an age-old technique (British Library Add MS 42130 fol. 163v)

FOUR

Farmers in roundhouses:
The Bronze and Iron Ages

B Y about 3,000 BC, there were some regional differences in British agriculture. Parts of East Anglia were flooding as sea levels rose; many areas of the
wide central chalklands were largely cleared of woods and being heavily grazed;
the Severn and Wye valleys were less open than the chalklands, and herds of
pigs were kept in the remaining woodlands everywhere. But the idea that most
of the population was concentrated in the south and east is almost certainly an
illusion due to incomplete modern knowledge. For example, hardly any early
sites were known near Peterborough until work began on the New Town in the
1970s; now it boasts more and better examples than many other districts.

Fast-forward a thousand years to 2,000 BC and the picture is much clearer.
There are three major reasons for this. Firstly, after nearly two millennia of
farming, populations had probably risen, resulting in more people leaving their
mark on the land. Secondly, these people were living in recognisable settlements,
which can increasingly be identified from the air, even in Herefordshire where
they are often now buried deep beneath heavy soils. And thirdly, metals began
to be used after about 2,500 BC, for tools as well as weapons and ornaments.
With modern detection methods metal is far easier to find than flints, stones
and antlers.

Of course, the great majority of people at this time were farmers, and most
buildings related to farming

SETTLEMENTS AND FIELDS
Farming in the southern Marches seems to have been livestock-focussed until
about 1,500 BC. The population could thus have maintained some of their
ancestral mobility, with only a minority needing to live permanently at the
sites where cereals were grown. This could help to explain the relative scarcity

of early monuments – of the henges and barrows that are so characteristic of regions further east, where people may have been more rooted to their immediate landscape. But there is nevertheless evidence for some arable farming here. In places, there was significant soil erosion and alluvial deposition in the valleys, consonant with woodland clearance and bare soil. Rather than see this preference for livestock rearing as evidence for a primitive society, we could view it as a positive choice, so that the Herefordshire region at this time might have looked rather as it does now, with mixed 'wood-pasture' but less arable.[1]

Then, around 1,500 BC the archaeological evidence suggests there was probably a further significant rise in population, associated perhaps with a switch to a more settled way of life. Farmers began to build more robust and longer-lasting houses (usually round, but occasionally rectangular), which were initially unenclosed but later sited within soil banks. Some of these houses were isolated, standing alone in their farmland, while others seem to have been clustered together like hamlets. It is not possible to put any actual numbers on the population, but enough burials, jewellery, tools and weapons survive to give a picture of the lives of these people. Most of the roundhouses found in Herefordshire so far seem to be isolated, but it may just be a matter of time before more are found here in groups. In East Anglia and parts of southern Britain, many such clusters have been found, typically numbering from two to five but sometimes more. At Rotherwas an eight-post roundhouse with a classic small porch facing south was excavated in 2007; close by, a field project in 2013 found what seems to be a series of other houses, similarly dated to 1,500–900 BC; and near them runs the much older cobbled track known as the 'Rotherwas Ribbon'. These discoveries may represent the first example of a significant Herefordshire settlement of this date.[2]

After 500 BC, there are many more settlement sites. On the border with Gloucestershire, for example, at Great Heath in Donnington, there is evidence for what might be a group of roundhouses, between seven and nine metres in diameter, associated with a system of enclosures or fields. In all, there could potentially be over 370 sites now known within the county. It is impossible as yet to translate this into any population estimate, since few have been excavated and most are only known from aerial surveying of their filled-in ditches. Also, of those which have been excavated, some were only occupied relatively briefly; for example one on Garway Hill seems to have been in use from about 150 BC for a period of 200 years.

The post-holes of a Middle Bronze Age house, c.1,500 BC, at Rotherwas; the porch is facing south, towards the camera (© Worcestershire County Council; Ray 2015, fig. 3.28)

Coinciding with the earliest roundhouses, the landscape began to be divided up into what seem to be fields and trackways. This process appears to have taken place across much of southern England in the same period, lasting some 500 to 1,000 years. Until a decade ago, it was thought that these field systems were largely restricted to the south and east, but now they have begun to be found in Herefordshire too. The number of tracks, watering places and major boundaries involved shows they were often associated with livestock management. Most of the systems are roughly rectilinear, and the largest can cover many hundreds or even thousands of acres, with huge numbers of individual fields, suggesting both a large population and also social cohesion. Apart from the ditched drove-ways which seem designed to allow movement through this landscape, the majority of the enclosures have large areas all on the same basic axis, with transverse subdivisions. Where stone is freely available in the landscape, it is frequently used to divide off the main fields; otherwise ditches and banks were used.

There seems to have been significant regional variation and specialisation. In the Thames estuary and the London Basin, for example, many drove-ways and holding pens have been identified, especially along rivers and at confluences.

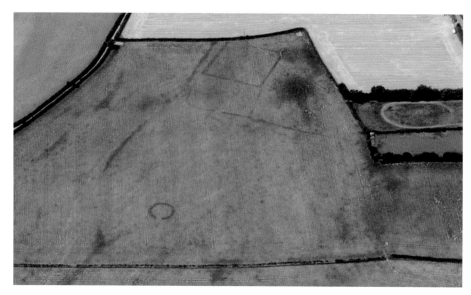

A probable Iron Age landscape at Stapleton on Lugg, paralleling some of the later features.
The rectangular enclosures are thought to be a farmstead and fields or paddocks, with a
trackway to the left; the dark circular area in the foreground is probably earlier,
with ceremonial significance. (Herefordshire Aerial Archaeological Survey
© Historic England/Herefordshire Council [06-CN-2525]; Ray 2015, fig. 4.2)

Dorchester-on-Thames by contrast has lots of field systems, perhaps implying
this area was being intensively farmed. The High Cotswolds, on the other hand,
have so far produced little comparable evidence. In the Severn Valley just downstream from the Malvern Hills, however, there is an area of very dense finds.
Field systems and trackways dated to about 1,400 BC onwards stretch from
Bredon and Tewkesbury along the Avon into the Vale of Evesham, associated
with burials, ditches, rectilinear enclosures and evidence for contemporary
forest clearance. At Huntsman's Quarry, Kemerton, evidence for a field system
of at least 17 acres was uncovered, with extensive domestic settlement.[3]

Close inspection of patterns of field boundaries in Herefordshire suggest that
here, too, there was some cohesive landscape design from soon after 1,000 BC
if not before. Most obviously, perhaps, the Roman road through Stretford and
Birley cuts across the predominant trend of the surviving old fields, indicating
that the road is likely to post-date the fields. In some places, the antiquity of the
field systems can be pushed back still further: the Iron Age hilltop site of Wall
Hills, Thornbury, seems to disrupt the pattern, so the fields may predate that,
too. Other examples of these prehistoric field systems have been recognised

in the Lugg Valley near Stapleton, where aerial photography has revealed a trackway running for over a mile beside a set of small fields or enclosures, and excavation has found a characteristically Iron Age V-shaped ditch around one square enclosure.[4] Further examples exist at Bircher Common; near Pembridge; and south of Ledbury in the Leadon valley. Thus, although there are as yet hardly any securely dated field boundaries in Herefordshire, and nothing on the scale or complexity of the Kemerton site, we do now have enough evidence to suggest that here, too, there was a phase of major landscape reorganisation and rationalisation between about 1,500 and 500 BC.[5]

WHAT CAUSED THIS INTENSIFICATION OF LAND USE?

Although these changes took place quite slowly in human terms (over some 20 generations), they nevertheless represent a dramatic alteration in agricultural practice and the appearance of the landscape. After a gradual adoption of the key elements of farming over about 2,500 years, it is as if the population suddenly boomed and pressure on the available land intensified over the next four or five hundred years.

A major factor, if not the single cause of this, seems to be the climate. After a long phase of relatively warm and dry weather, it gradually became cooler and wetter. The temperature probably only fell by between 1 and 2°C on average, but this was enough to have big effects. The maximum altitude at which cereals could be grown was reduced by about 100 metres, as the growing and ripening season shrank by up to five weeks. This would have thinned out the population living in upland areas including the Brecon Beacons, putting increased pressure on lower-lying land. At the same time, the lowest-lying areas became more water-logged: dating evidence from ever-higher wooden trackways built over parts of the Somerset Levels confirms that ground-water levels were rising there between 1,000 and 500 BC.

With more people dependent on the lower-lying and well-drained areas, there would therefore have been a knock-on effect, limiting the viability of the remaining semi-nomadic livestock farmers and pushing them towards a settled style of agriculture, which would in turn increase the pressure on the land still further.[6]

Copper working was known in Western Europe from the late fourth millennium BC. Ötzi, the man found mummified in the alpine ice in 1991, has been dated to between 3,400 and 3,100 BC. Ötzi was carrying a copper axe, although his knife was made from flint. Copper reserves in Brittany were exploited at this time, and then, in about 2,500 BC, immigrant miners appear to have set up a camp on Ross Island in County Kerry, bringing with them their own distinctive style of pottery. Shafts and galleries up to 18 metres deep were dug to extract the rich ores, which were smelted on site. Because the Ross Island copper had a very high arsenic content, the trade routes can be traced all over Ireland and on to mainland Britain: 80% of early copper goods found in Britain came from this one source. Ross Island's mines ceased production abruptly after about 500 years, when they were flooded. By this time the technology had spread and other copper – in County Cork, in Anglesey, Aberystwyth, the Great Orme (Llandudno), Alderley Edge and elsewhere – was being used.[7]

The most famous British Copper Age graves are those of the so-called Amesbury Archer and the Boscombe Bowmen, near Stonehenge, which was still being built when they were interred between 2,500 and 2,290 BC. The Archer's grave goods include a copper dagger and two copper knives which, intriguingly, are very unlikely to be made from British copper (the ore was probably mined in Iberia or western France). In fact, research on the skeletal remains suggests that most of the men buried in these graves had themselves made journeys to or from Continental Europe. So, these may have been among the first people to bring knowledge of metals to southern Britain.[8]

In 1996, a less well-known Copper Age burial was found at Wellington, central Herefordshire. This has been dated to 2,500–2,050 BC (most likely about 2,450 BC), and like the Amesbury Archer it included among the grave goods a set of characteristic flint arrow heads, a stone wrist guard (probably made from West Country slate) and fragments of a small copper knife blade about 10.5 cm (4") long. In view of the known mainland copper sources that were then in use, it may be that Herefordshire was on one of the major routes through which copper was being carried to customers in the south of England.[9]

Soon after copper began to be used, someone discovered that if a small quantity of tin was added to the copper at a higher temperature, it produced bronze, which was much harder and better for both tools and weapons. It is possible that as the naturally harder Ross Island arsenical copper became depleted, British and Irish smiths began to look for ways to harden the other ores they were having to use. With huge reserves of tin in Cornwall and also Brittany, it is plausible that the transition from copper to bronze may have been completed in the British Isles and northern France first, with the relatively tin-poor Aegean and Anatolia (once thought to be the seat of the Bronze Age) lagging behind.[10]

Thus, in the space of about 300 years, Herefordshire farmers went from a complete dependence on natural materials – stone, flint, wood, antlers – for their tools, via the first sight of copper knives, of limited use for many practical purposes, to the arrival and proliferation of much harder bronze axes, spears and knives, all of which could be repaired, sharpened and reshaped repeatedly.

The final phase of the adoption of metals did not take place until about 700 BC, when the weather had become colder, wetter and less reliable. A resulting demand for better tools may have been a factor in the eventual transfer to iron, since the ore is both widely available (locally it is readily accessible in the Forest of Dean) and the skills and temperatures needed to extract and work the metal were not vastly more challenging than for bronze. The earliest evidence in the Forest of Dean, from about 500 BC, suggests that ore and charcoal were initially burned in a shallow pit to produce an iron-rich bloom; however, within three centuries increasingly sophisticated kilns were used, controlling the amount of oxygen reaching the iron and so improving the quality of the metal produced. The resulting iron tools were significantly harder and more versatile than bronze. In particular the new iron-tipped wooden ploughs or *ards* meant that it became possible to exploit heavier soils. This may in turn have enabled population levels to rise still further, as is implied by the many farmsteads which have been dated to shortly after 200 BC. Meanwhile, of course, the old traditions lived on. Old-style flint blades continued to be widely used, and many examples have been found on the Iron Age sites at Croft Ambrey and Midsummer Hill. Recent experiments have shown that they were as good as the contemporary iron blades for most butchery tasks.

FARM ENTERPRISES: LIVESTOCK AND WATER SUPPLIES

A characteristic feature of the Bronze Age is the large number of ponds and wells that were dug. In Herefordshire, the artificial ponds that have been identified are often called 'pool', which may be a British name indicating their antiquity, or may in some cases link them to Welsh-speaking drovers who used them much more recently (from the Welsh *pwll*). Some watering holes were shallow scoops, others were deeper, but all needed safe and easy access for animals large and small. On light soils with fluctuating water tables, more complex designs were used, for instance at Chigborough Farm near the Blackwater estuary, Essex, a watering hole on a sandy site had steps cut into the sides to access water in dry weather.[11] Few examples as obvious as this have yet been found in Herefordshire, but at Moreton-on-Lugg, a water hole with partially-collapsed waterlogged timbers of what may have been a retaining wall was found, and among the fill were sherds of mid to late Bronze Age urns, showing that the timbers predate 1,200 BC. An adjacent area paved with burnt stones may have been an access path.[12] Bronze Age people often deposited valuable items in water, some in what were perhaps natural marshes, but often in the vicinity of pools. Examples include a former pool near Urishay Common, Vowchurch, and at Admarsh Meadow, Eardisland, where a filled-in depression had a short bronze sword buried in it.

The Bronze Age Belle Tout Shaft, Sussex: left, in section soon after the cliff-fall; right, close-up of the shaft, showing footholds. (© David Freke, 1976)

In some parts of the country, it seems that when a water source went out of use, perhaps when a settlement was abandoned, there was a formal 'decommissioning'. Bronze objects or occasionally whole cattle carcasses might be buried near the water, and also near or in houses. The precise meaning may be obscure, but it is not surprising that a water-source was so valued in the eyes of a farming community.

One thing that has not yet been discovered in Herefordshire is an early well, even though they were developed in England soon after 2,000 BC. It may, however, just be a matter of time, since the most spectacular one yet found, at the Birling Gap in Sussex, was thought for a long time to be just another shallow pit in the middle of a Bronze Age enclosure, originally built several miles from the coast. It was only when a section of the chalk cliffs collapsed in 1976 that the whole 40-metre shaft was exposed. On the freely-draining chalklands, where many streams only flow in winter, such extreme measures would be vital, but here in Herefordshire few farms would have been far from a natural source of water, so there are perhaps few prehistoric wells of any great depth.

ANIMALS AND THEIR USES: THE GREAT SHEEP AGE

The sizes of prehistoric livestock are notoriously difficult to estimate, but on the whole the cattle and sheep were small (half the size of most modern breeds, the sheep being the size and build of Soays). The pigs were relatively large, nearly as big as a Berkshire but similar in conformation to a wild boar. This fits with the theory that only the pigs are likely to have inherited genes from the wild British species, while the sheep and cattle stock were brought here from the Continent.

Feral Soay sheep, on St Kilda

As noted before, a practical consequence of this is that a succession of sheep could be slaughtered as needed, providing the same total amount of meat as one cow, steer or pig. These larger carcasses would be inconveniently big except for major communal feasts. Until salting technology was mastered in about 800 BC, this could have contributed to the apparent popularity of sheep, as suggested by factors as diverse as bone residues and the smaller size of cooking pots and cauldrons which seem to have been used. Survival of animal bones from different places hints that there may have been some regional variation, with more sheep on downlands, and cattle in the north and in the upper Thames Valley, but in practice local variations are likely to have been more significant. Cattle and perhaps also occasionally horses might have been used for traction, including ploughing, although firm evidence is scarce, and where woodlands remained it would make sense to keep pigs, hence their localised abundance, but apart from these this era seems to have been the 'Sheep Age'.[13]

Another advantage of sheep was that their manure was a valuable fertilizer for the newly-enclosed fields. There is now clear microbial evidence for this. Neither cattle nor pigs are equally suited to this role. As soon as farming settlements became more permanent, it would become apparent that a steady supply of manure was needed. A simple system of folding sheep on fields overnight and moving them back onto pasture by day would have served this purpose well, and there is correspondingly plenty of evidence for the use of dogs, both in the occasional skeletons about the size of modern collies, but also many characteristically gnawed bones of other species which have been found in domestic environments.

If meat and manure were the only products from sheep, it would be logical to keep most animals to an optimum size while taking account of fodder supplies: most would be slaughtered at some stage during their second summer. In fact, there is clear evidence that by about 2,000 BC, sheep farmers were already following specialised strategies and looking beyond meat and manure.

A study of the age at slaughter of sheep from nine sites from the East Anglian Breckland to Somerset, showed that in some flocks, especially on downland, animals were being kept to three or four years, even though carcass size had ceased to increase with additional age. Occasionally, the bone conformations suggest that wethers (castrated rams) were being kept as well as ewes. Together, this indicates a concentration on wool production, which is supported by an often-dramatic increase in the number and size of both loom-weights and spindle-whorls. At Huntsman's Quarry, Kemerton, for example, the cluster of

Bronze Age farmsteads that have been excavated have produced over 30 loom-weights. Many were complete or nearly so, and they were a variety of shapes from pyramids to doughnut-shaped, which is thought to relate to their date or the fabric-types being produced. No spindle-whorls were found, but this is also the case at some other sites where loom-weights and sheep bones are common, so they may have been made of wood and so not survived.[14] By the time of the Roman invasion of Britain in 43 AD, Roman writers certainly thought of Britain as a source of woven woollen blankets and cloaks, and some experts believe that wool became an important crop in southern England as early as 2,000 BC, gradually replacing flax and linen as fleeces were improved.[15]

Iron Age spindle-whorls: left, Yarkhill; right, Preston Wynne (Hereford Museum acc. nos. 4493/2 and 1995-64/2)

We can go even further. A specialised analysis of sheep bones and the residues found on pottery from the nine sites suggests that even wool was often only a secondary enterprise. Sheep farmers at this time probably had all the wool they needed for domestic use and could still concentrate on managing their flocks for their most valuable product: dairying. A major advantage of milking sheep must have been that it ensured a regular but modest supply of food, and once the technology of butter- and cheese-making was mastered, it became a product that could be stored. And once salt became available, the storage duration would have increased significantly (a subject that will be returned to shortly).

When analysing pottery for evidence of ancient dairying, it is lipids and proteins that are usually the focus of interest, since lactose is rapidly degraded and lost. By contrast lipids, which do not dissolve in water, can remain on pottery in the soil for thousands of years. Although methods for analysing these residues are complex (not least because of the scope for contamination in the intervening millennia), there is growing evidence that dairying may have been widespread from the Bronze Age or even earlier. New shapes of pottery seem to have been associated with this, particularly in the Copper and early Bronze Ages and including some vessels which were perhaps designed as sieves. At Wellington Quarry, 73% (19 out of 26) of the earlier Neolithic (*c.*3,700–3,000 BC) potsherds tested showed signs of animal lipids which were compatible with ruminants, and many were closer to dairy fats than adipose tissue. Crucially, this evidence suggests that the beginnings of Herefordshire dairying probably lie well before the Bronze Age.[16]

A survey of world-wide sheep dairying systems has shown that the most intensive regimes slaughter some ram lambs at about two months, while less intensive ones keep all the lambs to four to five months, to benefit from their meat. No traditional sheep systems seem to slaughter new-borns to release more milk. In a milking flock, then, there is a clear peak age of slaughter at two to four months, and then the older animals as they lose fitness, or meat is needed. Two of the nine sites in the study referred to above (Runnymede, and East Chisenbury on Salisbury Plain) had between a quarter and a third of all the animals killed at two to three months; and two other sites, in East Anglia and on a greensand ridge in Wiltshire, had nearly a third slaughtered

Clay Iron Age loom-weights from Sutton Walls. (Hereford Museum acc. no. 6747)

between three and nine months. These four sites, representing nearly half of the sheep flocks investigated, were probably focussing on dairying, with only replacements being kept into the first winter and beyond. As yet, the only data for Herefordshire is from Iron Age Croft Ambrey, where about half of the 7,000 bone fragments could be identified. The great majority were domesticated species, with slightly more head of sheep than either cattle or pigs. But whereas the cattle were mostly being kept to at least their second summer, and most to their fourth, suggesting that the main cattle enterprise was beef and that winter fodder supply was not a major concern, in the sheep flock about a quarter were killed in their first autumn, and most were overwintered at least twice if not three times. The most likely conclusions are that cattle could be overwintered to optimise beef production, the sizeable flock of sheep was managed for a combination of wool, dairying, and mutton, while pigs were being kept to feed in adjacent woodland.[17]

One other change that occurred at some point in the final centuries BC was that greylag geese and ducks were domesticated. While they were not a major part of the diet, they widened the choice, and perhaps might have been tended by the older children. There is no evidence as to whether eggs were deliberately farmed at this stage.

Gooseherd boy; based on a sixth-century AD mosaic restored by Justinian I (527–565), in the Great Palace Museum, Istanbul

CROPS

In the early Bronze Age, cereal farming seems to have taken off. Querns for grinding corn, and partially or wholly burnt grains, are found on increasing numbers of sites, and many pots have impressions of grain, as if they became stuck there while the clay was drying. The amount of burnt grain suggests that it may often have been necessary to dry cereals after harvest, perhaps by spreading the grains on a hide resting on hot stones, or in purpose-built cool ovens of the kind the Romans used. As the weather became cooler and wetter towards the Iron Age, this post-harvest drying must have become more necessary.[18]

At first, the main cereals grown were Emmer wheat (*Triticum dicoccum*), which prefers rich and heavier soils, and barley which would tolerate poorer conditions. Emmer would probably have been autumn-sown, and barley spring-sown. An advantage of this dual-crop approach in a system relying on manual labour is obviously that it would spread the ground-preparation work load, as well as spreading the risk of crop failure. It is less clear when rye and oats originated, but rye in particular seems not to have been common. After about 1,000 BC, the type of barley grown changed from the naked *Hordeum tetras-ticum* to hulled varieties (*H. hexasticum*) which appear to have predominated by around 500 BC. At the same time, emmer gave way to spelt (*T. spelta*) which is both higher-yielding and more tolerant of frost and wind. Such evidence as is available suggests that this switch from emmer to spelt happened over most of England, perhaps as far north as the Tees. Spelt could also be winter-sown, it could cope with the shorter growing seasons of the Iron Age weather and it was able to succeed on the heavier soils which were being cultivated. At first, the new barley and spelt may have been autumn-sown together, as so-called maslins, but over time they were probably more often treated separately.[19]

Little evidence survives for how these cereals were processed. Some flint sickles survive, and there are a few examples of bronze sickles, too. About six inches (132 mm) of the point of a blade was found at Minsterworth (Gloucester-shire) in 2006, and dated to 1,200–1,000 BC. More recently the Bronze Age site at Must Farm, Cambridgeshire, has produced an entire example from 900–800 BC.

The range of weed seeds found with cereals suggests that the harvest was cut high up on the stalk, leaving the low-growing weeds behind and presumably using livestock to graze off the straw and fertilize the ground.

As well as cereals, some linseed or flax was being grown in places, either as animal feed or for textiles. Bronze Age pots also quite often contain residues of

Copper alloy sickle c.800–600 BC, found in Oxfordshire; the integral socket contained fragments of what is assumed to be the wooden handle. (Rights Holder: The Portable Antiquities Scheme; BERK-AC4A08, CC license)

Harvesting with a bronze sickle, based on a painting in the burial chamber of Sennedjem, c.1,200 BC. *Note the distinctive Egyptian sickle, and harvesting the awned crop near the stalk tops*

a mead-like substance, so either wild honey was collected or bees were already being kept. Among the crops that appear at this time, 'horsebeans' (*Vicia faba*) have been found at a site near Colchester, while elsewhere peas were grown.[20] Since there is some evidence from weed-seed profiles that soils were becoming nitrogen-deficient in the later Iron Age, it is tempting to wonder if these leguminous, nitrogen-fixing crops were being grown deliberately.[21] Another possible 'crop' is fat-hen, which has oil- and starch-rich seeds. Nowadays thought of as a garden weed, it is found occasionally in late prehistoric contexts, for example at the hilltop site at Little Doward. This, incidentally, could be the plant referred to by a Greek adventurer who explored the coasts of Britain in the fourth century BC, who reported that people in Scotland ate 'millet'. The seed heads of fat-hen are similar to millet, which would have been well-known in the Mediterranean world.[22]

There are also some hints regarding alternative uses to which barley was put. It is less digestible than oats or wheat, although the discovery of barley loaves at Yarnton, Oxfordshire, dating to 3,620–3,350, suggests that it was occasionally used for baking. Fermented barley has been found in Bronze Age pottery from Fife, Orkney and Rum, together with traces of meadow sweet and bog myrtle, which may have been used to preserve and flavour the beer, as hops are now. If barley was being used in this way, it would seem to be a potent reason for the spread of this otherwise second-rate cereal.

Beer-making would have required several technological developments, but for a society already producing a range of fired pottery, managing sheep for their wool and milk (with all the complexities of corralling, fabric-making and food technology that these involve) and also developing metal-working, these are not impossible. Malting requires soaking the grain for a couple of days at about 65°C, then spreading it out in a dark but well-ventilated building for up to a week until it sprouts; thereafter, the malted grain must be dried carefully before use. Each stage needs skilful work, purpose-designed buildings and sophisticated expertise, but once made the malt would have had a range of uses. It could be ground and made into malted barley loaves or cakes; mashed with warm milk to make a sweet drink; run through with hot water it yielded additional sweet 'wort'; and of course it could have been made into beer. The residual spent grain would still have been useful, as a desirable feed-supplement for both ruminants and pigs: there is evidence from Orkney that this was done during prehistory, although how far into the winter it could be kept is not known.[23]

USING THE HILLTOPS

A major change in the last centuries of the Bronze Age was that Herefordshire people began to turn away from the river valleys, where many of the early farms have been found, and to start constructing so-called 'hillforts' on the summits.

Entrance to Credenhill fort (© Herefordshire Archaeology; Ray 2015, fig. 4.11)

Herefordshire, like Wessex, has a huge number of these sites, from the largest (Midsummer Hill and Credenhill are both over 30 acres/ 12 hectares), down to a dozen comprising just a few acres, of which more are still being discovered.

Pottery has been found on Credenhill dating back to about 700 BC, and by around 500 BC many of these sites were occupied. Croft Ambrey may have had a population of over 500 at its peak, apparently living in some sort of planned settlement, even if only for part of the year, while others seem to have been mainly a kind of monumental structure in the landscape. Although many or even most of these 'forts' were not primarily defensive, Herefordshire was probably not a very peaceful place at this time, with pressure on the available land, and standing as it did near the territories of three major groups of people, later known as the Silures, Cornovii and Dobunni. This period of hilltop use also coincided with an apparent increase in mobility, with long-distance trade in pottery, quern stones, salt and luxury goods, as well as increased metal-working.

Barely a tenth of these sites have been explored in any detail, so Croft Ambrey may well not be typical in any respect. But it has produced some remarkable material. Specialists believe it could have been a regional capital or a market centre, or perhaps a seasonal depot. Or maybe it was built on the boundary between tribal regions, as a meeting place. Or perhaps it had a very different function, rather as we would struggle to explain the purpose of Trafalgar Square. At nine acres (3.6 hectares), Croft is not huge, but it has evidence for being used right up to the arrival of the Romans, when some other hill tops had already gone out of use. At Croft, Credenhill and Midsummer Hill, there were some typical roundhouses, but also lots of square and oblong constructions, from about 2.5 by 1.8 metres to about 3.6 metres square. When these were first discovered, they were assumed to be later Roman buildings, but now it is thought that they may be Iron Age, and raised above the ground for storage, perhaps of salt, grain or animal by-products. The number of these granaries or storage rooms makes it almost certain that there was a significant acreage of arable nearby, even if the region was still dominated by livestock farming.[24] In places where the seed corn could be kept in underground pits, this would no doubt have been the preferred option. These pits are now known to have preserved all but a small percentage of the grain in a viable state, with only the outer edges germinating and thereby using the small amount of oxygen available; thereafter, microbes were unable to grow and the rest of the corn was preserved. This worked well in the dry soils of the chalklands, where such pits are most commonly found, but it was unlikely to be a success in Herefordshire's clays.

It may be no coincidence that domestic cats first appear in any numbers in the later Iron Age, at the same time as the arrival of rodents which must have been taking advantage of the greater bulk of stored grain.

Digs at Croft Ambrey and also at Sutton Walls have given many insights into farming in the last five centuries BC. Numerous loom-weights, spindle-whorls, shuttles and combs show there was almost certainly textile working there, while the many pieces of distinctive pottery used for carrying salt may indicate dairy or meat preservation. But many of the most striking finds are the Iron Age tools, so similar to their modern equivalents that it is easy to overlook their rarity and age. There is a nearly-complete sickle blade with a fragment of wooden handle, the tip of another sickle and several bill-hooks, a small mattock or spade, and part of a tiny saw blade with a rivet hole and in-situ rivet. Similar tools from this period have occasionally been found, for example at Glastonbury and Bredon Hill, but the spade is very rare, with the only comparable examples being non-metallic, such as wooden ones found in Shropshire.

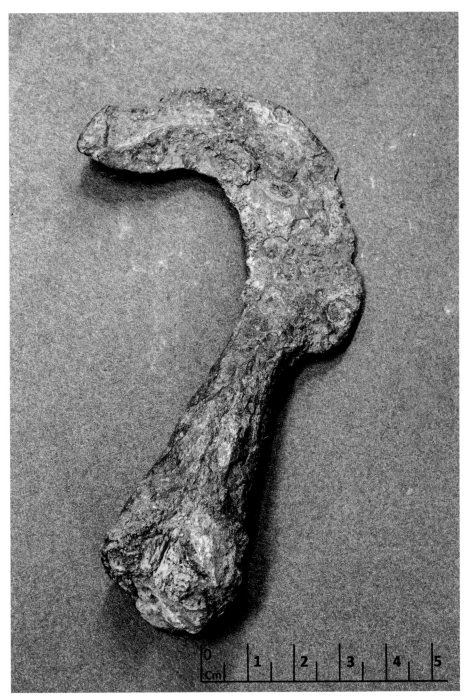

Iron Age sickle found at Sutton Walls, with the end of the wooden handle still within the socket (Hereford Museum acc. no. 6747)

One other development at this time was a great increase in quern stones. For many centuries these were saddle querns, which ground corn between a larger lower stone (which became more saddle-shaped through use), and a smaller handstone. Then in the Iron Age a more sophisticated rotary quern was developed, with stones of equal size, the upper one being turned with a handle through a hole near one side while the grain was fed into a second, central hole. Querns were of such value for preparing flour that they are often found deposited in gateways and at other significant points, as if to consecrate a site. Among the three dozen querns, broken and whole, found at Croft, many were made from sandstone from May Hill near Ross-on-Wye, which seems to have been a major regional source.[25]

Part of a small iron saw blade from Croft Ambrey, with a rivet for attaching the handle. (Hereford Museum acc. no. 8756-304)

Saddle quern from Croft Ambrey (Hereford Museum acc. no. 7975-3)

Unusual upper stone of a beehive-shaped rotary quern, with the handle hole down on the side; found at Sutton Walls (Hereford Museum acc. no. 2018-21)

Getting about by water

For many thousands of years, there must have been countless boats plying the inland and coastal waters and making longer voyages too. In the Bronze and Iron Ages, these water-borne links must have intensified. It is important to include them in any consideration of the practicalities of early farming, since we are now so conditioned to think mainly about transport by road.

For simple river-crossings, log-boats would have served, although the oldest ones excavated, dating back to the cusp of the Bronze Age, have very little free-board and poor stability. Even one sheep might capsize them. The best examples from Britain are the eight found at Must Farm, Cambridgeshire, from around 1,500 BC, and a huge fragmentary one from Poole, probably dating to 400–200 BC.

Another class of ancient boat, known from written sources of about 400 BC, was made from hide stretched over a wickerwork frame. This style survives as the small coracles and larger sea-going curraghs now found chiefly in Ireland, while a golden model of one formed part of the Broighter Hoard, dated to the first century BC. These hide boats are easier to make even than log ones, and experiments have shown they can be constructed using only flint tools.

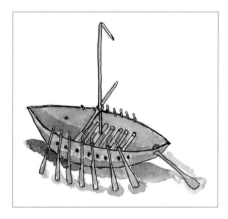

Curragh, based on the golden model in the Iron Age Broighter Hoard (18 cm long), found in County Londonderry and now in the National Museum of Ireland

Larger wooden boats were also made, using a sewn plank technique. They have so far been found at four sites in Britain – the oldest on the Humber Estuary where the North Ferriby boats, dating to 2,030–1,700 BC, include the oldest of this type in Europe. Part of one was found at Dover; one on the Test Estuary in Hampshire; and several fragmentary examples from the Severn Estuary from 1,750–1,000 BC. All these boats have sturdy planks, usually oak, sewn together with yew or other fibres, caulked with moss and held rigid with lath cappings and cross-timbers fed through cleats on the main planks. The largest section discovered so far, 'Ferriby 1', was over 43 feet long (13.2m), with three surviving planks over three inches thick. How sea-worthy they were is hard to assess, but replicas have performed well in trials and they are much the best candidates for cross-Channel voyages in the Bronze Age.[26]

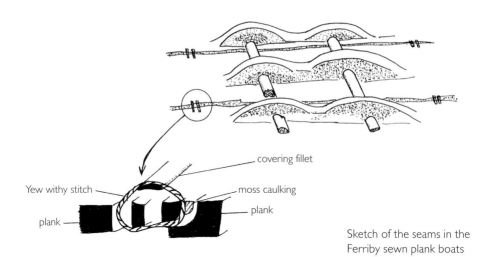

Yew withy stitch

plank

covering fillet

moss caulking

plank

Sketch of the seams in the
Ferriby sewn plank boats

THE CENTURIES OF CHANGE

The thousand years after 2,000 BC seem to be when 'true farming' became securely embedded in Herefordshire. Population levels were increasing, and cereals joined livestock (particularly sheep) as major enterprises. But the evidence is skewed by the transition to metal tools and, increasingly, occupation of recognisable settlements, both of which are much easier to find with modern research techniques than their precursors. Earlier farmers were certainly here, but they left a lighter trace on the land.

The great majority of households must have been focussed on producing food and clothing most of the time. Monumental community activities, such as henge or hillfort construction, evidence for which is now so visible in parts of the landscape, suggest a food surplus, however it was achieved. But these may never have occupied many adults, and surely not in most years. A more regular agricultural surplus would have encouraged trade with other regions, and there is certainly evidence for increasing exchange networks from this time onwards.

Salt

Salt was pivotal in the development of early farming. With salt, diets could not only be made tastier, but opportunities arose for a transformation of animal husbandry. Once salting methods were devised, farmers no longer had to eat or exchange all the meat from a slaughtered animal within a few days; dairy products kept better and could be traded over longer distances; pigs could be butchered, salted and distributed piecemeal, avoiding the difficulties of herding them to feasting sites. Through the Iron Age, there are increasing numbers of examples of animal carcasses being cut into sides, with the vertebrae divided by chopping, and this may well relate to salting. Even into the modern period, many farming families were salting their own pigs.

There is evidence for sea salt extraction at several British sites from late prehistoric times, particularly along the Channel and east coasts. Inland, the main salt centres were Cheshire (near Northwich, Nantwich and Middlewich) and Worcestershire, at Droitwich. In these places, layers of rock salt lay below Mercian Mudstone (alias Keuper Marl), through which welled up highly concentrated brine. Far saltier than sea water, this inland brine requires less boiling to process it: one gallon of Droitwich brine makes two and a half to three pounds of salt (four litres for a kilogramme); sea water only makes a tenth of the amount. Once these inland sources of salt were discovered, it is easy to see why they were developed, and Herefordshire was conveniently located in between them, able to benefit from both.

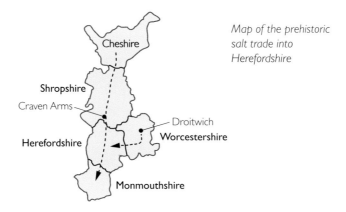

Map of the prehistoric salt trade into Herefordshire

Of the two inland sites, Cheshire salt was probably exploited first, with the earliest securely dated evidence being from the late Bronze Age (1,000–800 BC). Cheshire salt extraction and export, including south along the well-established trackways through the Church Stretton Gap, seems to have increased from about 800 BC, and it was certainly brought right across Herefordshire, down to the Monmouth area at Little Doward hillfort. By 300 BC, the purer and less bitter Droitwich salt was also in production.

The earliest salt workings at Droitwich seem to have used a shallow pit, in which the brine accumulated and from which it was transferred to watertight wood-lined tanks, where grit and other coarse impurities settled out and the first stage of

Iron Age salt extraction, based on excavations at Upwich (Droitwich).
(Carolyn Hunt, © Worcestershire County Council)

evaporation happened. Whether the brine was then transferred to shallow pottery containers over fires, or whether fires were lit near the tanks to encourage evaporation, is not clear, but charcoal residues abound. What is beyond doubt is that the last stage involved packing the wet salt into small, specially-designed coarse pottery vessels, allowing the remaining water to seep out and the salt to dry and harden. These vessels may have been arranged round hearth pits, or clamps may have dried the salt with a cool firing process.

The fabric of the jars in which the salt was packed and then transported is so distinctive that it is possible to map in some detail the trade in Cheshire and Droitwich salt. Cheshire salt was initially used all over Herefordshire, but during the later Iron Age the Droitwich product came to predominate here, reaching a peak shortly before the Roman invasion. At Kenchester, near Hereford, both sources were represented, even though the Cheshire sites were 75 miles (120 km) away. Because of its desirability and relative scarcity, it is likely that the exchange and trade of salt was controlled by an elite, or at least involved specific social networks. Droitwich salt may have been organised from the hillfort at Hanbury, where the church now stands. We can only speculate how the salt was actually paid for.

Droitwich-type coarse pottery for drying and transporting salt: left, interior of rim fragment from Sutton Walls (Hereford Museum acc. no. 6747); right, partly reconstructed pot, found at Croft Ambrey. (Hereford Museum ac. no. 7975 CA62 162; Ray 2015, fig. 4.24, photograph © Adam Stanford)

The Romans reached Droitwich soon after the 43 AD invasion, and built a small fort and military road. By the late first century, there was also a farm, and it seems that salt processing was continuing. Certainly in the early years of the second century the brine workings were extensively rebuilt. One wood-lined tank from this period has had its timbers dated: they were clearly reused and had originally been felled in 61–65 AD, immediately after the Boudiccan revolt, when a second fort was added to Droitwich's defences.

Salt was important for the Roman establishment. Despite popular myth, the army was probably never paid in salt, but it was highly prized and its manufacture and supply came under central control. At Droitwich, excavations have identified large tanks up to 1.5 metres (5 feet) deep, and a series of wine barrels originally imported from the Continent, all apparently used to settle and evaporate the brine. Later in the Roman period, shallow lead troughs may have been used. The characteristic Iron Age pottery went out of use and must have been replaced by another (as yet unknown) means of drying, packing and transport.

An important Roman industrial road ran from Droitwich down to Worcester. Salt could thereby be taken to the port at Gloucester or east over the Cotswolds, while branch roads carried it west into Herefordshire. The road system is far from fully mapped, but the major settlements at Kenchester, Ariconium near Ross, Canon Frome, Leintwardine and Blackwardine near Leominster would all have been markets for salt distribution.

After a period of decline in the fourth century, salt extraction at Droitwich began to develop in earnest in the post-Roman period and especially from about 700 AD, when the production process took on roughly the form it maintained for a thousand years, until other sources began to compete. The brine was heated in shallow lead trays, over stone-lined hearths up to 2 metres long and half a metre wide. Wooden paddles, perhaps used to stir the thickening brine, have been found from this period, as well as pieces of broken shovels (one with a series of perforations), presumably used to scoop out the crystals as they formed.

This Saxon era also reveals much more about the transport routes used. The new unit of measurement was a 'mitt', probably equal to one packhorse load, although a charter dating to between 884 and 901 shows that salt was carried by both packhorses and in cart-loads: tolls at Droitwich were charged at either a wagon-shilling or a pack-load penny. The best roads were used for salt carriage, and were usually called 'straet', signifying a major made-up surface, as opposed to a poorly-maintained 'weg'. Those who know and love Herefordshire's roads will not be surprised that the earliest reference to salt transport along a minor, inferior route is the 'saltera weg' on the boundary of Acton Beauchamp, where the salt came in over the modern county boundary.

Early charter evidence for Herefordshire is scarce, so for details of involvement in the salt trade we rely heavily on Domesday. There were at least eight brine centres near Droitwich in 1086, with several hundred extraction points, nearly half under royal control. Eleven Herefordshire manors had some interest in the Droitwich works, in the form of a right or permission to take salt from specific wells:

Leominster, Much Marcle, Marden, Wellington, Tupsley, Moreton Jeffries, Eastnor, Ledbury, Ullingswick, Backbury in Mordiford and Cleeve in Ross, all in the eastern two-thirds of the county. No Herefordshire manor was reliant on Cheshire salt.

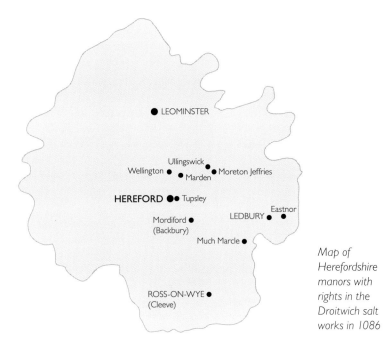

Map of Herefordshire manors with rights in the Droitwich salt works in 1086

Some insight into the complexities of the salt business at Domesday can nevertheless be gained from an entry in the Cheshire section, under Middlewich:

> In the same Middlewich Hundred there was a third Wich which is called Northwich and it was at farm for £8 in the days of King Edward [Nantwich was even more valuable, at £21] ... and the earl and the king divided the renders. Anyone who brought a cart with two or more oxen from another shire gave 4d. in toll. A man from the same shire gave 2d. for a cart within the third night after he returned from whence he had come. If the third night passed [without payment], he paid a fine of 40s. A man from another shire gave 1d. for a horse-load, but one from the same shire gave a mite within the third night as aforesaid. If a man living in this Hundred carted salt about the same shire to sell, he gave 1d. for each cart every time he loaded it. If he carried salt on a horse to sell, he gave 1d. at Martinmas [11 November]. Anyone who did not pay at that date paid a fine of 40s.

Place-names show that Droitwich was once in a well-wooded area, with many early references to '-leah', a woodland clearance, as in Beoley, signifying bees (reminiscent of Yeats' 'bee-loud glade'). Many of the early charters, too, refer to woodland. But salt production used large volumes of wood, for the fires most of all, but also for trackways, pit- and well-linings, housing, workshops and smaller poles for tools, windbreaks and all the other needs of industry. Pollen analysis supports the place-name evidence for early woodland clearance: several sequences suggest much of it was gone by Roman times, so that the landscape became dominated by grassland and arable, with some oak, alder and hazel which could have been coppiced.

Charters from the tenth century onwards begin to include the need for wood. In Domesday, seven of the eleven Herefordshire manors with salt rights mention timber, and at Leominster and Much Marcle the woodland is specifically linked to the salt. Thus, at Much Marcle, 'there is woodland rendering 5s. which are given to Droitwich for 60 mitts of salt.' A more complex system was described for Leominster, where the haulage costs were being avoided (or their own wood saved) but at a worse exchange rate: 'there is wood ... rendering 22s. Out of this 5s. are given for buying wood in Droitwich and 30 mitts of salt are had from there'.

By about 1400, when some 1,500 tons of salt were produced annually (from 11.4 million litres, 2.5 million gallons of brine), the wood supply for the brine industry began to fail and Droitwich turned to coal, brought in by cart-loads from the Black Country, to supplement it. There were, unsurprisingly, complaints about the damage this did to the roads. King John had already sold off his salt rights for the huge sum of £100 a year, and production was controlled by the town councillors, with an effective monopoly on output resulting in high prices. Would-be buyers came to two annual salt fairs, in October and December, and Droitwich traders also took the salt to other markets and fairs, over an increasing distance. Their product continued to be preferred to Cheshire salt for domestic use.

The final links with the centuries-old production systems were broken in 1771, with coal having finally replaced wood for fuel, the monopoly of the town burgesses being successfully challenged in the courts, and lastly the construction of the Droitwich canal in 1767–71, which meant the saltways became historical curiosities and no longer arteries of a much-prized trade. Other sources of salt were by then becoming available, and its unique links to Herefordshire farming were severed. The current rebranding of Droitwich Salt as a luxury product has some echoes of its prehistoric ancestry, but sadly lacks its epoch-making potential.

FIVE

Farming in Roman Herefordshire

H EREFORDSHIRE was not significantly influenced by the Roman Empire until the invasion of 43 AD, under Claudius. South-eastern England, however, was directly affected by Julius Caesar's two visits, in 55 BC and 54 BC, and remained in touch with the emerging Roman world until the Claudian invasion. Strabo, writing between 7 BC and 24 AD, implies that the main exports of the south-east of Britain were grain, cattle, gold, silver and iron, as well as hides, hunting dogs and slaves, and seems to assume there were ongoing trade links prior to 43 AD. But Strabo is not always reliable: the gold and silver presumably originated further west, and he completely omits the tin for which Britain had long been famous. Perhaps he was talking of potential new revenue.

One indication of the extent of 'Romanisation' before 43 AD is the number of Iron Age coins found in different parts of England. In the south-east they first appear *c.*80 BC, a generation before Caesar's visits, implying some pre-existing contact. Herefordshire currently has Portable Antiquities records (random finds, usually reported by amateurs) of 56 of these coins, Worcestershire has 195, while Kent has 3,900. The south-east, by this measure, was much more heavily influenced by Rome in this initial stage, and for a century longer in total.[1]

Although the Claudian fleets landed in 43 AD, it was only in 47–49 AD that the Herefordshire region had first-hand experience of the legions. This area was briefly on the front line, before the invaders pushed on west into Wales, leaving behind roads, forts, camps (some demolished but others to be maintained) and embryonic towns. As the occupation settled, the nearest major legionary fortresses were at Chester and Caerleon, and there was a *colonia* city for army veterans at Gloucester.[2] Between these large centres, Herefordshire was a land of small towns and rural settlements, with few villas. It seems to have mostly

Gold stater of the western Dobunni type, c.20 BC–5 AD, found in Allensmore. The reverse shows a stylised horse with wheel below; the obverse shows a leaf (Rights holder: Birmingham Museums Trust; The Portable Antiquities Scheme HESH-F48C56, CC license)

looked to Cirencester and, in the north, to Wroxeter. In complete contrast to this, the region from Somerset up to the Yorkshire Wolds and over to the Chilterns was a heavily Romanised and apparently affluent area, with many towns, a well-developed road network and by far the highest density of villas in the country, several of them seemingly palatial.

Even though Herefordshire lacked a continuing heavy garrison, there must always have been some military presence. Evidence is scarce for Britain, but other provinces certainly used soldiers to supervise markets, and to oversee postal stations and vital supplies: the fort guarding the Droitwich salt-works, for instance, was well used. In addition, the army was involved in tax collection and transmission, sourcing military supplies, surveying, census taking and many other roles. The militarised zone in the north and the many 'non-productive' urban inhabitants needed a surplus of produce, and for the first time there is evidence for a market economy.

At its peak, the army in Britain numbered 50,000 men, with a wide range of supply needs. Assuming that each man had a new tunic, cloak and blanket every two years, it has been calculated that this would require half a million days' labour, using the wool from 200,000 fleeces. The Scottish garrison at its peak was about 25,000 men, consuming 10,000 tons of wheat, 8–9,000 tons of barley, 2,000 head of cattle, 5,000 pigs and 5,000 sheep, plus huge quantities of leather and 520 remount horses, every year.[3] Some of this demand could be met by local requisitioning, but much would have involved complex long-distance supply chains.

View from Kenchester Roman town to Credenhill, which was used by the military as a grain store

Although the Roman Empire was fundamentally literate, there are no written sources that describe farming in Britain during this period. All the surviving Roman agricultural manuals relate to Mediterranean conditions and were written by members of the rich elite, so they are of limited use.

The best general source for Britain at this time is the *Agricola,* written by Tacitus in praise of his father-in-law Agricola, Governor of Britain from 77–84 AD. Although it deals mainly with the subjugation of the north, it includes descriptions of the land and people, supposedly taken from Agricola's own recollections. This awareness of the conquered people may fit with the evidence of Roman-period place-names, about 500 of which are known. All but 50 are 'British', implying an interaction with native culture, and even these remaining 50 are mostly descriptive, for instance *Salinae Dobunnorum* (Salt Springs of the Dobunni: Droitwich) or *Horrea Classis* (The Granary of the Fleet, or Naval Storehouses: a fort at Carpow overlooking the Tay Estuary).[4]

The paucity of narrative sources makes the material that does survive all the more precious. Foremost from an agricultural perspective is the collection of wooden tablets from Vindolanda on Hadrian's Wall. Unlike most Roman tablets, which were covered with wax and written on with a stylus, leaving only occasional scratches in the wood, the Vindolanda letters are wafer-thin sheets of wood, with ink text. Over 400 have been translated, yielding information about foodstuffs, supply systems and the domestic economy of the upper echelons of society on the provincial frontier shortly after Agricola's governorship. Some letters have been found in other parts of Roman Britain, notably London and Carlisle, but nothing comparable survives for the Welsh Marches.

Even though Herefordshire had no large towns and no major garrisons, agriculture here must have evolved to meet the demands of the 20% or so of the national population which was 'unproductive'. As well as the army and its associated networks, this included many inhabitants of towns and cities, the administrators, lawyers, magistrates and everyone who supported and maintained them. Together these were the more Romanised parts of society, and their diet seems to have reflected this.

There is plenty of evidence, especially from Vindolanda, that grain merchants and cereals were travelling long distances within Britain. Some letters refer to the delivery of cartloads of grain by Britons, or include requests for payment for consignments needing threshing. It used to be thought that the army diet was heavily cereal-based, but it now seems that this was only true while campaigning. Wheat does feature prominently at Vindolanda, but for pasta, a range of named breads and even semolina. Barley was used for fodder for horses and mules, and for brewing: the army may well have adopted the native drink for the ranks rather than import all the wine it would otherwise have needed. It has long been known that a standard feature of permanent forts was their granaries; in addition, numerous corn-drying ovens have now been excavated, many of which may actually have been heated floors for malting grain.[5]

Despite Strabo's optimistic initial assessment, it is likely that grain was only exported from Britain twice in the Roman period: early on and again towards the end in about 360 AD when the Emperor Julian was trying to defend the Rhine frontier. Most of the grain needed by the army of occupation and the urban elites was probably supplied from native sources, although there is evidence at Alchester (Oxfordshire), London, Caerleon and South Shields for some importing.

There is also ample evidence for military consumption of meat, probably by all ranks. Beef was clearly the staple, representing about 90% of the meat intake at most sites; however, perhaps because it was so basic, it is seldom mentioned in the letters. Instead, pork seems to have been highly sought-after, perhaps eaten particularly by higher-ranking families, as ham, bacon, trotters, crackling, fat/ lard and especially suckling pig. Lamb and mutton seem to have been undesirable, but goat, venison, chickens, geese, hare, fish, oysters, eggs and butter are all topics of interest. More sheep and goat was eaten here than at military sites in Gaul or Germany, which perhaps reflects different native supplies.

Apart from meat, evidence for the elite military diet at Vindolanda suggests it was as close to the Mediterranean one as possible. There are frequent references to olives and olive oil, wine (both these are also witnessed in the numerous shards of the amphorae used to import them), beans, honey and exotic introductions including pepper, plums, apples, lentils, radishes and lovage.[6] Analysis of the sewerage system at Bearsden, a small fort in the middle of the Scottish Antonine Wall, found seeds of a wide variety of foods: wheat, barley and beans, but also fig, dill, coriander and celery.

The diet of the elite urban population seems to have been broadly similar to the military one, with more beef and pork, and much less sheep and goat than in the rural diet. For example, beef formed nearly 70% of the diet according to the results of research at Silchester, a regional and tribal capital of comparable status to Cirencester.

Buttressed building on the Wye, just south of Kenchester; perhaps with a commercial or religious function, several of its rooms had mosaic floors

For much of the Roman period, then, Herefordshire farming would have been skewed towards generating a surplus of wheat, beef (probably on the hoof), some barley and maybe salt pork, to meet the demands of the army and cities elsewhere in Britain and even abroad. Military supplies were largely handled by contractors, with some requisitioning (with or without compensation). Transport was by ox-cart or mule train. Horses were quite common in late Iron Age and Roman-era Britain, but they were more likely to have been high status animals for the elite, for pulling chariots or as military mounts.

This increased demand for arable produce may well have been the reason for the introduction of mechanical mills into Britain during the Roman period. While hand-powered rotary querns certainly remained in domestic use, there are some 20 known British sites where water-powered mills may have operated. Two of these are in Herefordshire, at Field Barn Farm, Kenchester and near Weston-under-Penyard. At Kenchester, a strongly-constructed and buttressed building, probably three storeys high and with evidence for a raised floor, is likely to have been a granary; another building contained seven millstones, many of them worn or fragmentary. The adjacent stream had been partly canalised, with a cobbled bed. The complex was probably a military mill, operating from the late first century for about 100 years until it was destroyed by fire. It could have begun life serving the nearby fort, and might have continued in use as the small town of Kenchester (Magnis) developed around it. Later, both these Herefordshire mill sites were also a focus for iron-working.[7]

FARMING FOR TAXATION

A necessary consequence of conquest, indeed one of its aims, was to generate a surplus that could be used by central government. This mainly took the form of agricultural produce, either collected in kind or sold and converted into cash for taxes, but it was also achieved by controlling mines, salt workings, quarries, ports and markets. The imposition of this system naturally led to the development of a coin and market economy, which lasted as long as Rome's rule: this partly explains why coinage ends quite abruptly in the early fifth century. The Roman road system also facilitated access to markets, both for supplies and

Three low-denomination, early fourth-century AD Roman coins from Aston Ingham. Clockwise from top left: Constantinus, Crispus and Maximinus II. (Hereford Museum acc. nos. 2012-167-27, -31 and -11)

the payment of taxes. Public and military roads, of which only a few are known in Herefordshire, were characterised by having bridges at major river crossings; they were built and maintained by the state for the army and the imperial messenger service. Smaller roads were financed by the town councils, and the minor roads were built by the new landowning elite, at their own expense.

Much of the tax revenue was used to pay the civil service and army, and for public building works. Censuses were used as the basis for land allocation, taxation and administration, and the land was then measured and parcelled out. In theory, spreading taxation over the whole province meant no one area was impoverished as long as the people did not rebel, but on the other hand an area like Herefordshire, with few new roads or other building projects, and relatively few imported luxuries, might be considered to have been disadvantaged.

RE-SHAPING THE LAND

Once an area had been conquered and 'pacified', Roman surveyors were tasked with measuring everything, defining boundaries and ownership under the new regime. In areas where the conquest had been relatively easy, like Herefordshire, the natives might retain some measure of independence, at least initially, but they would still be liable for taxation. After a revolt such as that of the Iceni in 60 AD, and in the hinterland of *coloniae* like Gloucester, land was appropriated and reallocated for Roman citizens and veterans, even though the original owners might find themselves still doing the farming work. Other parcels of land were allocated to the Imperial Estate and leased out to make further income for the ruling classes. Yet another category was the land near the smaller towns, which was assigned to the councils to generate revenue to provide for the needs of local government, road-building and so on.[8] In Herefordshire, then, while taxation and the obligation to provide an agricultural surplus was now a fact of life, the absence of major towns means that the degree of land appropriation was probably less than in many parts of Britain.

Three clearly-visible routes framed Roman Herefordshire. Two ran broadly north-south: one from Gloucester to Wroxeter via Stretton Grandison and Leintwardine, and a more westerly one from Kenchester up to Leintwardine. A third crossed them, running roughly east-west from Stretton Grandison to Kenchester and on towards Brecon. Within this network there were at least five small towns, four of which were little more than villages on the trunk roads: Leintwardine, Blackwardine, one in the Stretton Grandison-Canon Frome area, and Ariconium near Ross. The last of these was apparently an industrial centre, with extensive iron-working.[9] On a larger scale, with late-Roman stone walls and a partial grid pattern of streets, was Kenchester, which could have been the local capital. Despite their small size, however, all these places would have served as markets, both for imports and for local agricultural produce and pottery.

Perhaps befitting its somewhat larger size, the environs of Kenchester seem to have been the only place in Herefordshire where a major reorientation of the earlier fields took place, in order to form a Romanised landscape. The fields to the north of the town were re-aligned to lie along the road, and south of the Wye another group of fields near Madley are similarly oriented. The Kenchester area is also where most of Herefordshire's villa-type rural dwellings are found, with as many as seven within a few kilometres of the town and all on the same left bank of the river.[10]

Map of the main Roman roads and settlements in Herefordshire referred to in the text

Domestic farming

In the Roman period, we know that Herefordshire would have looked rather similar in some respects to the way it does now, with half a dozen small towns and large numbers of individual farmsteads or small clusters of houses. But Hereford itself may not have existed, and instead the urban centre was at Kenchester. In the last few decades, many more of the farmsteads (presumably home to 'British' farmers) have been found by aerial survey, but only a few have yet been analysed in detail. Several hilltop sites seem to have been occupied into the late first century AD or even beyond, notably Sutton Walls, Dinedor, Aconbury and Poston Camp near Peterchurch, while it seems that Credenhill was occupied at the same time as a small settlement below it, adjacent to the site of Kenchester.[11] While Romano-British farmsteads sometimes continued the earlier circular floor plan, others changed to a rectilinear form. Two rectangular ones that have been excavated, at Westhide in the Little Lugg Valley, and at Garway, had corn-driers indicative of a relatively high status.[12] In many places in the county, it now seems that the pre-Roman clearance and farming was sufficiently intense for the impact of the new occupiers to be much less than once thought. In between the towns, farming could have continued within broadly the same infrastructure but at increasing density.

Pollen sampling can sometimes give quite a detailed picture of what was growing at a particular time and place. One such analysis compared the Central region of England with the Western Lowlands region (including Herefordshire), and found that the Western area had twice as many woodland species and half as many arable (including arable weeds), about the same amount of unimproved

Roman ploughing scene, based on a first or second-century AD mosaic from Cherchel, Algeria

pasture, and less improved pasture as the Central region in the Roman period. This follows the pattern that was established as far back as the Bronze Age, with more woodland and unimproved grazing in the Marches than the areas further east. Detailed sampling within Herefordshire has suggested that during the Roman era there was nevertheless a reduction of woodland species and an increase in pastoral and arable-type vegetation.[13]

The Roman period certainly featured some new crops. Where grapes were grown they may have been for the use of the elite rather than for general consumption. Orchard fruits were also introduced: apples, pears, medlars, cherries and plums; and among the new vegetables were asparagus, beet, cabbage and carrot, as well as assorted culinary herbs. Mortaria, used for grinding spices and herbs, are particularly found in high-status sites and rarely in rural locations, and many Herefordshire examples originate in Oxfordshire or Caerleon.

But rural and small-town Britain may well have remained a butter and beer culture rather than oil and wine. Dioscorides (40–90 AD), a Greek doctor who served in the Roman army, describes both barley- and wheat-beer from Britain.[14] At the villa-type site at Huntsham, on the Wye just south of Goodrich, a substantial aisled barn seems to have been adapted in the fourth century by adding a water tank and a large oven, perhaps to make a commercial brewery. There was also convenient access to the river as an exporting route.[15]

There is evidence for considerable silting up of several river systems towards the end of the Roman period, and this is probably because of the increasing population, combined with the central demands for cereals, resulting in higher arable acreages and consequent loss of topsoil.[16]

Native livestock farming seems to have continued much as before. Sheep and goat continued to be most common, perhaps being reared for milk and wool, with pigs and cattle also present. There is some evidence for regional variation, perhaps associated with market forces, including possibly Romanised religious practices. A demand for lambs for sacrifice could have fitted well with dairy farming, although in some temple sites poultry seem to have been preferred.[17]

Farming tools reveal a great deal about crops and techniques, but although many have been found in Britain and northern Europe, very few are known from Herefordshire. The best local example is perhaps a double-tined pickaxe, an *ascia rastrum*, found in Lydney, Forest of Dean. Many variants of this versatile tool are known from all over Roman Britain and they were also carried by legionaries, perhaps for making marching camps. Their agricultural uses included preparing ground for vines, trenching, breaking up earth, root-cutting and so on.[18] In parts of Britain with more Roman remains, billhooks, scythes and sickles are common, as are a whole range of specialist spades (including wooden ones) and forks; and parts of wheeled carts, especially axles and tyre-bands. Finally, there is the question of the design of ploughs. Most still seem to have been symmetrical, broader variants of the earlier ards, but in the late Roman period heavier and asymmetrical shares appear; these would have thrown the soil to one side and some are as much as three feet (90 cm) long and capable of cutting deep into heavier soils. This may reflect the demands of a growing population, or of central government, but it was certainly a major new technological development.

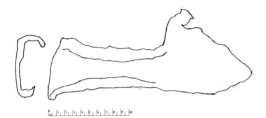

Left: Sketch of a late Roman period asymmetrical ploughshare from Dinorben hillfort, Denbighshire; 25 cm (10") long (National Museum of Wales, 56.444/181)

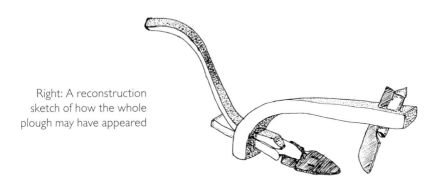

Right: A reconstruction sketch of how the whole plough may have appeared

THE END OF AN ERA

The Roman era in Britain is unusual because, unlike most historical time-periods, it is relatively easy to say when it ended. If the years from 350 to 400 saw an economic downturn, the next 50 years was an economic catastrophe. Imperial pretenders had weakened the British garrison to wage their Continental wars, until in 409–410 control collapsed. By this time, coins and pottery cease to be reliable for dating farms, fields or other sites. Over the next century, many urban settlements seem to have been partly or wholly deserted, or rebuilt in wood. At Kenchester, there is some evidence for the last gasps of 'Roman' administration, in the form of 85 coins minted between 365 and 395. Later still, a well-worn coin of Eudoxia (383–408) found in what is now Hereford, and one of Honorius (393–423) in Blackwardine may hint at the future shape of the county, as church and lay leadership began to coalesce around the site of the future county town.[19] Meanwhile, the sudden freedom from the obligation to produce large surpluses for tax must have made survival somewhat easier for most rural communities, even as they looked ahead into a profoundly uncertain future.

SIX

Archenfield interlude

T HE decay of Roman rule meant that the weight of taxation, chiefly in the form of grain, was significantly reduced. Farmers were able to focus instead on local and domestic needs, with urban life only persisting in the largest centres such as Wroxeter, which survived in a modified form until the seventh century. Pressure on the land also decreased because of a fall in population. This was less drastic than once thought, but significant nevertheless because of major outbreaks of plague in the 540s and 660s, which affected much of Britain.[1]

Herefordshire is unusual because in the post-Roman period it lay on the boundary between two cultural regions. The south was part of the 'Welsh' Christian lands, particularly Gwent, to the west, but the north was increasingly linked to the pagan Germanic culture of the south and east. For perhaps two centuries, the south of the county formed a separate 'kingdom', called Ergyng by the British (Welsh) and Archenfield by the Anglians who eventually established the powerful kingdom of Mercia. The rump of Ergyng survived into the Norman period, with references to it in Domesday Book.

These two parts of Herefordshire have left different evidence of their farming.

SOUTH HEREFORDSHIRE

In the immediately post-Roman era, southern Herefordshire became increasingly Christianised. This has three relevant effects for us here: the Church needs wine and wheaten bread for Communion services; it is a literate religion, so some fragments of documentary evidence become available; and the early British ('Celtic') churches were arranged around numerous small estates, which have left place-name and structural clues in the landscape. One such possible site, known only from traces of a large (200-metre diameter) circular enclosure, and its place-name Stowe, is in Whitney-on-Wye.

The written evidence about any particular religious foundation is usually scarce, and references to food production are vanishingly rare. But these communities were part of a much wider culture, and probably had many things in common. Putting all the many saints' 'Lives' and other material together, it is clear that the seas in particular were open highways throughout this period. To give just two examples: St Samson (c.485–565) was born in South Wales, made prolonged journeys to Ireland and Cornwall, and ultimately settled in Brittany;[2] when St Columbanus (c.542–615) had to return to Ireland from the mouth of the Loire, he arrived at Nantes and is said by a near-contemporary source to have found an Irish trading ship loading up for its return voyage.[3]

A model of an Irish religious settlement, c.600 AD

Although some early grants and charters have clearly been edited centuries after the original bequest, to assert rights over long-lost or spuriously-claimed lands, some things are certain. Wine, ale and mead were commonplace in many communities; Samson was unusual in being teetotal, in contrast to his predecessor as abbot of Caldey, who is said to have died from an inebriated fall down a well. If possible, vineyards would have been maintained, but if not then wine must have been imported from the Continent. Many religious settlements emphasised simple food, but were not necessarily vegetarian. Columbanus, for example, stipulates in his own *Rule* that his disciples' food should be 'coarse', recommending cabbage and other vegetables, and plain flour biscuits, but in his *Life* there are not only examples of the brothers using hoes and reaping hooks, and threshing and storing grain in barns, but also stories of fishing trips, beer made from both wheat and barley (and a cellarer), loaves and wine.[4] Some communities certainly kept dairy herds and there are often mentions of milk pails, cheese, cattle and shepherds.

From the tenth-century *Wish of Manchan of Liath*:

This is the housekeeping I would undertake, I would choose it without concealing; fragrant fresh leeks, hens, speckled salmon, bees.
My fill of food and clothing from the King of good fame ...

From an anonymous tenth-century Irish prayer:

I should like to have a great ale-feast for the King of Kings;
I should like the Heavenly Host to be drinking it for all eternity ...

Two tenth-century texts celebrating Irish Christianity's relationship with nature and feasting[5]

THE RELIGIOUS SETTLEMENTS OF ERGYNG

The principal holy man of southern Herefordshire seems to have been Dyfrig, Latinised as Dubricius (*c*.460–550). He is thought to have been born in or near Madley, which, according to a supposedly eighth-century charter, was later given to a religious community and named in honour of Dyfrig's mother. Hentland was probably founded by Dyfrig as a religious settlement, and place-names there relate to this early phase of its life. His other major local foundation was at Moccas. Dyfrig would now be described as a bishop. He ordained St Samson, among others. However, the British churches lacked fixed boundaries, and their bishops taught and ministered widely. In this, Dyfrig was no exception. He spent time on Caldey Island and he died on Bardsey, the 'Island of the Saints' in north-west Wales.

Many of the charters in the Book of Llandaff, although heavily edited when the book was assembled in the early twelfth century, probably have a basis in truth. Those dated to the sixth and seventh centuries, before Mercian overlordship began, show that the kings of Gwent and Ergyng were able to make a succession of grants of land (usually of at least 100 acres) in perpetuity, many without much in the way of rent. Those for Welsh Bicknor, Llandinabo and Dorstone are thought to date back to the sixth century, and Ballingham, Garway, Llancillo and Much Dewchurch are perhaps seventh-century.

All of these have specific associations with early British saints, and Llandinabo has a conspicuous near-circular church-yard which is a sign of potential antiquity (although not always a reliable one). The only other near-circular churchyard among these early charter-locations is Kilpeck, which, perhaps significantly, is described as a pre-existing church when it was granted in the mid seventh century.[6]

All these religious estates must have had a significant effect on land-use and farming, even though we cannot be precise about the details. Three have specific written evidence. Llancillo was bounded by a 'dyke through the wood to the open'; Much Dewchurch (St David's church) has Welsh place-names for 'the big wood' and 'forest clearing' (though these first appear in thirteenth-century records); Moccas has a meaning of pig-marsh.[7] The problem with relying on place-names, of course, is that they may

Memorial slab, probably for an early Christian priest at Llangarren. Among the place-names in the parish is Llangunnock, perhaps relating to St Cynog, a prince of Brecknockshire (active c.450 AD)

be highlighting very unusual aspects of the landscape which are therefore con-spicuous, rather than ordinary or typical ones. Also, these earliest 'pre-Mercian' charters and boundary descriptions are mostly fragmentary, as we shall see below.

Inscription to Guindda, wife of a ninth-century Christian, at Clodock.
St Clydog, to whom the church is dedicated, was a sixth-century ruler of Ergyng

NORTH HEREFORDSHIRE

Until very recently, little could be said with any confidence about the political and social situation in northern Herefordshire between about 450 and 650. This shadowy period ends when the first bishop of the new Anglian Kingdom set up a different style of diocese soon after 650, based in Hereford and associated with the Roman church not the British ones. He had died by about 688. The first known king of this district was Merewalh, but since his name can be translated as 'celebrated Welshman' it may be that he was a native client ruler, founding a dynasty under the umbrella of the incoming Anglo-Saxon culture.

Research in the last decade has proposed a way to fill this two-century

The Marden hand-bell, similar to those associated with other important early Christian sites in the western British Isles. (© Hereford Museum acc. no. 488)

gap in the story. In the same way as Gwent expanded east and north to fill the post-Roman vacuum in south Herefordshire, forming Ergyng, it is suggested that Powys expanded to the east and south, ultimately producing three sub-kingdoms centred respectively on Leintwardine in the north west, on the *Lene* district in a band in the middle from Huntington up to Wolphey, and a big block to the east from Bromyard down almost to Ledbury. These regions, based around some or even most of the 14 big 'minster' churches, could have provided both religious and civic structure in this period, especially since the minsters seem to have often been located on royal estates.[8]

In contrast to the south-western parts of the county, the extreme north east has many references to farming in its place-names, some dating back to Domesday or earlier. Much Cowarne as a name first appears in the early eleventh century, and suggests a specialised cattle building, either for oxen or perhaps for a dairy. Ullingswick is one of several -wick names indicative of dairy farming of some sort, others being found in Whitbourne, Winslow and Wolferlowe (Poswick), while Kimbolton has (Cow) Bach. Cradleigh includes Cowleigh Gate (cow pasture) and Wacton has Butterley, from 'butter pasture'. There is a possible reference to goats in Buckenhill by Bromyard (billy-goat hill), but no sheep, even though loom weights of this period have been found and most of the dairying was almost certainly based on sheep. There are few crop names, supporting the theory that place-names often highlight exceptions not norms: Linton and Linley refer to flax, which was used for fine lamp wicks and some

Peasants milking their goats, based on a sixth-century mosaic from the reign of Justinian I (r.527–565) in the Great Palace Museum, Istanbul

textiles, and further south there may be one reference to beans, at Benfield Farm in Bredwardine. It is thought likely that many of these Old English place-names reflect the situation when the Anglian culture first began to develop here, rather than describing the farming they introduced.[9]

MORE DETAIL FROM LATER DOCUMENTS

Even in the northern section of the county, few early documents survive, limiting what can be deduced about farming. There are just two charter bounds (descriptions of the perimeters of estates), compared with 90 for Worcestershire.[10] In the west of Herefordshire, Staunton on Arrow's bounds date to about 958. They state that King Edgar (r.959–75) gives the estate to a thegn (a free but non-noble courtier), in exchange for a cash payment; and while there is no mention of any crops, there are boundary fences and a hedge, three gates, a metalled road and a mill on or very near the River Arrow. So here there was, or had been very recently, a substantial acreage of cereals as well as livestock. In the extreme east, on the Worcestershire boundary, Acton Beauchamp was first mentioned in charters of 716 and 727, and the full bounds occur in a document dated 972 when it belonged to Pershore Abbey. This mentions a 'horse brook', a hawkridge, an 'oat clearing gate' (again suggesting a mix of arable and pastoral farming); then a 'fold of bee keepers' (which is interesting because a century later in Domesday Book bee-keeping was specifically mentioned very near here); an Irishmen's path and further over a salters' way (probably a continuation of the same ancient route); loam or clay pits (perhaps for pottery making); flax, and lastly a grove, a term often used for small areas of intensively-managed coppice.[11]

As well as these boundary descriptions with their precious nuggets of information, there are two other relevant Herefordshire documents, one a lease and the other a will. The lease was for part of the bishop's lands at Bromyard, and dates to between 840 and 852, when Mercia was the major power in England. The annual rent indicates what surplus production was believed feasible, including a full cask of pure beer, a vessel of honey or its equivalent in mead, one plough-beast, 100 loaves, one sheep and one pig. The will of Wulfgeat of Donington is later, dating to about 975, when Herefordshire was under the overlordship of Wessex and ruled by the descendants of Alfred the Great. Wulfgeat held land in four modern counties and his will gives some insight into the social networks linking the upper echelons of agriculture in this period. He gave a brewing of malt to the church of Worcester, specifying where the grain was to come from; an estate at Thornbury went to one of his daughters, with four full-grown bullocks to the Leominster clergy and one bullock to Bromyard; land at Tardebigge in Worcestershire was for another daughter, and a bullock was gifted to the church at Clifton-on-Teme; another three estates in Gloucestershire and Shropshire went to his wife for her life, and two bullocks to the church at Tong, Shropshire.[12]

There are numerous Worcestershire charters which shed additional light, although some aspects of farming there were certainly different, not least because the value and management of timber and woodland was affected by the demands of the Droitwich salt industry. Many Worcester charters include cattle and honey, like the Herefordshire ones do. For example Worcester's cathedral clergy agreed to lease out Kempsey and part of Bredon in 847 for three barrels of ale, three casks of Welsh ale (one to be sweetened with honey), three barrels of mead, three fat cows, six wethers, six hams, 60 cheeses, 600 loaves of white bread, four large candles (presumably beeswax, for the altars) and oil (almost certainly imported) 'for all the lamps of the minster'. Soon after, between 863 and 866, the king of Mercia leased land in Upper Arley to a thegn, including a specific mention of pasturage for 70 swine in the common wood, the right to take five cart-loads of brushwood, one oak annually and timber for building as well as firewood. For this he had to pay a temporary rent of a sum of money, two colts (of unknown age) with all their tack, eight oxen, 50 swine, 200 acres of corn and 30 bushels of threshed and winnowed barley.[13] Despite the differences between the counties, it is reasonable to assume that many Herefordshire estates would have been capable of producing similar rents.

Pigs might not be as common in Herefordshire's place-names and its few written records as in Worcestershire, but they must still have been an important element in the farming system. In the spring and summer they were fed on grassland until berries and seeds became available. In the autumn they were allowed into the woods for the acorns and beechmast, but this was strictly con-trolled. There was a national court case in the early ninth century concerning these pannage rights at Leigh Sinton near the Herefordshire border: the bishop successfully claimed that even in years when the crop of acorns was large, a maximum of only 300 of the king's swine need be fed in his woods. When the pannage fodder was gone, pig herds were moved back to the fields and fed on fern roots. Also from western Worcestershire, a charter of 855 exempts Bentley 'on the west of the Severn' from providing 'fern pasture' for the royal swine.[14]

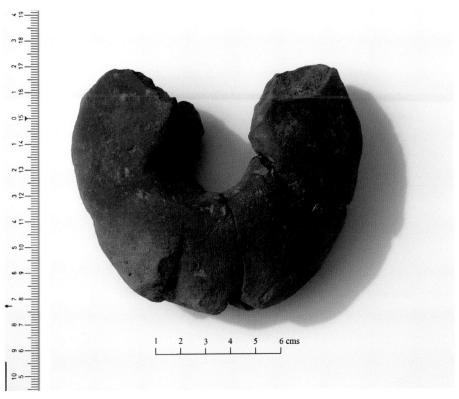

Mid-Saxon loom-weight, from Upton Bishop. (Photograph Tim Hoverd, Herefordshire Archaeology/ Herefordshire Council; Ray 2015, fig. 6.13)

Some more detail can be gleaned from two tenth-century Worcestershire charter bounds which lie on or very near to the Herefordshire border by the Malvern Hills. Firstly, Longdon Manor included the modern Bushley, Birtsmorton and Castlemorton parishes, and its western boundary ran up from a 'pease field' in Birtsmorton to the crest at Winter Coombe and on to 'swyn geat' (the pig gate or fence, now Swinyard Hill). The boundary then crossed an area 'cleared by burning' and dropped down again to the east of the hills. Secondly, Powick Manor was even larger, covering what is now Great Malvern, Guarlford and Leigh Sinton. Near Wyche was Abbandun's dairy farm, and thence the boundary ran north with several mentions of woods and clearings, including those which had been the subject of the pannage dispute; Powick itself is described as 'Poha's dairy farm'. Linked to this are the bounds of Leigh, which run from Crumpton Hill with mentions of hedges, enclosure gates and a spring (later called Holywell), along to the River Teme.[15]

A POSTSCRIPT IN DOMESDAY BOOK

Much of the south-western part of Herefordshire remained subject to medieval Welsh law until the mid twelfth century, and much of this was clearly intended for an agricultural population. Part of the Welsh system of fines, which applied in the time of King Edward the Confessor and presumably had done for many years before, is recorded in the Herefordshire section of Domesday.

> If one of the Welshmen steals a man or woman, horse, ox or cow, upon conviction for it, he first restores the stolen [goods] and gives 20s. as a forfeiture. For a stolen sheep, however, or a bundle of sheaves, he pays a 2s. fine ... If anyone conceals a sester of honey due by custom, upon proof of it he renders for 1 sester 5 ...[16]

Here, as we come to the end of the period that used to be referred to, unfairly, as 'the dark ages', we see the farmers of south Herefordshire illuminated clearly. Animals for riding and ploughing were as valuable here as slaves, while the other highly-regarded agricultural products were sheep, corn and honey.

SEVEN

The Millennium

THE last phase of Anglo-Saxon England and the first century of Norman rule (approximately 900–1150 AD) was a period of generally warm temperatures, benign climate and a growing population. It is also the first time that detailed information is available about individual settlements and the roles of some farm workers.

Herefordshire was by this time clearly identifiable as a county, although its borders were slightly different from those of the modern county, especially in the south-west. It had a small urban population, which had to be fed with an agricultural surplus. Pressure on land must have been increasing as the rural population rose, even though the towns here were tiny compared with other regions such as East Anglia. Mercia was no longer the dominant English power, but had been absorbed first into King Alfred's Wessex and later into England as a whole, which for a century before the Norman Conquest in 1066 had been (notionally at least) one kingdom. Many laws were applicable over wide areas of the country, but local customs and the detail of how particular estates were managed still varied widely.

Despite the mostly favourable conditions, there were some years of dearth. *The Anglo-Saxon Chronicles* (a group of texts continuing from those begun at King Alfred's court in about 890) include one compiled at Worcester. Although the Chronicles mainly cover national events, they also give some insight into local conditions. In 1048 the winter around Worcester was very harsh; the following year there was an earthquake and then a pestilence affecting both people and cattle; in 1052, Gruffydd of Wales raided far into Herefordshire 'very near to Leominster'. Elsewhere, mention is made of such poor harvests that wheat prices rose sharply. In 1044 the Peterborough and Abingdon Chronicles both record that there was a great famine 'over the whole of England' and the price of wheat rose to 60d. and even higher – more than anyone could remember. In February 1047 the Abingdon text reports the worst winter in living memory, with snow and storms and widespread starvation and death.

WORK ON THE LAND

Ælfric's Colloquy, a manuscript written in about 990, gives the first detailed look at farming in southern England.[1] Although written by an ordained 'academic' monk with limited practical experience or direct contact with the land, at least some of the picture it offers must be accurate. Its author Ælfric (*c*.950–1010) was brought up in Winchester, and lived and taught for many years at Cerne Abbey in Dorset before becoming abbot of the Benedictine abbey of Eynsham, Oxfordshire. There were undoubtedly differences between the farming Ælfric saw around him in Dorset and that in Herefordshire, but much of it was common to most of southern England at that time, as other documents show.

Ælfric's text is a conversation between master and pupils, as an aid to learning Latin, with the pupils describing and perhaps acting out the work of people from ploughmen to blacksmiths and salt-makers. From it, some things become very clear.

Most of the work was done by people who were not 'free', but were tied by duty to the lord of their manor. Ploughing was with oxen, using a metal ploughshare, and these animals were highly prized; they were fed on hay in their stalls when they were not out working or grazing, and their dung was then carted out onto the land. They were given regular access to water, especially at night.

Sheep were also significant, especially as dairy animals for both butter and cheese (which was salted to preserve it). Sheep dogs were used to protect them from wild animals, and folds, probably made from woven wood, were used to contain the flocks. Hunting provided part of the diet of the wealthy, and goats were at least sometimes included as legitimate targets. Hawking was a winter pursuit, but only for the rich.

King Harold hunting with a hawk, based on an image from the Bayeux Tapestry, probably made in England c.1075

The manorial estate system developed long before the Norman Conquest. In fact, one of the most constant features of Domesday Book entries is the listing of both the present lord and the person who held that land in the time of King Edward (up to 1066). The resulting social system was an essential part of farm management, and although the social classes were not absolutely fixed, it is the fundamental basis for another document describing rural society, the *Rectitudines Singularum Personarum*. This was probably written in or near Worcester around the millennium, under the auspices of bishops Oswald (+961–992) and Wulfstan I (+1002–1016).[2] The text stresses that not all places were the same, but 'this is how we do it here'. The Worcester bishops held no land in Herefordshire, but being neighbours we can perhaps use it as a guide to the basic pattern of farming and social life on big estates in this region. There is one major proviso, however, in that this is a Mercian or 'Anglo-Saxon' document, so will be less relevant to the western and southern (Welsh, or 'Celtic') parts of Herefordshire.

At the bottom end of the scale, slaves were entirely under the control of their lord, but they also had customary rights, varying in detail between estates. Thus, according to the 'Worcester' document, slaves should be given their own 'plough-acre', and could be fed while working for the lord as well as joining in the feasts at Easter and Christmas. Each slave woman should have 8lb of bread-corn (perhaps for seed) and one sheep or 3d. for her winter food, one *sester* (a volume perhaps equal to 12 bushels, about 100 gallons) of beans for Lent food, and milk-whey in summer or 1d. in lieu. A male slave should have 12lb of good corn, the carcasses of two sheep and a cow, and the right of cutting wood for fuel or building. These people might have been born slaves, or sold themselves into slavery to avoid starvation, but equally they were not infrequently freed in their lord's will.

Above a slave but barely free, a *cotsetla* or 'cottar' on this estate was given at least five acres of land for life in exchange for labour-dues: one day each week, three days a week in August at harvest-time. One day's work was reckoned to be enough to reap an acre of oats and half an acre of other grain, for which they were given one sheaf as a perquisite.

Both slaves and cottars could be employed on specific tasks, each with their own perquisites which are listed in detail. A cowherd should have the milk of a mature cow for seven days after calving, or a heifer's milk for two weeks per calf; a goatherd should have a year-old kid, the milk of the herd after Martinmas

(11 November) – in other words the back-end of the season – and his share of the whey, but only if he looks after the herd properly! The shepherd is entitled to 12 nights' sheep dung over Christmas, one lamb, the fleece of one bellwether (a castrated ram wearing a bell, to help control and lead the flock), a week's milk from the flock at midsummer, and a bowl of whey or buttermilk daily through the summer. Again, this shows the importance of sheep as dairy animals. It is also clear that the (female) cheese-maker collaborated with the shepherd: she could keep a hundred cheeses for herself, and, having made butter for the lord, she had the buttermilk that the shepherd did not take.

Small iron bell, probably for animal herding, found at Croft Ambrey; context undated.
(Hereford Museum 8756-271)

Among those who specialised in the care of crops, the granary-keeper was watched by an overseer, and if he did his work well, he could claim any grain spilt at the barn door (perhaps his duties included ensuring that the potholes were repaired before harvest, so there were not too many spillages?) The hayward was given a piece of land adjacent to the meadows or pasture, so if he had not maintained the fences, his own grass would also suffer. The woodward managed the manorial woods, and was allowed every tree blown down by the wind: perhaps this means that most of his work related to coppiced timber and not mature trees, or that the decaying timber was not useful to the lord.

All the men (in some cases also the women) who were tied to the manor were obliged to help at peak seasons, and for this, too, they had customary rights. In some places they were given winter and Easter provisions, or specific feasts for reaping corn and making ricks, drink for ploughing, festivities after haymaking, and one log from each load carried to the manor house.

Further up the social scale were people who farmed a larger plot of land (typically a *yardland* of 30 acres) for life, after which it reverted to the lord of the manor. The *Rectitudines* says they should each be given two oxen, one cow, six sheep and, by implication, some poultry and pigs, when they were set up on their land. Seven acres (half his land under arable in each year) should already be sown for him, and he should be supplied with all the tools he needed to begin farming. Such people were known in late Anglo-Saxon England as *gebur*, 'boors', and in many respects they were equivalent to the *villeins* of the Norman period. For the first year they paid no rent, but thereafter 10d. a year at Michaelmas (29 September); on 11 November they typically paid two hens and 23 *sesters* of barley, and at Easter a lamb or 2d. They also still had to do work-dues, but if they owned a horse and sent that to the work they might be excused attending in person. Another interesting feature is that every two *gebur* on this particular estate were obliged to feed one hunting dog.

A hunting dog runs down a deer. Hereford Cathedral misericord

On the top tier of the manorial workforce were the *geneat*. These people were free, although not in the modern sense of the word. They paid rent in labour, money or kind for their land. Their duties varied widely, perhaps maintaining deer hedges and the hides from which deer were shot, feeding the lord's horses or assisting with reaping and mowing. They might have their own servants, as well as horses which were at the disposal of the lord of their manor.

INFORMATION FROM DOMESDAY BOOK

The great survey of England ordered by William the Conqueror at Christmas 1085 and carried out the following year, gives a unique picture of farming right down to parish and sometimes hamlet level. In places – notably the detailed account of how the lands of Leominster were managed – there is even information about members of the workforce. No other European country has anything comparable. But despite its immense importance, some words of caution are needed, because it is surprisingly difficult to extract a clear picture of contemporary farming from it.[3]

Firstly, Domesday usually only records the farming of the demesne land: that belonging to the lord of each manor. Where it says 'the men' or the *villeins* of a place had a certain number of plough-teams, part of their work must have been on the demesne land. It is unclear, for instance, how to interpret the entry for Archenfield, that the king had '96 men' who held 73 plough teams 'with their men'.

Secondly, many modern settlements are not included in Domesday, while others cannot now be identified. The entry for Almeley states that 'the men of another vill labour in this vill . . .', but the place that supplies this workforce is not named (a later document gives it as Upcote, now a hamlet within Almeley); nor is Whitbourne, a large bishop's manor, included. Conversely, 45% of Herefordshire Domesday places do not appear on the modern parish map. Some of these have survived as the names of hamlets or farms, for example *Baissan* is now the hamlet of Baysham in Sellack, while *Alcamestune* is Chanstone Court Farm, Vowchurch. Twenty-nine Domesday place-names in Herefordshire (9%) cannot be identified at all, but fortunately they were mostly very small, with a combined recorded population of only about 2% of the county.

Thirdly, and in some ways most unfortunately for an attempt to describe Herefordshire farming, there are regional variations in the information that Domesday includes, so comparing one county with another is perilous. The survey seems to have been carried out or collated in about seven regional circuits before being assembled at the Exchequer, and many distinctive features have crept in along the way. For example, two-thirds of the national total of swineherds are listed under Devon, while Herefordshire apparently had only one, even though under Leominster, for example, pigs are specifically mentioned. Does this mean that swine-herding was more highly regarded in Devon? Were the pigs not usually herded collectively in other counties? Or was this job simply omitted from most Domesday lists?

Similarly, meadow is only recorded for about a sixth of the places in Herefordshire, compared with Berkshire's two-thirds. How much of this contrast is due to them being in different circuits, and how much reflects a genuine difference in farming is hard to ascertain, although in places it may be realistic. In Berkshire, for instance, most of the meadow recorded is in the north of the county, along the Vale of the White Horse watered by the River Ock and its tributaries, where many manors had over 200 acres of meadow listed and were apparently specialising in dairying. For instance, Shellingford (near Faringdon, Oxfordshire) had several areas of meadow (one of 104 acres) and paid customary dues for cheese valued at a huge £4 16s. 8d. By contrast, nowhere in Herefordshire is recorded as paying any dues for cheese, and nowhere had more meadow listed than the 28 acres at Hampton Bishop.

Even more extreme, the Domesday county of Shropshire had no meadow recorded at all, although six places now in Shropshire (but then listed under Staffordshire or Warwickshire) did have some, averaging just seven acres. It seems likely that there was much more meadow along the Severn and its tributaries, but for some reason it was not recorded. For example at Stokesay on the River Onny there was a rich manor, with a mill and land for 14 ploughs: surely this must have had some meadow, to feed the oxen if nothing else?

WHAT WAS HEREFORDSHIRE LIKE?

Despite all the above provisos, some comparisons can be made between Herefordshire and other counties. Being a small county (half the area of Somerset), some of the true picture gets lost until acreage is taken into account. The table overleaf summarises some basic information.

county	acreage	no. 'rural' villeins (per 1,000 acres)	no. mills	mills (per 1,000 plough-teams)	boroughs (no. burghers or free citizens)
Herefordshire	545,000	1,704 (3.1)	99	41 (2,421)	Hereford (10) Clifford (16) Ewyas Harold (2)
Gloucestershire	790,000	3,835 (4.9)	258	67 (3,812)	Bristol (?) Gloucester (73) Tewkesbury (13) Winchcombe (29)
Somerset	1,030,000	5,273 (5.1)	381	97 (3,886)	Axbridge (32) Bath (178) Bruton (17) Frome (?) Ilchester (108) Langport (39) Milbourne Port (67) Milverton (1) Taunton (64)
Suffolk	900,000	3,094 (3.5)	246	55 (4,480)	Beccles (26) Bury St Edmunds (342) Clare (43) Dunwich (316) Eye (25) Ipswich (112) Sudbury (138)

Table comparing Herefordshire and three other counties at Domesday

The most obvious difference between these four counties is the disparity of urban population (final column). Even allowing for regional differences of definitions, there are some real distinctions. Herefordshire had no surviving Roman towns, no great abbeys with their associated infrastructure, and no significant ports. This had a knock-on effect on farming, because the big inland urban populations, like that of Bury St Edmunds, must have been a drain on local production, even if ports such as Gloucester and Dunwich were not. Perhaps this is also linked to the relatively low number of rural villeins in Herefordshire compared with Gloucestershire (which was assessed in the same circuit and so might be judged on the same terms). Ancient towns might have resulted in a more developed hinterland and a higher rural population. But the survey is so notorious for using different categories to describe the population, not only between circuits and counties but even between and within Hundreds, that this might be an inference too far!

The effects of Gruffydd ap Llewellyn's raids

By Domesday, the situation for Herefordshire had altered, due to the career of Gruffydd ap Llewellyn, who united much of Wales and the western Marches under his rule in the mid eleventh century. *The Anglo-Saxon Chronicles* for 1052 describe him raiding and spoiling the land far into Herefordshire. He married the daughter of the earl of Mercia, and was settled by Edward the Confessor with the lands to the west of the Dee. Or at least, that is the English version of the story; it is more likely that King Edward was simply forced to accept the status quo. After Gruffydd was killed in 1063, these lands reverted to the Bishop of Chester and others, as Welsh unity disintegrated. In place of this recently-collapsed power-block, William the Conqueror created three Marcher earldoms, based on Chester, Shrewsbury and Hereford, with a particular social mix of 'militia' found almost nowhere else.

As a result of this unsettled past, the Welsh March, including much of Herefordshire, had a distinctive pattern of land use. There was, in general, a substantial amount of 'waste', partly due perhaps to Gruffydd's raids, and in places at least the region may have been relatively thinly-populated. Domesday is clear that most of this waste land, particularly in north Herefordshire, dated back to before the Conquest. In addition, the whole of the county had patches of waste, and settlements which were not being farmed as intensively as they might have

A bird taken by a hawk is retrieved by a dog. Hereford Cathedral misericord

been. This shows up particularly in the enumerations of plough-teams, relating to the amount of arable land being worked: in a seventh of Herefordshire's named places, the survey says *'there are x ploughs but y more could be there'*. For example, at Stoke Lacy, on the lands of the powerful Roger de Lacy, there were nine ploughs and could have been six more. Roger also held Staunton on Wye, with four and a half plough-teams, with potential for four more – and so on. Most histories of the eleventh century mention the Conqueror's infamous harrying of the north, which left swathes of the country derelict for years, but fewer include the less-dramatic but still significant damage to the Welsh March two decades earlier.

Some of the waste had already been put to a new use by the time of Domesday, as small hunting grounds known as hays. Only seven counties list hays, which seem to have been carefully maintained as hedged enclosures used for driving animals during hunting. As mentioned above, this work could form part of the dues of the free *geneat* to his lord. Curiously, of these seven counties only Cheshire also records large numbers of hawks' nests, despite their value and status for hunting. The only additional records for hawks were one in each of Surrey and Buckinghamshire.

county	number of hays	number of hawks' nests
Warwickshire	1	0
Gloucestershire	3	2
Worcestershire	3	2
Herefordshire	10	1
Shropshire	42	3
Cheshire	52	23
'Beyond the Mersey'	Not specified, but 'to be made'	9

Table of hays and hawks' nests at Domesday (adapted from Darby's *Domesday Geography*)

Some waste land in north-west Herefordshire and west into Radnorshire, had been repurposed as woodland for hunting. Eleven manors held by Osbern fitzRichard, from Brampton, Presteigne, Titley and Knill over to Discoed and Cascob, together tell the tragedy that had befallen local farmers: they had 'land for 36 ploughs, but it was and is waste . . . [and] on these waste lands have grown up woods in which the same Osbern hunts, and thence he has whatever he can take. There is nothing else'. Similarly at Clifford, near Hay-on-Wye, Harewood 'has all been converted into woodland. It was waste and renders nothing'.[4] If, as seems likely, these lands had been laid waste by Gruffydd, the new trees would have been about 30 years old by Domesday.

WOODLAND

Despite millennia of clearance, Domesday suggests that England was still relatively well-wooded. The problem, as will be clear by now, is that the detail is still obscure for this period, and comparisons are parlous. We know that in places new woodlands had recently grown up in Herefordshire, but how much tree cover was there, and how did it compare with that of other counties?

Domesday uses five different ways to record woodland: how many swine the settlement could support by its production of acorns and beechmast; the annual render or payment of swine owed to the lord in exchange for pannage; the length and breadth of woodland (usually in leagues and furlongs but sometimes perches[5]); area in acres; and a miscellaneous minor group 'for fuel', 'for house repairs' and so on. The first two of these emphasise how important woodland remained in the annual routine of pig production, and what a valuable source of tax it was.

Even in counties like Herefordshire where they were seldom mentioned, we can assume that pigs were a major part of the rural economy. Very occasionally there is some information. At Pembridge, there was 'wood for 160 swine, if

Harvesting acorns to feed swine, based on *The Queen Mary Psalter*,
British Library Royal 2 B VII, f.81v, c.1310–1320

[the trees] bore mast'; at Leominster, which included 16 outlying manors, 'The woodland rendered 24s. and pannage ... Each villein having ten pigs gives one pig for pannage'.[6] Since the entry states that there were 224 villeins, a substantial number of pigs could have been paid annually.

Domesday suggests that Herefordshire was only a moderately-wooded county, without the large areas of woodland implied for places like Derbyshire, for example. However, there may in fact have been rather more generous tree-cover here than first impressions indicate, since over half the references to royal hunting forests in the county say that these lands were wooded, even though the legal term 'forest' could often include land with only sparse tree-cover.

settlement	description of royal hunting forest (with folio number in Domesday text)
Brocote [unidentified]	2½ waste hides are in the king's wood (181)
Bullingham	The wood is in the king's forest (184 & 186)
Burton in Holme Lacy	The wood is in the king's demesne (181)
Didley in St Devereux	Of these 9 hides, part is in the jurisdiction of Alured's castle at
Stane [uncertain]	Ewyas Harold and the other part is in the king's enclosure (181)
Dinedor	The king has the wood of this place in his demesne (183)
Madley	Wood is half a league long and one furlong broad. This wood is in the king's enclosure (181)
Ross	The wood is in the king's enclosure (182)
Cleeve in Ross	The land in the forest rendered 6 sesters of honey and 6 sheep with their lambs (179)
Harewood	The forest renders half a sester of honey and 6d. (181)
Turlestane in Marcle	One hide used to render 50 masses of iron and 6 salmon. Now it is in the forest (179)
Cowarne	One hide of this land lies in the king's wood (186)
Moor near Clifford	Most of this land is in the king's enclosure (182)

Table of Royal Forests in Herefordshire (adapted from Darby's *Midland England*, 87 and 88)

The top eight entries in the table above indicate that these forests included or were largely wood; the next three have no mention of woodland, but are close by, on the Archenfield border. The last two places, Cowarne north-east of Hereford and Moor, near Clifford on the Welsh border, are both some distance away from other recorded forests. Apart from these two anomalous pockets of royal hunting land, it may be, therefore, that there was a belt of woodland, partly within forest law, along the Archenfield border. Unfortunately, the lack of detail for most of Archenfield and the almost total lack of information on Ewyas Lacy means that it is not possible to say whether this woodland belt extended down to the important royal Forest of Dean, or indeed how well-wooded that then was.

One other place is of interest in the context of woodland and its use for hunting. The royal manor of Kingstone (near Hereford) had a wood which provided venison for the king in Hereford, and the villeins living there were obliged to carry it to the city. The renders of this manor also included one hawk per year.

Even at Domesday, woodland does not always seem to have been rigorously managed or tightly controlled. Herefordshire is unique among all the counties in its specific mentions of 'assarts' (from the French *essarter*, to grub up bushes and trees). In Kent and on the Sussex Weald there are hints that this process had begun, as a growing population put pressure on the land, but only in Herefordshire is it spelled out, for four manors. In Much Marcle there were 58 acres 'assarted from the woodland' and it was stated that three men including the reeve – a senior local figure – held part of these assarts. In Leominster, Weobley and Fernhill the assarts are described in terms of the extra tax they paid, averaging 11s. each. Whether these four places were unique in facing this encroachment on the commons, or there was merely a greater willingness or determination to highlight it, is an intriguing question.

MEADOW AND PASTURE

Domesday makes great play of the difference between meadow and pasture. Nationally, meadow is often described in terms of the number of oxen it could support, generally at a rate of two acres per ox. Much of this must have been for haymaking for winter fodder. It is odd, then, that with a minimum of 2,400 plough-teams (nearly 20,000 oxen) in the county, the Herefordshire account only mentions meadow in a few places in the centre and east of the county. There must have been a great deal more, and perhaps the carelessness of two entries is a clue to how much more general it was: at Bodenham, 'there is meadow for the oxen only' and at Bartestree the manuscript has a gap: 'there is meadow __'.

Pasture, by contrast, is seldom mentioned in the Survey. The word is used in association with less than 1% of Herefordshire settlements, but this is clearly irrelevant to the actual situation. All farm livestock, including pigs and geese, must have needed grass pasture in substantial quantities.

SHEEP, GOATS AND PIGS

The amount of grazing needed in a given settlement relates fundamentally to the quantity of livestock. The problem is that for most counties, including Hereford-shire, Domesday is focussed on recording plough-teams, not even stating how many oxen were in a team nor how many followers a team needed. There are, however, other invaluable sources that can help here, two of which are Domesday accounts from other parts of the country.

Firstly, within what is now known as Domesday Book there is the subsection called Little Domesday, covering Essex, Suffolk and Norfolk. These are much more detailed than the entries for the other counties. For example, the entry for Parham, Suffolk, includes the information that since King Edward's time there have always been two ploughs in demesne and one for the men; eight acres of meadow; the woodland used to be rated for 20 pigs but now only for 10; there were actually 50 pigs, now 30; then as now there were five head of cattle; then there were 24 sheep, now 38; then there were 50 goats, now 58 – and so on.[7]

Secondly, the so-called Exeter Domesday, a separate document covering Cornwall, Devon, Somerset, part of Dorset and one manor in Wiltshire, is possibly a preliminary compilation of local returns, saved in the West Country when the official copy was sent to the central Exchequer. This includes a lot of detail about livestock of many kinds, and can help reveal patterns of farming for comparison.

livestock	Suffolk (900,000 acres)	Somerset (1,030,000 acres)
sheep	37,817	46,868
wethers	–	948
she-goats	4,348	4,482
pigs	9,789	6,980
cattle (not oxen): cows	9	123
cattle: non-ploughing stock	3,052	4,343
pack horses	527	448
all other horses and mules	241	391

Table summarising demesne livestock in Suffolk and Somerset
(adapted from Darby's *Domesday England* 164)

Sheep were obviously by far the most numerous, and although their wool is known to have been used, they were also the foundation of the dairy industry, together with the smaller number of goats. It would seem that cows were chiefly kept as breeding stock, rather than for milk (only very occasionally is there a mention of a cow providing milk for the lord's household). In addition to these demesne flocks, there were an unknown number of sheep belonging to the peasant farmers. This is hinted at both when their renders are given, and also when the Domesday text says that the night's folding of sheep was owed to the lord of the manor. In other words, the lord could claim the benefit of the manure for his own land. This was especially common when a big abbey held the lordship. For example, Bury St Edmunds' lands in Suffolk included Hessett, where 54 of the 60 freemen were obliged to fold their sheep on the demesne land. There is no indication of how many additional sheep this represented, but it must have been several hundred on a large manor.

Incomplete late-Saxon clay loom-weight, from the Castle House Hotel dig, Hereford. (Hereford Museum acc. no. 2011-92-2)

Further detail is available nearer to home from a survey carried out in about 1113 of the lands of the Abbaye aux Dames at Caen, Normandy, including its seven English manors. Three of these were in Gloucestershire, at Minchin-hampton and Pinbury, and Avening which was in lay hands at Domesday but was gifted to the Abbey soon after. On these abbey manors, there are some clues to how stock was managed.

	Minchinhampton, Glos.	Avening, Glos.	Pinbury, Glos.	Felstead, Essex
cattle: cows	6	–	6	8
cattle: milk-cows	1	–	–	–
cattle: calves & young	20	–	5	15
Total cattle	**27**	**–**	**11**	**23**
oxen (ploughs)	40	64	24 (3)	28
sheep: milk ewes	–	600	50	–
sheep: maiden ewes	–	36	21	–
sheep: wethers	223	60	21	–
sheep: lambs	–	496	30	–
sheep: unspecified	344	–	–	42
Total sheep	**567**	**1192**	**122**	**42**
goats	29	–	–	30
pigs: boar	1	1	–	1
pigs: sows	5	8	2	54
pigs: yearlings	14	24	–	100
pigs: piglets	20	27	–	40
pigs: unspecified	–	–	8	5
Total pigs	**40**	**60**	**10**	**200**
wheat (acres)	–	–	155 (maslin)	150
oats	–	–	50	150
peas	–	–	–	–
other crops	–	–	–	–
mills (value) [cf at DB]	8 (–) [8, 45s. at DB]	4 (–) [5, 22s. 8d.]	1 (33d.) [40d.]	2 (15s.) [2, –]

Table of livestock on the Gloucestershire and Essex possessions
of Abbaye aux Dames, Caen, c.1113[8]

This survey confirms that the sheep were being milked and also kept for wool, and demonstrates how large the flocks were on some church manors. Other documents from Caen show that the western manors were being used to supply the abbess and her households in Bristol and Gloucester when she was resident, while the manors in East Anglia were more geared to grain production and cash rents. Felsted had by far the most pigs of any of the English manors of Caen, and Domesday notes that it had woodland capable of supporting 600 pigs. Pinbury, by contrast, was the smallest of these manors and the one with fewest pigs in 1113, and had no woodlands mentioned in Domesday.

Hunting wild boar: as well as damaging crops and pasture, boars were liable to inter-breed with domestic pigs. Note that the man prefers to spear it from the safety of a tree.
Hereford Cathedral misericord

This relationship between the area of woodland and pig numbers compared with sheep seems to hold generally true. The Breckland area of north-west Suffolk had no woodland at Domesday, and was a strongly sheep-farming area: the king had a demesne flock of 1,000 at Mildenhall; Eudo the Steward had 800 sheep and just 20 pigs at Eriswell; at Santon Downham there were 21 pigs and 900 sheep. Conversely, the higher and heavier land towards the centre and south of Suffolk had more woodland, more pigs and fewer sheep: Bildeston had woodland for 10 pigs and a herd of 40, but only 80 sheep; Assington had woodland assessed for 30 pigs and a herd of 60, with 90 sheep and 12 goats. If, as seems plausible, this pattern could be extrapolated to Herefordshire, then the wooded areas to the south-east and along the Welsh border would be those with most pigs, while other parts might have tended to have more sheep. One major proviso, however, is that the largest flocks were often associated with religious houses, and Bury St Edmunds Abbey owned large parts of the Brecklands. Herefordshire, lacking very rich and dominant abbeys, is not strictly comparable.

It is also instructive to look at the soil types in the parts of Suffolk with most sheep. The Brecklands are notable for their light soils – often little better than sand over gravel – but they produce a good sward for sheep. Similarly, in a county of predominantly heavy soils, the Archenfield district is one of the few areas with relatively light soil. Only a dozen Archenfield manors are listed in Domesday, and none have woodland mentioned, but the entries are very brief so this proves little. However, of these, four specifically mention a render of sheep: Kings Caple paid with honey, cash and five sheep with their lambs; Pontrilas rendered three sheep; at Linton, the sheriff paid all the customary dues of honey and sheep because he was controlling Archenfield; in addition, land at Cleeve in Ross which used to render six sheep with their lambs no longer did so because it had been incorporated into the forest. The only other mention of sheep in the Herefordshire account is under Eardisland, which had woodland worth only 3s. 4d., but here six freed slaves together rendered three sesters of wheat and barley and two-and-a-half sheep with their lambs and 2 ½ d. Do these mentions of sheep only relate to surviving traditional Welsh law, or do they reflect a genuine focus on sheep farming on the lighter soils? Is this even, perhaps, the early beginning of the later emergence of the great Ryelands sheep breed in this same area?

Early thirteenth-century bee-keeping, based on British Library Royal MS 12 C. xix, f.45r, which probably originates in central or northern England

PLOUGH-TEAMS AND ARABLE

At one extreme, Domesday sometimes only lists one plough-team or less per square mile, perhaps because the soil was light or the land was mostly pasture, or because the population density was low. Much of Cornwall seems to have had this sort of density, as did the Suffolk Brecklands and much of the westernmost edge of Herefordshire. The highest densities, of four or five teams per square mile, were on the alluvial loams and clays of the coastal plain of Sussex, much of central East Anglia, large parts of Worcestershire and in eastern and central Herefordshire.[9] Even these seem quite low densities by modern standards, so it is easy to understand why the demesne ploughmen were expected to work all year, as described in *Ælfric's Colloquy*, moving on from one task to the next through the seasons.

Using the additional information available in the Exeter and East Anglian regions, it is clear that a normal plough-team would have had eight oxen. On lighter soils, however, a smaller team was apparently sufficient. In the great majority of cases, the oxen are in even numbers, so an extra four at Eastrip, Somerset, in the Exeter text equals half a team in the main Exchequer version. At Cheriton, also in Somerset, three oxen are listed and are to be charged as half a team, but it is not clear if this represents a genuine team of six, or some opportunistic tax-hiking. There are also a very few entries for Herefordshire where the number of oxen is given, not teams: at Garway, three bordars had three oxen; at Yarsop there were two slaves and four plough beasts; at Newton there were three oxen on the demesne and the four men also had a full team. This last-named place is one of the many for which it is specified that 'there could be one more plough'.

There is very little information in Domesday on the arable crops being sown. At Leominster and its associated manors, it says that the men (over 300 are enumerated) plough and sow 125 acres with their own wheat. At Much Marcle, the 36 villeins sowed 80 acres of their own wheat, and 71 acres with oats. At Eardisland the render included wheat and also, unusually, barley.

The 1113 Caen survey provides useful additional information on crops. The abbey's manors in Normandy mostly paid their dues in grain, mainly oats, then barley and malted grain. Three of the English manors also give relevant information. As shown in the table on p. 94, Pinbury was growing 155 acres of maslin (usually a wheat and rye mixture) and 50 acres of oats, while Felstead in Essex was growing equal areas of wheat and oats. A slightly different system was being followed at Tarrant, in Dorset, a large manor with a flock of 900 sheep; the arable included 50 acres wheat, 50 of oats, 116 of maslin and half an acre of peas. Taken together, it would seem that demesne crops were mainly wheat, oats and maslin, with smaller quantities of barley and some peas.

Bere, a medieval barley possibly brought to Britain by the Vikings and now grown in the Orkneys (The Barony Mill; photograph © John Wishart)

A further and more general indication of the extent of arable land is the number of mills that were operating. There were about 99 of them spread among the 312 settlements within modern Herefordshire, and only three of these (Avenbury, Letton and Aston Ingham) had no value, although a fourth, one of the two at Much Marcle, only paid for the maintenance of the miller. In other counties, many of the mills made little or no profit. The national average for Domesday counties was 75 mills per 1,000 teams, so at 41 per 1,000 Herefordshire seems at first rather poorly supplied. But in fact, Wiltshire's 144 and Norfolk's 107 per 1,000 may actually be because these counties lacked suitable gradients, or had inadequate river systems, and so their mills had a smaller capacity. Five places in Suffolk specify that they only had winter mills, apparently relying on streams while they were in spate. Gloucestershire (67), Shropshire (53) and Hereford-shire may actually have had better mills. In any case, the huge increase in the number of water-mills in the two centuries leading up to Domesday represents an enormous investment of construction and engineering resources and must have transformed arable production and processing.

The basal timbers of the earlier of two eighth-century Mercian water-mills, excavated between Wellington and the royal manor of Marden, the church of which is visible behind. It probably included some Rhineland millstones. (© Worcestershire County Council; Ray 2015, fig. 6.15)

HEREFORDSHIRE FARMING AT THE MILLENNIUM

In its essentials, Herefordshire agriculture at this period was similar to that of many other regions of England. Sheep were by far the most common livestock, being raised for wool, meat, but above all dairying. Much smaller herds of goats were also kept for milk and cheese, and very occasionally there is a mention of a milk-cow, but this is very much the exception. Dairying meant sheep. Sheep predominated in less-wooded places, with more pigs where there was more woodland. Demesne flocks could be several hundred ewes strong, and bell-wethers were used to help manage and control them, with other wethers kept for their wool. It is tempting to suggest that the Archenfield region was to some extent already specialising in sheep production, but the slim evidence of Domesday does not really justify this.

Oxen were clearly still the dominant and probably the only animal used for farm traction. Domesday has one reference to an 'animal' used for harrowing (in Cambridgeshire), which could be a horse, but the great majority of the horses recorded in counties which have this detail were pack-animals, with a few apparently being kept for riding. Associated with the active and trained oxen, of which there must have been at least 20,000 in Herefordshire, there would have been at least one bull on all but the smallest manors. Additionally, there would have been enough cows and their young to supply replacements for the plough-teams – perhaps an additional 10,000 head of cattle if the Caen survey is representative of prevailing management systems. This large number of cattle for traction power would in turn have absorbed huge quantities of labour and land for their fodder and care.

A rare early English example of horse-power for harrowing, based on an image from the Bayeux Tapestry, c.1075

A fifth of Herefordshire's many mills paid renders in fish, most commonly eels, and there were also a dozen fisheries listed on the Dore, Teme and above all the Wye and its tributaries. The render due for the Marden mill, for example, was 25 sticks (25 eels held in a bundle with a rod or cord through their gills made one 'stick'); at Kingsland it was 500 eels; at Fownhope, three fisheries rendered 300 eels (12 sticks). Occasionally, salmon are mentioned: at Much Marcle the dues used to be in salmon but were no longer paid.

One way in which Herefordshire farming already differed from that of many other counties related to the pattern of land ownership. Instead of powerful abbeys, often dating back several centuries, Herefordshire was dominated more by the new lay lordships of the Marches, in particular the de Lacy family, the Mortimers at Wigmore and the lesser de Tosny family at Clifford. Leominster Priory, a seventh-century foundation, had about 80 hides but in Gloucestershire, by contrast, there were nine important land-holding houses of which Winchcombe and Gloucester Abbeys together held over 170 hides. The situation relating to 'foreign' religious houses was similar: a total of two and a half hides of land in Herefordshire were held by Norman abbeys, but in Gloucestershire there were 88. As the survey of the Caen lands suggests, the needs of essentially absentee and distant religious houses for goods that were either readily converted to cash renders, or transportable over significant distances, compared with the more often present Marcher lords and their very different requirements for agricultural produce, and would have translated into rather different farming regimes on their lands.

Another difference is that no vineyards are recorded in Herefordshire. Perhaps this relates to the border nature of much of the county, because the cathedral and the many long-established churches would surely have needed wine, quite apart from the tastes of the new Norman overlords. Domesday mentions about 45 vineyards in total (five of these may be duplicates). There were certainly some in Saxon England, and numbers were increasing: for example, at Westminster and at Hampton in Worcestershire, Domesday specifies that the vines were newly-planted. In many cases, the vineyards were associated with the great abbeys, from the seven in Somerset to the furthest north at Ely. The rest (as at Stonehouse, Gloucestershire, on the lands of William de Eu) were linked to tenants-in-chief, confirming that these were high-status enterprises.

Above all, even though Herefordshire was a mixed-farming county without large areas of woodland cover, it did have a significant acreage of hunting land, under the forest laws. Much of this, particularly in the south, came under direct royal control and perhaps this was linked to the relative proximity of the regional capital at Gloucester, where the Christmas court and crown-wearing ceremonies were often held. Along the western border with the Welsh-controlled lands, noble tenants held sway and managed the hunting for their own pleasure and benefit.

So, at this pivotal time in English social history, when rural life first comes into fine focus, a picture emerges of Herefordshire being farmed in a way that is in some respects very familiar, in others quite different from today. The county was to a considerable extent following the patterns and constraints of most of southern England, with each settlement or manor needing to be largely self-sufficient, but at the same time it was continuing to forge its own path.

EIGHT

From peasants to yeomen?

T HE later medieval period, from about 1100 to the late 1500s, encompassed huge changes. Partly this was because of civil and political developments, but from a farming perspective the driving forces were a combination of unsettled climate and dramatic epidemics. These external factors pivot around the fourteenth century, a time of intense social and agricultural upheavals, from which emerged a distinctive new way of managing the land, with new crops, tools and theories.

POPULATION LEVELS AND LAND HUNGER

If Domesday Book gives us a first vague idea of population levels in individual places, thereafter we have increasingly reliable sources from which to draw comparisons.

Over most of England, the 200 years from Domesday to about 1300 was a time of population growth, and a combination of the surviving national tax information and records for church estates allow this to be approximately quantified. The widespread estates of the Bishop of Worcester, for example, were surveyed several times, including in 1170 and 1299. Where both figures are available, all but two manors show a big increase in the number of tenants (*see overleaf*).

A more extreme example, from East Anglia, is Norwich Cathedral Priory's manor of Martham, Norfolk. In a 1220 survey, there were 104 tenements recorded, but by 1292 this had been subdivided into 900 plots, held by a total of 364 tenants, 220 of whom (60%) held under two acres; some had barely a garden and only ten had over ten acres. On manors like this, with most of the population holding plots too small for subsistence, tenants were trapped in servitude unless they managed to move to less overcrowded places. Some lords allowed a few people to leave, for a fee; others fined the relatives of absconding peasants.

103

Manor	c.1170	1299	change c.1170–1299
Alvechurch	42	150	+257%
Bredon and Welland	77	110	+43%
Hanbury	45	90	+100%
Hartlebury	69	113	+64%
Kempsey	102	154	+51%
Ripple	86	111	+29%
Wick	122	126	+3%
Whitstones	189	179	−5%

Numbers of tenants on a sample of Worcester diocesan manors[1]

Some tenants found ways to sell or pass on their holdings to others, who could thereby amass a viable or even generous acreage. Many of these transactions may never have been officially enrolled, and so the detail is lost, but there does seem to have been an embryonic peasant land market in some regions by the turn of the fourteenth century, including in parts of Worcestershire.[2]

In Herefordshire, the Red Book of the bishop's estates, dating to about 1285, lists the tenants, their land-holdings and dues. It too reveals pressure on the land, but less than at Martham.[3] Thus, in the three rural townships of Bromyard Foreign, surrounding the borough, and in the neighbouring parish of Whitbourne, over a third of tenants held ten acres or less.

Approximate size category (acres)	≤10	11–20	21–40	41–60	61–80	81–120	>120	total
number of holdings in: Bromyard Foreign	59	47	29	3	1	0	2	141
Whitbourne	32	34	7	0	0	0	0	73

Holding sizes of episcopal tenants in Bromyard Foreign and Whitbourne c.1285

The status of villeins seems to have declined during this century, as stricter controls on the peasantry were enforced in the face of increasing population pressure and a consequent reduction of freedoms for individual workers on the land. Whereas villeinage once implied a family of prosperous peasants with a substantial holding, now it was more likely to mean a household of more-or-less unfree tenants bound to their manor. In Worcester diocese at least, a whole range of categories came into use. In the 1299 survey, the episcopal estate distinguished between the free rent-payers with few obligations, and the others, subdivided into several classes, from tenants who held their land by clear customary duties, down to those little better than slaves. In reality, the precise distinctions probably varied with local custom. Superimposed on these regulations were standard fines and fees, in particular the heriot payable in kind or money on inheriting a holding, which applied to free and unfree alike, and which was a real burden on many tenant families.

The number and extent of assarts (areas newly brought into cultivation in the manor) also indicates pressure on land. Bromyard and Whitbourne for example shared a boundary over Bringsty and Badley Commons; the Hereford Red Book lists 53 acres of assarts on the commons from the Whitbourne side and 33 acres from Bromyard, charged to many people including Robert of Brockhampton with a one-acre assart, and Matilda of Stubmershe with 12 extra acres (*see overleaf*).

In neighbouring Worcester diocese, the episcopal estate in 1299 covered 30–40,000 acres, of which some 2,000 acres (5%) was from assarts made since 1150, including 300 acres of the old Malvern Forest and a further 600 acres between Ripple and Kempsey.

In many counties, there is widespread evidence for medieval 'ridge and furrow' arable land in fields which are now pasture. Herefordshire was previously thought not to have many surviving examples of this, perhaps because the population never got so high. More recently, disused ridge and furrow indicative of temporary medieval arable has begun to be found. The difference here is that the areas brought into cultivation as the population rose, are now often hidden beneath woodland on steep slopes and hilltops. In some parishes there is so much that every coppice seems to cover traces of old ridge and furrow.

While the generally benign weather and high demand persisted, agricultural prices rose and so for those with a big enough holding and some capital, it was a time of relative prosperity. As we have seen, however, it was a harsh time for most of the poorest, and not just in the occasional years of bad harvests. In this Medieval Warm Period, there was a tendency to change to growing the finer bread wheat, the modern sub-species, which needs fair weather. Peasant farmers could expect in a good year to harvest about a quarter of grain per acre,

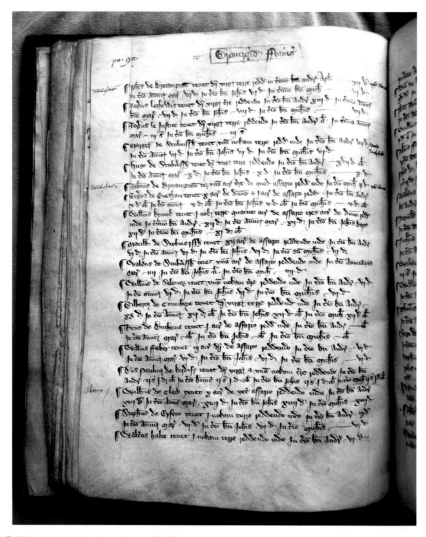

The Hereford Red Book, showing the Bromyard Foreign assart holdings of Robert of Brockhampton and Matilda of Stubmershe (lines 11 and 20). (Herefordshire Archive Service)

so if they had a full 30 acre yardland, then allowing for fallows, meadow and so on they might hope for 20 quarters at harvest. They would need to reserve five or six quarters for next year's sowing and ten quarters for domestic use, leaving them a surplus for sale in a very good year of about five quarters.

Grain prices nearly doubled through the century, incentivising a move to arable and benefitting those with surpluses to sell. On the Worcester diocesan estate, the surveys of 1290 and 1299 show that by this time about 80% of the land was arable, 12% meadow and 8% pasture.[4] But prices varied by both location and season, as revealed in the household accounts of the Bishop of Hereford for 1289–90. In that year, wheat prices were far higher in London than in Herefordshire, at over 6s. a quarter during the winter compared with barely 3s. in Hereford, rising to 4s. in March and 5s. at Ledbury market in July, just before harvest.[5]

The 1299 Worcester survey seems to imply that a two-course rotation was being used, so in alternate years the livestock could graze and fertilise the large acreages designated for sowing the following year. This system also allowed some freedom to switch between winter- and spring-sown cereals, according to need and weather. Of the principal crops being grown, wheat (generally by far the most important on demesne lands) and rye (mainly a poor-man's crop although monkcorn bread, made from a wheat and rye mix, was used in monasteries) were winter-sown, while barley, oats, peas and beans were spring-sown. Wheat was generally worth about twice as much as barley, weight for weight, and while barley was sometimes used for ale in a mix of other cereals, malted wheat or oats were more usual. Hops were not used, but the wealthy flavoured their ale with spices.

Some of the many spices used to flavour beer for the aristocracy: cinnamon, cloves, peppercorns and nutmeg

Evidence for the sowing regime comes from the Worcester episcopal manors of Fladbury near Evesham and Tredington, near Shipston-on-Stour, for the season 1246–47. In neither case are the acreages known, but the wheat and rye must have been extensive because these winter crops were relatively thinly sown.[6]

	wheat	rye	barley	peas and beans	oats
Fladbury	17qrs 6bsh	26qrs 4bsh	26qrs 5bsh	5qrs	31qrs 4bsh
Tredington	45qrs 6bsh	–	16qrs 1bsh	3qrs	16qrs 7bsh

Quantities of cereals sown on two Worcester diocesan manors, 1246–47, in quarters and bushels (see Weights and Measures on p. *xiii*)

The thirteenth century was thus a time when plough animals were in high demand, rigid adherence to fallowing sequences slackened in order to grow more corn, and the use of farmyard and domestic manure may have increased as witnessed by spreads of pottery in fields. On some richer estates at least, investment was made in higher sowing rates, new stone floors in barns and increased meadow management and hay cropping. In the east of England, on larger fields, horses began to be used as plough animals where the feed costs could be borne. On the down side, population pressure was rising, and most people had a nutritionally poor diet, low in protein, relying heavily on grain supplemented with a small amount of dairy produce.

Ploughing with a half team of oxen, based on the Luttrell Psalter, probably illustrated in East Anglia, British Library Add MS 42130 fol. 170, c.1320–40

LIVESTOCK

Manure, which was so vital to fertilise the arable land, came partly from plough animals but more from the sheep which were becoming a key component of the national economy. Thousands of peasants with bigger holdings were beginning to specialise in wool production as well as sheep dairying, and the national tithe data show that two-thirds of the national flock were on peasant holdings, with an average flock size of 20. The remainder were on church estates, and the largest flock in Herefordshire at the time of Pope Nicholas' detailed taxation assessment of 1291–92 was at Dore Abbey, which had 40 cows, 1,760 sheep, and at hay-making they carted 51 wagon-loads of hay, 40 of which came from their nearby grange at Morehampton.[7] The much larger Worcester episcopal estate ran an integrated livestock enterprise, with a total of 226 cows (mainly on the low-lying lands) and 5,650 sheep, concentrated on the Cotswold manors in summer but being moved lower in winter.

Nationally, the peak export year for wool was 1304–05, when 46,382 sacks were shipped to the Low Countries, representing the fleeces of 12 million sheep.[8]

TIMES CHANGE

By the late thirteenth century, land hunger was so severe that even wood was in critically short supply in this well-wooded county. In 1288, the bishop's court concluded that a grant of wood-rights to the Ross woodward and his heirs was a forgery, and cancelled it; in 1305 the same woods were raided at night and several trees were carried off. But the bishop's servants saw what happened, recognised the ringleaders, and Thomas and John Clarkson were excommunicated and denounced by name in six local churches each Sunday until finally they confessed, returned the stolen timber and did public penance.[9]

For the rich, however, things still seemed good. The bishop of Hereford had vineyards at Hereford and Ledbury, as well as smaller suppliers in the county who had vines around their farms. These made white wine, generally regarded as an inferior drink but still consumed in quantity. The more favoured red was imported through Bristol, shipped up to Haw, south of Tewkesbury, and thence carried overland to Bosbury, the principal episcopal cellar.

Then at the end of the thirteenth century and into the fourteenth, the benign conditions ended. Over 70 years, temperatures fell slightly, just enough to prevent the growing of vines. The Medieval Warm Period was replaced by the Little Ice Age, with harsher winters, high rainfall and unpredictable harvests from soils that in some cases were already becoming exhausted. An early sign of the trouble ahead is in the Worcester records for 1306, when Alvechurch, Hanbury, Kempsey and Wick were all said to lie in a 'barren district', while from Shropshire to Cambridgeshire areas of land went out of cultivation between the national taxations of 1291 and 1341, due to their infertility or the poverty of the tenants.[10] The earlier assarting was likely to have brought in relatively poor land, which would quickly loose fertility unless generously manured.

The colder weather was compounded in 1314–17 by sustained and torrential rains, resulting in a run of poor harvests. At this time, many people could endure one poor harvest, two in a row was disastrous for the poorest, while a succession of three – especially when, as in 1317, there was in places an almost complete failure of the winter corn (wheat and rye) – resulted in famine. This one is called the Great Famine. Yields of wheat on the Winchester diocesan estates, which are well documented and covered a huge area from Somerset to Surrey, fell to 60% in 1315 and 55% in 1316. In England and Wales, as far as can be calculated, the 1315 national wheat harvest was reduced to 40%, in 1316 to 60% and in 1317 to just 16% of normal (only partly offset by the oat and barley crops). Prices more than doubled, rising to 16s. a quarter for wheat (briefly 23 to 24s. in early summer 1316) and 10 to 11s. for barley, and remained high for two years. There is some evidence that the more fortunate poor switched to eating oats, although the price increased five-fold in places. Accompanying these poor harvests were a widespread disease of sheep (perhaps liver fluke), resulting in a loss of milk, cheese, wool and meat; a big reduction in salt production so slaughtered livestock could not be preserved; a fall in the price of draught animals as the market was flooded; and a 10–15% human mortality rate in southern England, a similar level to the Irish Potato Famine. Overarching all these factors was the tragic lack of information. If someone had money, they had no reliable way of knowing where to go for grain; if they had goods to sell, where should they take them?[11]

The harvest of 1319 was good, but that year saw the start of a devastating cattle 'murraine' (probably viral rinderpest), which entered England in Essex and by early 1320 had reached the Welsh border. Part of the spread may be attributed to sales of already-sick livestock, and its rapid transmission north was probably because cattle were taken with the army then moving up to Scotland. Overall, the murraine killed 62% of all bovids in England and Wales. Some 50% of oxen, 64% of cows and 56% of calves and young stock died. To put this in context, the 2001 foot and mouth outbreak, hideous as it was for those affected, involved the slaughter of about 700,000 cattle out of a national herd of 6 million, or 12%.[12] A characteristic of the murraine was that some manors were far worse hit than others, in an unpredictable way. There is no precise data for Herefordshire, but the table opposite gives examples from nearby.

	mortality (number slaughtered)*	herd size	% mortality
Gloucestershire			
Hardwick (Stroud)	55 (7)	63	87
Bourton-on-the-Hill	13 (1)	26	50
Worcestershire			
Chadsley Corbett	5 –	16	31
Pershore	27 –	38	71
Monmouthshire			
Llangwm (Usk)	10 –	33	30
Trellech (Monmouth)	14 –	20	70

Some examples of bovine mortality on manors near Herefordshire, 1319–20 (*some manors had a policy of pre-emptive slaughtering of sick-looking cattle, but most were left to die, or were sold)

The trauma of this single pestilence is hard to overstate. In some places, all the stock are reported to have died in a few weeks. For instance, on the Westminster Abbey manor of Hardwick near Stroud, 'all oxen died between Christmas and St Hilary' (13 January). Almost at a stroke, farmers both rich and poor lost many of their draught oxen, imperilling their capacity to grow grain as well as a major source of manure, their bovine breeding stock, part of their supply of milk and cheese, and for the lucky few a valued meat. Bulls could be replaced in three or four years, but although oxen numbers initially increased, so by 1330 they were back to 85% of pre-murrain levels, they seem never to have fully recovered. Yet, neither did horses completely fill the gap: there was a temporary upsurge in their numbers, but by the late 1320s horse numbers fell back again over much of the country. It seems that the human mortality of the last decade had reduced the demand for corn.[13]

THE 'BLACK DEATH' AND LATER POPULATION LEVELS
One generation after the cattle murrain, an even worse disaster struck, in the form of the outbreak of bubonic plague later known as the Black Death, which spread north across Herefordshire through 1349. In all, about half the population probably died. In Cradley, Bosbury, Colwall and Coddington together, 158 tenants died in the plague year out of 320 in the Red Book; in Woolhope, a quarter of the population died in 1348–50.[14] In most cases, other family members would also have caught the plague, so total numbers of burials must have been far higher.

A poor man and the king meet Death, in two of Holy Trinity Church Cherbourg's
late fifteenth-century *Danse Macabre* bas-reliefs

Clergy appointments to parishes give a glimpse of the extent to which these varied disasters disturbed the normal rhythms of life. In 1316 the numbers of appointments were double those of 1285, and most were after harvest. Few clergy may have died during the famine, but their glebe and tithe incomes were decimated, and many seem to have opted to move. Then the Black Death obviously hit hard, with a peak in the hottest months; many clergy died, others may have been frightened away.

Months	1285[1]	1316[2]	1349[3]	
Jan–March	10	9	13	*1. One of the last 'normal' years*
Apr–June	5	1	35	*2. During the Great Famine and sheep plague*
July–Sept	1	12	85	
Oct–Dec	2	13	26	*3. The year of the Black Death*
Total	18	35	159	

Table showing clergy appointments in Hereford diocese 1285, 1316 and 1349

There were major national recurrences in 1361–62, 1369 and 1375, before the plagues became less devastating but more erratic and unpredictable. In 1377, after the first four plagues, a Poll Tax was imposed by King Edward III and the data from this taxation is detailed and reliable enough for it to be used to compare population levels with those at the end of the thirteenth century, before the decades of disasters began. It is, crucially, believed that there was only about 10% evasion of this first Poll Tax. Much later, the Compton Census of 1676 is even more accurate, providing an end-point to this series of population estimates. Together these make it clear that these decades were so traumatic that population levels did not recover until at least the late Stuart era. This was after the final outbreaks of plague here, which in Worcester was 1637–38, when 1,505 people died in ten months (about 20% of the city's population).[15] In Herefordshire they were spread through the 1580s and 1630s. In Hereford itself, mortality was concentrated in 1580 and 1636–37, while in Much Cowarne, for example, it peaked in summer 1587 at three times the normal death rate, and again in 1630 and 1636. In Ross, plague carried off 315 out of 1,800 people in 1637, while many others fled the town.

Left: the Ross plague cross, commemorating those who died in the last assault of the plague in the seventeenth century

Below: the inscription on the Ross plague cross, with the date, 1637, and the number of burials recorded as 315 souls

Combining the available data for a sample of the Herefordshire episcopal manors gives a picture of the effects of this period on the county population.

	Domesday Book, 1086	Red Book, c.1285	Poll Tax, 1377 on those aged 14 and over	Compton Census 1676 on communicants aged 16 and over
Calculation used:-	Listed x 4.5 = total population (only very approximate)	Tenants x 4.5 = total population	+10% for evasion; Payees x 3.5 = total population	Communicants x 1.33 = total population
Eaton Bishop (Webtree)	90	240	85	133
Upton Bishop (Greytree)	205	360	180	314
Whitbourne (Broxash)	–	370	275	400
Grendon Bishop (Broxash)	–	180	70	93
Cradley (Radlow)	190	410	230[i]	400
Colwall (Radlow)	105	510	190[i]	350

i. Many of the Herefordshire Poll Tax listings are now illegible or lost. These Radlow figures rely on the 1379 (second Poll Tax) data, and are possibly an underestimate.

Comparison of manorial or parish populations at four points in time[16]

The Domesday listings are incomplete and sometimes unfathomable, but they give some indication of the population increase on these manors in the centuries before the Red Book. There is then a decline to about half by the Poll Tax and sometimes much more, with the population in most cases still not fully recovered by the seventeenth century.

Although these manors are all episcopal and mainly in the east of the county, they may not be too atypical. A recent reassessment of county population figures supports the idea that although Herefordshire was relatively badly hit by the combined effects of the fourteenth-century crises (compared with Somerset, for instance), it had recovered significantly by the seventeenth century (compared, for example, with East Anglia and Wiltshire).

county	1086	1290	1377	1600
Cambridgeshire	31 (1.82)	137 (2.89)	53 (2.12)	73 (1.76)
Herefordshire	32 (1.87)	73 (1.53)	30 (1.21)	62 (1.51)
Norfolk	148 (8.7)	487 (10.3)	177 (7.07)	171 (4.16)
Somerset	78 (4.57)	151 (3.18)	101 (4.06)	169 (4.11)
Wiltshire	63 (3.72)	160 (3.36)	83 (3.31)	115 (2.80)
Worcestershire	26 (1.55)	60 (1.27)	29 (1.16)	66 (1.59)

Estimate of county populations in thousands (with % of English population)[17]

NEW TIMES, NEW WAYS

For those who survived these calamitous years, new opportunities appeared for new ways of farming. Indeed, it ushered in a time when the very word *farm* came to the fore, meaning to rent part of the old demesne lands, with freedom to 'farm' them for personal profit. It would be wrong to think of the last decades of the fourteenth century as an entirely bright new dawn; however, in Worcestershire over half the lambs at one episcopal manor died in 1389–90, from 'le squyrt' (a condition modern farmers will recognise), and the enterprise was abandoned for several years. But it was certainly a time of opportunity, not least because the lower tiers of society were much less constrained by the old manorial ties and more able either to leave their place of birth or to work on their own land. In Kingsland, Herefordshire in this same year 1389–90, John and Thomas Kemsey were renting land – had they come from Kempsey in Worcestershire? Certainly, a century later it is known, for instance, that a John Pace of Hampton Lovett (a landless poor villein) moved to Elmley Lovett, while two of his sons were able to move to Woodstock and then back to Worcester, a son and daughter went to Bristol, and another son, William Pace, moved first to Martley and by 1526 was living in Tedstone (Delamere or Wafre), Herefordshire. For this family, and presumably for many like them, the world they now found themselves in had scope for much more freedom; where to live, whether to farm or to move to a town, how to manage their land.[18]

The bailiff's accounts for Kingsland survive for the year 1389–90, and they provide rare detail of this transitional phase of farming.[19] There are examples of the old custom of paying rent in spices (one tenant paid with 1 lb of cumin, which was sold on by the bailiff for 4d.). Some customary tenants were still liable for ploughing works and had to give hens as Christmas rents, but the ploughing seems to have been commuted to a money payment to the manorial lord, at 4d. a day (3 days in both winter and Lent and one day at the 'third ploughing', presumably just before sowing). Even the 30 hen-rents were turned into a cash profit, being bought at 1d. a head from the tenants and re-sold by the estate for 1 ½ d. The combined rents from free and semi-free tenants were now a substantial part of total estate income.

The income at Kingsland from farming out the pastures and meadows was a major component of the manorial economy. The grassland must have had a mix of uses, with specific mention of an obligation for the tenants to help at haymaking, and several hints about sheep, including a fulling mill and a sheep fold. As for the arable crops, the only clue comes from the tolls at the two mills, which were mostly in oats and a maslin mix, with a small quantity of winter corn and what may have been malting grain. The oats may have mainly been to feed horses, because an apparently unexpected visit from the estate steward and members of the lord of the manor's council caused the bailiff to purchase an extra cart-load of hay and half a bushel of oats. For storage of these crops, the great barn was let to two tenant farmers, and another barn had its thatched roof repaired at a total cost of 1s. 8d.

The Worcester survey of 1389 also shows how livestock farming had changed by the end of the century. As demand for arable land fell, so too did the need for oxen and cart horses, and sheep became relatively more numerous.

	horses	oxen	cows	other cattle	pigs	rams	ewes	lambs	2 yr olds	wethers	all sheep
Total on these 7 manors	27	107	84	13	468	23	922	220	431	934	2,530
Total on all 13 manors	58	202	96	63	740	29	1,164	835	451	2,159	4,638

Stock on demesne lands of seven west-Worcestershire episcopal manors (Bredon, Fladbury, Kempsey, Ripple, Stoke, Whitstones, Withington) in a September 1389 survey[20]

Cattle on low-lying pastures were beginning to be worth more as dairy animals than purely for breeding replacement oxen. Even though the bishop's household does not seem to have eaten very much cheese, there was an increasing trend towards letting out some grassland specifically for 'bovine lactage'. In general, the Worcester diocesan estate seems to have retained direct control of its land for longer than many. Thus the sheep data in the table on p. 116 show that the flock was still being managed centrally, with most of the two-year-old stock and ewes at these seven manors, but most of the lambs elsewhere. The woodland and meadows were often the last to be farmed out, and right up until the early 1500s the Worcester demesne meadows at Kempsey and Hartlebury were still held in hand for the bishop.

Harrowing with a horse, not oxen. Ripple misericord, Worcestershire, c.1420

THE LOOK OF THE LAND

A partial snapshot of what the landscape looked like beyond the church estates can be gleaned from the Inquisitions Post Mortem (IPMs). Until the system was abolished during the Commonwealth period, the monarch had rights over all the land held at the time of a lay person's death, and particular attention was of course paid to the richest families. If there was an heir who was of age, a fee had to be paid; if the heir was disputed, they had to be confirmed or the lands fell into the monarch's hands; if the heir was a child, the Crown collected the revenues until they came of age. In all cases, an inquisition was held following the death of the previous land-holder, involving a jury of local people. Although most IPMs underestimate the annual value of elements of estates, they are still a useful source.

An obvious bias is that IPMs only cover land held by someone who has died, so they cannot offer a full cross-section at a given date, in the way that surveys can. But a comparison of two superficially different counties, like Herefordshire and Wiltshire, can reveal some contrasts and similarities.

	Herefordshire	Wiltshire
% of the county covered	0.45%	0.2%
value of the manorial buildings	nil, even at Weobley castle	nil
additional buildings and income	weekly market 30s., 1 warren nil	1 old dove-cote 2s. 2d.
		5 water-mills, 1 nil, others mean = 24s. 2d.
rents from tenants	7 manors, mean = 57s.	9 manors, mean = 35s. 7d.
arable land	mean = 2 ½d. an acre	mean = 2 ½ d. an acre
meadow	mean = 1s. 3d. an acre	9 manors, mean = 1s. 2d. an acre
parks	4 manors had one, grazing over upkeep av. 5s. 10d.	none
pasture	6 manors, mean = 2d. an acre	7 manors, mean = 3d. an acre
woodland	5 manors, 3 nil value, mean = 2d. an acre	4 manors, 3 nil, 1 at 3d. an acre
*Herefordshire manors in the parishes of: Monington on Wye, Dilwyn, Eaton Tregoes (now Hole in the Wall on English bank, and on Welsh bank now Inglestone Farm; both now in parish of Foy), Lyonshall, Dorstone, Bishopstone, Snodhill, Credenhill, Tyberton and Weobley; **Wiltshire manors**: Little Bedwyn, 1 messuage in Chelworth, Little Bedwyn, Tisbury, Fonthill Gifford, Farnell, Trow, Figheldean, West Grimstead and Plaitford.*		

Comparison of IPMs for assets of ten manors in each of Herefordshire and Wiltshire 1420s and early 1430s, (all deceased land-holders were of the rank of knight or lower)[21]

Most of these manors were in a generally poor state of maintenance, had degraded woodland, and the landlords in both counties were now relying on rents for a large part of their income. Valuations per acre of arable, meadow and pasture were very similar, although pasture may have been worth more in Wiltshire. One should not read too much into this small sample, but the percentage of different categories of land-use on these 20 manorial holdings is interesting, as shown below.

	arable	meadow	pasture	wood
Herefordshire	65%	7%	10%	18%
Wiltshire	62%	5%	31%	2%

Relative areas of different land use in ten Herefordshire and ten Wiltshire manors

Both counties appear to have a reduced acreage of arable, down from the peak of about 80% a century earlier. The difference in pastureland may be exaggerated, not least because of unquantified free access to communal grazing land. At Monnington on Wye the IPM specifies that the estate gains nothing from the commons 'because the tenants have rights there'. But the woodland figures complement the pasture ones, and both fit with what is known from other sources, Wiltshire being an open pasture county while Herefordshire was more wooded. Interestingly, the Herefordshire parks seem to be in the process of changing from hunting grounds for the lord of the manor into enclosed private grazing land.

Autumn pig-killing — was this aspiration, or the new reality for many? Ripple misericord, c.1420

LOOKING AHEAD

In Herefordshire, the reduced population levels and new freedoms helped the development of new types of farming. The more prosperous survivors of the old peasantry were able to rent their holdings on more liberal terms, faced less pressure on the land and more opportunity to experiment with new methods and crops; but they still had enough labour available to help as and when needed. They called themselves yeomen. This system is markedly different from some other parts of the country, notably East Anglia, where the great church estates were often replaced after the Reformation by lay landlords and a dual 'lord and peasant' system persisted for many more years.

By the seventeenth century, the rural population here had evolved into four new categories. Gentlemen would aspire not to work the land. Yeomen were what we might now call farmers (many of them tenants). Husbandmen were smallholders, often needing extra employment to supplement their income. Labourers were cottagers who cultivated their garden plots and also worked for others. But self-identification did not always correlate with the opinion of the neighbours, and there was much overlap. For example, Anthony Browne of Avenbury died in 1674, leaving an estate valued at £167; his neighbours styled him 'gentleman' in his inventory. George Winton, of nearby Thornbury, died the following year with an estate of £210, but he called himself 'yeoman' in his will. Some yeomen were much poorer, for instance Giles Josling of Bridstow's inventory was valued at just under £6, while the husbandman David Price of Fownhope had an estate of £26, and the labourer Thomas Jones of Kington's was valued at over £14 (mostly in debts due to him); all these three died in 1675.

As we move into the modern period, we are suddenly able to name our Herefordshire farmers and their families, to focus in detail on what enterprises they were choosing, and in some cases to see what land they held, where they lived and how they marketed their produce.

Droving and Markets

Droving is one of the most romanticised aspects of farming, with a plethora of books claiming to trace and follow 'the old drove roads'. The best are based on fact – a handful of written accounts, or early photographs from the last days of droving before the railways became the main arteries of livestock transport. More often, the tales are probably hearsay, or an amalgam of individual events woven into a convenient story.

In essence, droving is the movement of live animals from any area of surplus (often but not always the uplands) to places where demand is greater. At its eighteenth- and nineteenth-century peak, this was mainly but not exclusively to feed London, with long supply routes for both cattle and sheep reaching back to Scotland and Wales. As early as the seventeenth century, however, Dorset and Somerset farmers were already fattening and sending cattle to London, as noted by the contemporary antiquarian, William Camden.

No matter how far the driven stock went, they needed a good route to market, and in many cases between successive markets along to their final destination. A classic example is that of Anglesey cattle being collected and swum to the mainland at a safe crossing-point, as described in this eighteenth-century journal:

> at the ferry, it fortunately happened that several herds of black cattle that had been
> reared in Anglesey were then crossing the strait, on their road to Abergeley fair,
> where they are bought up by drovers, and disposed of at Barnet fair to farmers
> in the neighbourhood, who fatten them for the London market ... The town of
> Abergeley is a place of considerable resort on account of its large cattle fairs,
> where the Anglesey oxen are for the most part disposed of to the English graziers.[1]

Where there was a choice, drovers would have picked level, well-drained and shel-tered routes, for the benefit of themselves and their charges alike.

Both drovers and driven also needed food and drink, whether grazing and water from ponds, or supplied by inns and farms along the way. Even after the three-week walk from central Wales to the outskirts of London, Welsh drovers are reputed to have aimed for a maximum 5% loss of weight in their cattle. Partly this was achieved by protecting the feet of the animals, especially if they were being driven on hard roads. Geese, which from the sixteenth century were brought to London from Norfolk and Suffolk for the Christmas market, could have their feet protected with soft tar and sand, making a hard-wearing surface. Sheep and the occasional herds of pigs wore leather boots, or woollen ones with leather soles. Cattle needed something heavier, and they were usually shod with half-moon shaped metal *cues*, one for each half of the hoof.

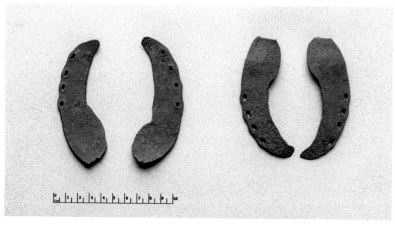

Ox cues, from Hampton Lucy, Warwickshire. (Hereford Museum acc. no. 873)

The Earliest Evidence

Analysis of livestock bones and teeth has revealed important information on late Stone Age droving. The technique relies on the fact that grazing animals absorb strontium from the grass, and this is deposited in their bodies. Strontium has two isotopes, Sr87 and Sr86, and the ratio of these varies according to the underlying rocks. It is deposited permanently in tooth enamel, while the inner dentine and the bones lack this permanent marker and instead reflect recent grazing pastures. Because livestock teeth erupt at specific known ages, it is possible to establish where they grazed while immature, by analysing their successive 'strontium signatures'.

At Durrington Walls, a site near Stonehenge that has been dated to about 2,500 BC, the rubbish pits contain large quantities of cattle bones. Analysis of some of the teeth has shown that only a few animals were bred on chalk land, while over half came from some distance away. The most likely places of origin for these were the Malverns, Devon or Cornwall, Wales, Herefordshire, Cumbria or just possibly Scotland. In some cases, it seems that the cattle were moved in stages, with different isotopic ratios in different age teeth, compatible with being bred in south central Wales, perhaps, and stopping for some time en route. It is interesting in this context that the famous 'bluestones' of Stonehenge themselves come from an area of Wales with a strontium signature compatible with that found in the older cattle teeth.[2]

Livestock cannot normally be driven through another farmer's land without their permission. This is perhaps self-evident, but it tends to be overlooked in many discussions of droving. It means that wherever stock was moved through farmed land, there must have been thoroughfares available for 'through traffic', suggesting a high degree of landscape organisation. This would be true of pastoral farming, and even more so with a higher proportion of arable. So, if Herefordshire was indeed seeing the passage of 'Welsh' cattle from this early period, this should help shape our understanding of the development of the early field boundaries and trackways.

A more local excavation, on the site where the Hive building in Worcester now stands, provides evidence for the movement of cattle to supply the Roman city. Strontium, oxygen and carbon isotope analyses of late-Roman cattle teeth show that none of the animals whose remains were tested had been born or fattened around Worcester, but came from a variety of possible locations to the north or west, including the south-west of England, Herefordshire, south Wales, Cumbria and the Malverns. Two in particular were consistent with having been raised on the Old Red Sandstone of Herefordshire. Again we have evidence suggesting early 'droving' from and through Herefordshire, although by this time the availability of salting technology means that some of this meat may not have arrived on the hoof, but pre-butchered.[3]

Welsh Cattle to Herefordshire Markets

The impulse for the flourishing of historical droving across Herefordshire is likely to have been the marketing of upland Welsh livestock and their dispersal around the lower-lying richer land where they could be fattened. This was mediated through several relatively specialised and heavily regulated fairs, which sometimes lasted for several days. Fairs often coincided with a religious festival, so that the owner of the fair and the local church could both benefit. A market of some sort is mentioned at Hereford in Domesday Book, but the earliest official fair in the county was an annual three-day event (later extended to nine days), established by Royal Charter in 1121 at Hereford, for the Feast of St Ethelbert. The bishopric was granted the right to levy tolls on those bringing produce to sell, and the cathedral gained from having more pilgrims visiting. By the early nineteenth century, the city's fairs had become spread through the year, on the Tuesday after 2 February, the Wednesday in Holy Week, 19 May (the Eve of St Ethelbert), 1 July and 20 October.

On the same route as Hereford, going towards the Worcestershire border, Ledbury received a charter for a Sunday market a few years later, in 1138.[4] Elizabeth I granted the town a weekly Tuesday market and two fairs, on the Festivals of

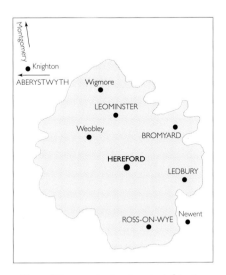

Map of the county showing stock fair sites

Ledbury's impressive two-storey market building, built in 1617

St Philip and St James the Less (1 May) and St Barnabas (11 June), and then in 1617 a group of eminent townsmen built The Market House, around which the Tuesday and Saturday markets are still held today. In the eighteenth and nineteenth centuries, there were seven annual fairs, including one on 21 December for 'horned cattle', pigs and cheese.

On a more northerly route, Knighton seems to have been established very early as a market place for Welsh cattle. An Anglo-Saxon fortified settlement, it became a borough in 1203 with a charter for a weekly market and an annual fair. The town was in England until 1536, after which it was transferred to Wales under the Acts of Union. It is at a key point on the road from Aberystwyth into England as well as on the route from Montgomery down to Hereford, and for many years it held one of the three largest fairs in Wales.[5] Unlike most small towns, the importance of Knighton to stock farmers has continued. There is a weekly market for lambs and cull ewes, fortnightly ones for store cattle and sheep, and special autumn sales of cross-bred ewes, weaned calves and young store cattle. As in many towns, the stock were tethered in the main streets until the twentieth century when they were moved out to new market places.

Further to the east, Wigmore had a small St James' Day fair in July and, after 1610, a second one in April. On this same route, Leominster also had an ancient stock fair, established for Michaelmas (late September) by Henry II in 1170. But after a century, the superior political weight of Hereford had resulted in this being stopped, for fear of competition. Trading continued, however, focussing more on animal by-products as time went by, especially wool, leather and cloth. The fair was re-founded by Mary Tudor in 1554, for horse and cattle sales, and by the early nineteenth century there were seven fairs spread from February to December. A measure of its continued importance as a marketing hub is that at the turn of the nineteenth century Leominster had more pubs per head of population than any other town in the county. The name of one, *The Bull's Head*, hints at its role in the cattle trade.[6]

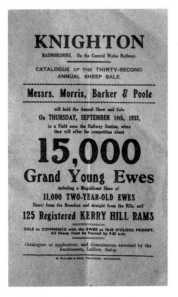

Knighton sheep sale catalogue, 1933 (Knighton Museum)

From Leominster, and following the approximate route of the modern A44, eastward-moving livestock would next reach Bromyard. The fairs and markets in this episcopal borough were probably founded before 1285, when market tolls, fines and other profits totalled £14, representing almost a fifth of the bishop's income from the manor.[7] For many years, the main Bromyard fair was on Whit Monday, with five or six others added later, on Mondays in January and May, and three Thursday fairs for Lady Day (March), the feast of St James the Great (July) and one in October. Although the main market area was approximately where the present market square is, an early map suggests it was much bigger, extending over some neighbouring streets. A large Market Hall was demolished in 1844. The Bromyard fairs seem to have been more mixed than many, and the early street names shed light on the arrangement of their livestock zones, with Sheep Street, Swine Street and some evidence that cattle were sold at the western end of High Street, while the horse fair was probably on the Tenbury Road towards the Fair Cross and Porthouse ('portus' meaning a market). There must also have been a substantial market for arable goods and non-perishable items including wool and leather goods. The Bromyard Bushel, dating from 1670 and used to test the accuracy of traders' own measures, still survives (*see overleaf*).

Two other towns, Ross and Weobley, also held fairs, while Newent, just over the border into Gloucestershire, had a weekly cattle market founded in 1253, the charter for which refers specifically to it being for 'the Welshmen who come ... to

The Bromyard bushel, 1670

sell their cattle'. In later centuries, the Newent fair mainly acted as a distribution point for the cattle of North Wales, which must have been driven diagonally down across Herefordshire.

The Legal Framework

The earliest written evidence for droving here may be in the laws of King Æthelstan, grandson of Alfred the Great, from about 926. While being mainly concerned with controlling the Welsh border, it refers to the abuse of cattle tracks along and across the lower Wye, presumably by cross-border rustlers, and could imply that there was already a regular cattle trade. Having been brought up in Mercia, King Æthelstan must have understood Herefordshire well.[8] His Laws included detailed clauses aimed at secure cattle ownership, trade and punishments for theft, and also prevention of 'forestalling', the age-old practice of selling outside markets so as to avoid tolls and price-regulation, which was particularly relevant for high-value goods like cattle.

By the sixteenth century, fear of vagrants was mounting as their numbers increased, and concerns about the potential cost of maintaining them (and controlling their perceived predisposition towards petty crime) grew. This led to new legislation regulating the drovers who by this time must have been making regular journeys from Wales over the border, including into Herefordshire. Edward VI (1547–53) and later Queen Elizabeth I enacted statutes requiring drovers and livestock dealers to be married householders aged at least 30 and of good character, and not hired servants. This meant that they could be traced more easily. They had to apply for and obtain a licence for a shilling, from the local Quarter Sessions. For a further 8d. they then registered the licence with the Clerk of the Peace, who recorded the name, address and licence type of each drover. This legislation was not repealed until 1772, and means that in some places there is a significant amount of personal detail about individual drovers.

Under the Stuarts, further laws aimed at the cattle trade were introduced, including one of 1676 which required that 'no drover, horsecourser, waggoner, butcher, higler or any of their servants shall travel or come into an Inn ... upon the Lord's Day ... on pain that each and every such offender shall forfeit 20s. for every such offence'. This law may be the one under which two Welsh drovers were convicted for profanation of the Sabbath by driving cattle through Mordiford in 1817.[9]

Road-side pond where the Aberystwyth to London road drops down from Bringsty Common before crossing into Worcestershire

The Buyers and Sellers

Until the eighteenth century, Herefordshire itself may have been the place where much of the fattening of Welsh cattle took place. The county developed a reputation as a prime location for mixed farming, epitomised by Camden's description of it in 1610 as:

> ... right pleasant for yeelding of courne and feeding of cattle in all places most fruitful, and therewith passing well furnished with all things necessary for man's life. In so much as it would scorne to come behind any one country throughout all England for fertility of soil, and therefore say that for three WWW, wheat, woll and water, it yeeldeth to no shire in England.

This mix of lush pastures and well-fertilised arable land, and specialising in 'corn-cat-tle' husbandry, is thought to have made it one of the few Midlands counties which had a surplus of grain for export.

One solitary document gives a glimpse into the shape of livestock trading in this period. Having been recently restarted by a charter of Queen Mary Tudor in 1554, the transactions at one Leominster 'horse and beast' fair of 1556 survive.[10] The fair was mostly dealing with horses and cattle, with a few small groups of sheep. Some of the 200 or so sales include the places of origin of vendor and purchaser and also the price paid, which enables some interesting comparisons to be made. Of course, this one isolated example may be unrepresentative, but some general patterns do seem to emerge.

Firstly, many sellers were from Wales, and most of the buyers were from Her-efordshire. (There were notable exceptions, such as John Addis from Chirton in Wiltshire, 85 miles (135 km) from Leominster, who brought three riding horses to the fair and sold them to Robert Hawley of Avenbury). Of the Welshmen, many had come from Radnorshire or further west along the roads to Aberystwyth and Cardigan. Most of the stock remained in the county or was taken further east, perhaps using pre-existing contacts and business networks. For example, Thomas Brook came over from Hampton Lovett in Worcestershire (32 miles) and bought up nine old cows from sellers from Radnorshire, Kington, Kingsland, Pembridge and Dilwyn. Many of the cheapest (and perhaps the oldest?) oxen were bought up by dealers from Birmingham, which was a leather and horn processing centre. But again, a few buyers were coming down from as far afield as Cheshire, Staffordshire and Lancashire.

The prices of stock traded at this particular fair give some clues to the state of the Herefordshire market at this time. The horses were much less valuable than cattle. Cows and bullocks were about 25s., while oxen were much the most expensive, averaging 30–40s. with several fetching 50s. or more. And when the sales are divided by place of origin, the role of the market in this west-east trade seems to become visible. The bullocks and oxen from Wales were sold for an average of 26s., the oxen being only slightly more valuable than the bullocks; the three oxen and three bullocks from Radnorshire averaged 31s. 6d., with almost no difference between them; but the 16 Herefordshire oxen sold for an average of 43s., with two fetching 53s. It might be inferred, then, that part of the function of this Leominster fair was to channel young bullocks and other stock from Wales into Herefordshire, to English cattle farmers who in turn brought their surplus mature oxen back for sale at a substantially increased price. Thus, Richard Grey of Norton bought two bullocks and a heifer from Thomas ap Evan of Llangeryk, Montgomeryshire, for a total of just 40s.; William Coulcombe of Dilwyn sold an ox to Rafe Good of Thornbury for 33s.; but Anselm Nott of Shelsley, on the Worcestershire border, bought what must surely have been a fine specimen from William Passey of Presteigne for 53s.

Droving to London

Although London was not the only urbanising area in Britain by the eighteenth century, its growth had the widest impact. From a population calculated by Gregory King in 1688 to be 527,000, it had increased to 630,000 in 1715, 740,000 in 1760, and then the city doubled in size by 1815 and more than doubled again (to over 3 million) by 1860.[11] At first, neighbouring counties were able to supply most of its demand for horses, grain, dairy products and meat, but before long many of these supplies had to be sourced from further away, including foodstuffs of all kinds, cereals for beer and increasingly gin, and cider. As part of this new situation, the droving trade rapidly expanded into the now-familiar long-distance routes which survived until they were finally supplanted by the railways in the later nineteenth century.

In London, the main meat market was still on the original livestock site at Smithfield, now much-diminished from its medieval green acres as it became hemmed in by the growing city through which the animals had to be driven. By the 1740s, the market was handling 500,000 sheep and 74,000 cattle a year, and the numbers continued to increase until a campaign to re-site the market in the suburbs began in the 1840s – led among others by Charles Dickens, who described the old market in *Oliver Twist*:

> The ground was covered, nearly ankle-deep, with filth and mire; a thick steam, perpetually rising from the reeking bodies of the cattle ... hung heavily above. All the pens in the centre of the large area, and as many temporary pens as could be crowded into the vacant space, were filled with sheep; tied up to posts by the gutter side were long lines of beasts and oxen, three or four deep. Countrymen, butchers, drovers, hawkers, boys, thieves, idlers, and vagabonds of every low grade, were mingled together in a mass; the whistling of drovers, the barking of dogs, the bellowing and plunging of oxen, the bleating of sheep, the grunting and squeaking of pigs, the cries of hawkers, the shouts, oaths, and quarrelling on all sides ... the crowding, pushing, driving, beating, whooping, and yelling; the hideous and discordant din that resounded from every corner of the market; and the unwashed, unshaven, squalid, and dirty figures constantly running to and fro ... rendered it a stunning and bewildering scene, which quite confounded the senses.[12]

The growth in London's population, and its rising demand for meat, coincided with two outbreaks of rinderpest in the first half of the eighteenth century. In 1714, about 5,500 adult cattle and 500 calves were destroyed in Middlesex, Essex and Surrey, but the Justices were able to prevent further spread by enforcing government regulations, including a generous 40s. compensation for every head of infected cattle killed and burnt, quarantine for infected farms and farm workers, and powers to prevent sick cows being moved and sold elsewhere. The second outbreak was less well managed and spread more widely, lasting from 1745–59; together these crises allowed long-distance droving to break into the London market.

For over a century, Welsh and Herefordshire drovers formed part of the chain moving stock into the capital. The last generation of these men can be seen in early photographs, taken shortly before the railways destroyed their way of life. But evidence for them remains, in other ways, not always reliable but tantalisingly evocative, and perhaps above all in the field-names they may have given to farms they returned home to or places they lived in for their old age.

Examples of London field-names in Herefordshire

field name	parish	field numbers
Smithfield	Almeley	11, 13
Little London	Sutton St Nicholas	95, 96, 165, 166, 167, 169, 170, 171, 174, 175
Little London	St Weonards	511, 512, 513
Little London	Yarpole	765
Picadilly	Craswall	168
Piccadilly	Ashperton	202 & 209
Piccadilly	Bromyard	60
Piccadilly	Vowchurch	220, 223, 224, 225, 226
Piccadilly	Walford	1/2
Hackney	Dilwyn	616
Hackney	Mathon	260
Charing Cross	Weobley	199, 200, 201, 206, 207, 209, 210, 211, 212, 213, 214, 215
Hyde Park	Bishops Frome	101
Holborn	Stoke Prior	544, 545, 547, 596, 597, 598, 599, 600
Holborn	Upton Bishop	54
Holborn	Ledbury	165

The height of long-distance droving coincided with the peak period for the operation of toll roads, and it is to this phase that stories of herds and flocks being taken over the higher ground, away from roads where charges were made, belong. But even so, overnight grazing entailed a fee, for some time a halfpenny per head of cattle. This may well explain the occasional 'Ha'penny Green', numerous Penny Meadows and similar field-names, for instance at Preston on Wye (field 298) near Hereford, and on Bromyard Downs (29 and 36). On the Welsh border near Hay-on-Wye, the Rhydspence Inn probably became a regular stopping point for drovers wanting either to ford the Wye in summer, or perhaps to shoe their cattle before continuing north of the river on hard-surfaced English roads. Three of the fields adjacent to the inn are called the Penny, Halfpenny and Farthing Fields.

The Rhydspence Inn, near Whitney on Wye

Herefordshire in Context

The traditional image of droving is perhaps of Scottish herds and flocks making their way down the Great North Road, some for breeders in East Anglia or for York and many for Smithfield, and this was indeed a major supply route for hundreds of years. Other, smaller, avenues made their contribution as well: in 1663 alone, over 18,000 cattle entered England through Carlisle, and by the late eighteenth century 10,000 left Anglesey each year at the start of a long droving journey. Later, Irish livestock were imported in increasing numbers through Liverpool, many to be driven across the Pennines for fattening in Yorkshire and then sold in the north of England: in 1831 for example, 90,000 cattle, 135,000 sheep and 156,000 pigs were moved in this way.[13] Droving from south and central Wales, together with stock reared or fattened in Herefordshire, was a long-standing part of this complex network, as we have seen, even if it is less well known. About 30,000 cattle were sold in Hereford in peak years, and many of these were ultimately taken on to London. So, it would be safe to say that much of the 'beef of Old England' consumed in our cities and on our ships was in fact not only Scottish or Irish, but Welsh too.

Draught Animals: Ox or Horse?

Mention of 'traditional' farming may call to mind images of heavy horses, whether for ploughing, carting or road-work, but there is no doubt that oxen were the early draught animals of choice in England and Wales, and continued to be used for many centuries. It was only relatively recently that horses replaced them, and even then the transition was uneven, with Herefordshire being one of the last bastions of ox-teams.

Domesday Book has unequivocal evidence that a standard team comprised eight oxen – four pairs – in every county where information was gathered – so much so that multiples of eight oxen also featured in land measurements. In Kent the basic unit was four yokes, and in the north-east the plough-land became a caracute in Domesday, divided into eight oxgangs or bovates. Elsewhere, including Herefordshire, land was divided into hides, varying in size according to its quality, but representing the area one team could plough. In Wales the same standard may have applied. The Laws said to have been codified by Hywel the Good (920–948) required 12 men to provide each team, with one supplying the wooden frame, another the iron share and coulter, and eight giving an ox each; one did the ploughing and the final man called commands to the animals, walking near their heads.[1]

Experimental ploughing with one yoke of oxen, at Butser Ancient Farm
(© Peter J. Reynolds)

As time went on, horses began to be used for farm work in some places. The earliest-known references are from twelfth-century East Anglian manors with light soils. An inventory for Bury St Edmunds includes a team of two oxen and three horses at Elvedon in the Breckland, six oxen and two horses at Groton, and two ploughs of six oxen and two horses and a third team of eight horses at Somer. There is similar evidence on the St Pauls' manor of Sandon, Hertfordshire, where teams ranged from six horses to six horses and four oxen, although the norm may have been four of each.[2]

There is no detailed early evidence from Herefordshire, but in neighbouring Worcester diocese a survey of the bishop's manors in 1290 recorded 67 horses and 542 oxen. Most of these horses must have been for riding. Even 100 years later, oxen were still clearly favoured there, with a total of 58 horses of all kinds on thirteen manors, compared with 202 oxen. Some of these horses were by now carthorses, but ploughing still seems to have been done by oxen.

The Worcester bishop's few medieval carthorses were seldom fed grain, unless doing very heavy work or if ill; only the riding horses of officials regularly had oats. In other counties, working horses were regularly fed supplements to grass and hay.[3] The thirteenth-century Bishop Swinfield of Hereford is known to have had many riding horses of his own, but carthorses were also used to transport his household goods on his frequent journeys, and he certainly found the horse-fodder a drain on his purse. They were grazed outside in June and July, then hay was added to their diet. From autumn through to June they were fed on hay and a significant volume of oats. Hay and oats often had to be carted around the diocese, further adding to the expense. For instance, in 1289 the surplus old hay from the last season was taken to Bosbury from Bromyard, where it had been made on the bishop's Upper Rompeney meadow. Sometimes, the episcopal horses' diets were supplemented with grain even in summer, as happened when the household reached Whitbourne on 17 June 1289.[4]

This costly feeding regime for working horses corresponds closely to the advice given in a seminal treatise, Walter of Henley's *Le Dite de Hosebondrie* (c.1270–1300). This was one of the earliest detailed descriptions of farming practice in northern Europe to be written by someone with practical experience (Walter seems to have worked as a farm bailiff before becoming a monk). He said that oxen are more sturdy and longer-working than horses, especially on heavy soil, as well as much cheaper to keep, but you needed more of them. Crucially, at the end of their working life, oxen were fattened for meat but horses were so seldom used for human food. Walter noted that horses were costly to shoe and recommended that from October to May, plough horses should be stalled and fed every night on 'at least a sixth of a bushel of oats and chaff'. In much medieval farm practice, this regime was exceeded. For instance, on the Westminster Abbey manor of Stevenage in 1273–74, draught horses had a bushel a night from 29 Nov to 1 April, and then for the rest of April ¾ bushel, perhaps because the heavy clay soils there began growing grass late. In the Pinchbeck Register of Bury St Edmunds, c.1333, the feed rate was set at half a bushel of oats. Oxen, by contrast, were able to work on a diet of grass and hay, occasionally supplemented with unthreshed oats, and Walter clearly considered them to be the principal draught animals.[5]

This fundamental distinction, costly but strong horses versus economical and versatile oxen, continued to dominate the debate about the choice of draught animals for centuries to come.

The Fourteenth-century Shock

One unique Herefordshire inventory for Garway, dated 1308, shows that oxen here were still the major draught animals at this time. This large estate had one riding horse, three carthorses and eight other farm horses. By contrast there were 60 oxen, 7 young oxen, 16 cows, 14 calves and 1 bull.[6]

The bovine murrain of 1319–20 began in Essex and spread west. No Herefordshire data is available, but whereas two-thirds of cattle died in East Anglia, in the western counties of Monmouthshire, Gloucestershire, Worcestershire and Shropshire mortality was 'only' about a half. In general the plough oxen, which had a better diet, survived better than other cattle, but even so this event was a huge shock to the rural economy. It took a minimum of four years to breed and train new oxen, even if bulls and cows were available, and it seems that in the short term horses took over at least part of the draught work. By 1330, oxen were back up to about 85% of pre-murrain levels nationwide, but the reduced human population caused by famine and then plague meant that the numbers never fully recovered. There was, however, a clear change in the east of England, perhaps in part continuing earlier trends and partly no doubt because of higher mortality of oxen in 1319–20. Horse numbers in the east doubled from 34% to 68% of farm draught stock between 1318 and 1350.[7]

By contrast, the sales at Leominster Fair in 1556, referred to previously, demonstrate that oxen continued to be very much in demand in Herefordshire, far exceeding the value of the horses on offer. Of the 16 Herefordshire oxen sold in this one day's trading, two transactions are representative: George Cowper of Wacton bought a black ox from Thomas Sucker of Logaston for 46s., while William Wynston of Dinedor sold a yoke of oxen, one black and the other red, to William Jeffries of Hom Castle, Worcestershire, for 96s. 8d. A few geldings sold for over 30s., but mares were typically valued at 20s. or less; one of the most highly-priced was a roan mare 'with a white face and four white socks', sold by Stephen Bull of Radnorshire to Thomas Stevens of Huntington for 24s.[8]

Regional Differences

Between about 1500 and 1750 there was a change to horses for farm work in most parts of England. Nationwide surveys of thousands of inventories and wills show that from 1580 to 1660 oxen were still common in the north and west, from Bristol and Devon to Lichfield, Stockport, Yorkshire and Durham. But they were already scarce or actually absent from areas further east, including Bedfordshire, Leicestershire and parts of Essex and Cheshire. It is not entirely clear what drove this divergence, but local traditions surely played a large part, since even gentlemen farmers were following the regional trends rather than leading the move to horses.

This contrast can be seen in two examples. Firstly, Robert Bulkeley of Anglesey kept a diary in the 1630s, which includes his sales at the annual August Newborough Cattle Fair by the Menai Straits. He was selling, or occasionally buying, draught beasts every year, presumably to balance the teams before autumn cultivation. He was clearly part of a continuing tradition of using oxen.

Robert Bulkeley of Anglesey's sales and purchases of oxen

year	sold	bought	price	price per head
1631	a yoke of oxen		£6	60s.
1632	6 oxen		£10 3s. 4d.	33s. 8d.
1633	4 runts*		£13	65s.
1634	4 runts*		£16	80s.
1634		2 runts*	£5 16s. 8d.	58s. 4d.
1635	8 oxen		£26 16s.	67s.

runt: a small ox, typically reared in Wales and Scotland at this period; not necessarily an inferior beast.

Between 1610 and 1620, on the other hand, the farm accounts of Robert Loder of Harwell, on the edge of the Berkshire Downs, reveal an area that had already opted for horse-power. His four farm horses were stabled from late October, while contemporary advice was that oxen could safely remain outside until December. In 1612, Loder notes that he had to begin feeding hay to his horses in early September, which was six weeks earlier than normal, and he seems to have fed them a better diet than many, supplementing even their summer grazing with vetches, barley-malt or peas. He calculated that the horses' hay this year cost him £16 12s. 10d., and their beans, malt and oats a further £9 12s. 8d. He also had to shoe the horses frequently, which added further to the expense, but on the plus side he estimated that the stabled horses had produced £3 worth of dung, or 60 loads.[9]

Another point of comparison was in the harness needed. Oxen used a yoke for each pair of beasts, a thick piece of wood lying forward of their shoulders, a collar

Ornate ox yoke, courtesy of Mrs Janet Legge

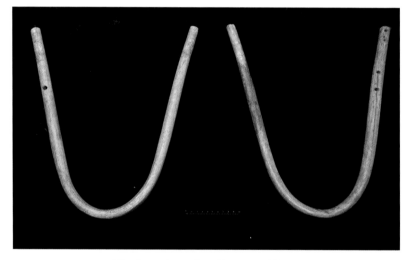

Wooden ox-bows, from Brampton Abbotts
(Hereford Museum acc. nos. 4276/1 and 4276/2)

traditionally of wooden ox-bows to hold it in place, and a simple system of traces. Horses, by contrast needed bridles, bits, nose bands, tail or back band, some sort of saddle pad to spread the weight, collars made from canvas, leather or tough hemp and then stuffed with straw or wool, and ropes (usually hemp) to run along the horse's side. Loder calculated that in 1612 he had spent over £1 on his farm horses' tack, apart from outgoings on fodder and on saddles and girths for riding:

Outgoings for 1612 for farm horses' tack

item	cost
flax collars	1s. 6d.
hames*	6d.
traces	2s. 6d.
hemp halters	1s. 5 d.
shoeing	10s. 11d.
white-leather**	5s.
TOTAL OUTLAY FOR THE YEAR	£1 1s. 10d.

hames: two pieces of slightly curved oak or ash (later replaced with metal), joined at the bottom and attached to the collar, with hooks and chains to take the traces;
*** probably for running repairs.*

As time went on, and especially as London grew to dominate the markets of southern England, increasing urban demand for dairy products, beef and horses together helped to change farm practice in areas closest to cities. Old coach and dray horses found uses on the farms of the southeast, as fallow acreage decreased and it became fashionable to harrow and roll more, for which the nimbler horses were more suited than oxen. Many farmers also preferred to keep a pair of horses for carting; even for tilling, with the new lighter plough designs, heavy horses were often able to outperform oxen. Cattle began to become specialised for dairy, beef or draught uses, and then they diverged into breeds which were described. By the late eighteenth century, oxen were largely restricted to the uplands and south-west, Herefordshire, the Weald and parts of Lincolnshire.

Tack for a draught horse, Bredenbury, 1920 (BDLHS Picture Archive)

Herefordshire Oxen

Devereux Pember of Newport House, who farmed land in Almeley, Kington, Brilley and Eardisley, left a series of livestock bequests to his wife and some of his 11 children in 1616. Together they indicate the relative numbers of oxen and horses he kept:

> ... unto my wife six oxen ten kyne two Bullocks and seven heyfers of three yeres old a peece ... my two best mares my best nagg, two Colts six weaning calves ... unto Frannces my sonne and heire fower oxen twoe bullocks of three yeres old a peece six kyne twoe heifers of two yeres old a peece ... a mare and one nagg. ... unto my sonne Thomas fower Bullocks of fower yeres ould a peece, fower kyne ... unto my sonne in lawe James Parrye and unto my Daughter his wife all such Oxen I gave in there use and possession.

In total, he bequeathed 10 oxen, 8 bullocks, 20 cows, 9 heifers, 6 calves and 7 horses to his wife and two eldest sons.

Some surviving records from the Wigmore fairs held around 1700 give more insight into the continuing demand here for working cattle. Neither horses nor bovids at market can be absolutely identified as draught animals in these documents: 'beasts', 'cattle' and 'cows with calves' might all be part of this enterprise. But including only oxen and bullocks, which are highly likely to be draught animals, there were at least 252 sold, compared with a total of 303 horses, geldings, mares and 'mares with colts', which had multiple uses beyond farm work. Most of the cattle were bought by farmers or dealers living within 15 miles of Wigmore, although a few went outside the county.[10]

Probate records give more specific information, and a large sample of these have been investigated for this book, to gain insight into the choices our farmers were making.

From a sample of 102 pre-1600 Herefordshire wills that mention farming, a third include specific bequests of oxen or bullocks. Two widows from the north of the county are representative. Maud Bouley of Humber, who died in 1567, first mentioned her wain, two oxen, yokes and a plough; she also bequeathed three other cattle to her children, a three-year-old bullock, a year-old calf and a red heifer; in addition there were bequests of 8 sheep, and finally her executor was given her grey mare. Elizabeth Partriche of Kings Pyon died in 1584 and her will gives even more detail. She left her family two head of cattle called Rosse and Rope, an ox named Scarlet, two other oxen and a bullock, a yearling bullock, one heifer and five young cattle; her three servants were given two sheep and a heifer calf; there are also mentions of a grey horse and hemp, wheat and other grain. All the remaining farm and household goods were left to her executor.

Of a sample of 120 farming wills from 1610 to 1640, chosen to capture all months and all parts of the county, 38 mention oxen, bullocks or yokes, but none have any mention of working horses or their harness. So at least a third of farms in the county still owned working cattle; those that did not, presumably shared or hired plough teams from neighbours. This is supported by the wills from after the Civil War, when inventories of personal effects survive in large numbers, so the detail of goods on each farm becomes visible. The table below summarises the working animals recorded in inventories from 1675 to 1750, when this information ends.

Summary of all draught animals itemised in sample inventories, 1675 to 1750

year (and sample size):	1675 (75)	1700 (68)	1725 (75)	1750 (31)
no. with oxen	29	37	25	9
mean number of oxen on farm	4	5	4.5	4.5
modal value of oxen per head	£4	£4 10s.	£4 – 5	£3 – 5
no. with bullocks	13	13	13	4
mean number of bullocks	3	4	2	4.5
modal value of bullocks per head	£2 10s.	very varied	a few over £4	£2 – 3
no. mentioning yoke	26	10	19	4
no. with working horses	0	2	3	4
no. mentioning horse harness	2	1	2	2

These probates suggest that it was only after the Commonwealth period that working horses became more numerous here. Whether the dislocation caused by the Civil War was a spur to innovation, or whether exiles returned to the county bringing novel ideas and wider trade contacts with them, oxen were clearly not immediately swept away and the few people who were using horses were still atypical. An early mention of a horse harness, in 1675, is by a Leominster dyer and clothier who was also cultivating some arable fields near the town. His inventory lists three mares (together valued at £7 3s.), 'saddles, other tacklings for horses, one cart, one plow and other geares for a horse team' (£1 15s.) and hay, fodder, muck and compost. Also in 1675, Thomas Parkes of Linton near Ross had 'cow bridles, a pack saddle and horse gears', but neither oxen nor any horses at the time of his death. Yet it was clearly a working farm, with hay, straw and the winter wheat already sown, so whatever stock he had owned may already have been passed on as a bequest.

In 1700, one of the two men with working horses was also in Leominster, and was an ironmonger. He had six horses with a waggon and its tack, with a combined value of £30 5s. Whether this horse team had been used for farming, or for other work, is impossible to say.

The first rural farm in this sample which definitely had working horses was Richard Hill's at Marston in Pencombe. He died in 1700 and his inventory totalling £163 was above average in value. He had eight oxen (£32), cattle worth a further

£80, and 'four working horses' (£10), as well as 'the tack of the team, wains, ploughs, towes, harrows and all other utensils and implements of husbandry'. Here perhaps we can see a yeoman farmer dividing the workload for his draught animals, using oxen for ploughing and horses for other tasks.

By the time we get to 1725, draught horses were perhaps less rare, although they are still on fewer than 4% of farms, whereas over a third had their own oxen. For instance, Thomas Vale of Kimbolton, gentleman, was using seven working bullocks in place of oxen, worth £25, and only had two old mares, one horse and a yearling colt, together valued at £8. One of the three farms listed in the table above as having working horses was just over the county boundary to the north, at Bayton in Worcestershire, where John Kinnersley had one yoke of oxen (£11) and seven horses 'with their tackle' (£12). Again, it is not completely certain whether his horses were for farm work, but the high value of the waggon and wain (£8) suggests they were. Within Herefordshire itself, Joseph Clark of Felton was definitely using both oxen and horses, with his three yokes of oxen and their tack, as well as five horses or mares and 'horse gears, saddles, pads, bridles'. He had a substantial 74 acres of arable mentioned, and three valuable wains and a waggon. The third example of possible horse-use from 1725 is from another Leominster farm, worked by John Pumphrey. Here, one waggon was listed, with no livestock apart from five individually described mares and horses and one yearling colt, one of which had a riding saddle, and 'six pairs of horse gears'; the muck heaps, at £1 8s., were 2% of the total inventory value!

In 1750, ten out of the 31 surviving farm inventories for Herefordshire and nearby parishes include either oxen or bullocks – one of which at Little Marcle had 48. Four inventories mention working horses or their tack, but two of these are over the Shropshire border, at Neen Savage and Bromfield. At Cradley, John Gwillam was clearly making both beer (or ale) and cider in some quantity and he had a cart, plough and harrows in a designated cart-house. He had no cattle except one cow (£4 4s.), but two horses (£5 total) and their 'gearing and two pads' worth £1. At Foy, meanwhile, Richard Fisher Collins, gentleman, who seems to have been taking his farming very seriously, had three yokes of cattle (£26), six carthorses and their gears (also £26), six different waggons and wains (together worth £15) and four ploughs, two rolls and five harrows. Here, for the first time, we have a Herefordshire farmer using an integrated system of oxen for ploughing and other heavy work, and horses worth the same as the oxen, perhaps mainly for road use.

So, we can be fairly confident from these examples that through much of the eighteenth century oxen continued to be the draught animal of choice for most of our farmers, although some individuals were changing over to horses.

The Napoleonic Wars

Even in landlocked Herefordshire, the long drawn-out wars between 1793 and 1815 changed the role of draught animals. Horses were in huge demand for the army, for haulage in London and the Channel ports and on the canals, and this slowed down their final adoption on farms. At the same time, there was a big rise in the acreage of cereals needed in particular (the number of men in the Royal Navy increased by a factor of 15 to nearly 150,000), and oxen with their minimal requirement for grain were well-adapted to this task. King George III even experimented with replacing horses on the royal Home Farms with Hereford, Glamorgan and Devon oxen in 1797, but it was only worth doing if oat prices were high, and despite attempts by several gentlemen farmers in the south of England to promote oxen, the idea never took off. Instead, the areas of the country that had already switched to horses began breeding them selectively, producing riding, racing, carriage and heavier farm and dray horses for different uses.[11]

One result of this changing demand was a series of county surveys, conducted around 1800 and presented to the Board of Agriculture, a private group aiming to improve farming methods. Although the reports vary in quality depending on the methods of their authors, they enable comparisons to be made between counties at the turn of the century. On the question of horses versus oxen for farm work, they show that in the five counties of the Marches and in northern Somerset, the transition was well underway.

Comments in The Board of Agriculture Reports on draught animals

County	Proportions of oxen versus horses	Authors of reports
Cheshire	almost entirely horses	Thomas Wedge, 1794 Henry Holland, 1808
Shropshire	oxen on heavy soil, horses on lighter, but horses widely used for carting, so they predominate on small farms which cannot afford both	J. Bishton, 1794 Joseph Plymley, 1803
Herefordshire	largely oxen, for both ploughing and road work	John Clark, 1794 John Duncumb, 1805
Worcestershire	almost entirely heavy horses	William Pomeroy, 1794
Gloucestershire	depends on the region: oxen especially west of Severn and on Cotswolds. Horses predominate in the Vale	George Turner, 1794 Thomas Rudge, 1807
N. Somerset	oxen preferred for ploughing, horses for other work but they cost 30% more	John Billingsley, 1798

The Final Demise of Oxen

Only in the nineteenth century did the use of oxen finally come to an end in Herefordshire, due to a combination of several factors. Demand for horses and grain for the armed forces plummeted and heavy horse prices fell after 1815, making oxen less competitive for farm work. Demand for good quality beef rose, especially in the expanding urban areas, encouraging a switch to faster-maturing animals and away from fattening oxen after many years of draught work. New plough designs increasingly favoured horses, as did the introduction of mechanised farm implements such as early capstan-based threshing machines which relied on the faster horses to operate them. The Swing Riots in the south-east in the 1830s were largely caused by fear of the unemployment these machines might bring. In Herefordshire there was less obvious unrest, but at a time of rural underemployment and rising poverty among the labouring poor, distinguishing motives for civil disobedience is not easy.[12] Lastly, road surfaces were gradually being hardened, with regular dressings of gravel or 'broken stones' on major routes, often using pauper or convict labour. Consequently, many farmers found it advantageous to have at least one carthorse. Although oxen were shoed for road work, farriers were seldom happy with the job, since cattle were far less amenable to holding their feet up, and the shoes fitted less securely.

Herefordshire, along with Monmouth and parts of the south-west, was one of the last strongholds of working cattle. For a few years after the 1793–1815 wars, fattened Hereford oxen could fetch high prices even in London. A Mr Westcar of Buckinghamshire, for example, regularly travelled to Hereford market in the early nineteenth century and bought up oxen which he then fattened and sold for huge profit at Smithfield, for between £50 and £100 a head. 'Nearly all ... these high-priced gigantic oxen had been worked, and had earned home money at the plough and other labour before they were fed.'[13] But by the 1840s, oxen were in rapid decline. Mr Cooke of Lower Lyde Farm was one of the last breeders of draught Hereford cattle in the county.[14] By 1865, oxen of any breed were reliably reported to be almost abandoned in Herefordshire, with only a handful of farms in the county still using them.[15]

Thus, oxen held sway here for several millennia as the draught animals of choice, while heavy horses then barely lasted a century before they were themselves replaced by modern machinery.

A horse plough-team, mother and daughter Holly and Ivy, courtesy of Crunchies Cobs

Improving the land

As long as oxen were used for farming in Herefordshire, demand for hay remained high and this was often reflected in elevated prices. Whereas grain was relatively cheap here, hay at Hereford between 1698 and 1701, for instance, averaged 50s. a load while in Norwich it was only 32s.[1] In a year like 1740, with a hard winter and a late spring after a dry preceding summer, any surplus commanded record prices and many animals in Herefordshire and Shropshire starved for want of fodder.[2]

Most of this hay came from the low-lying flood-meadows along the numerous rivers and streams in the county, and the remainder from pastures on higher ground, where the old open fields had been enclosed and livestock could be kept off the crops. Before enclosure, some was also produced on the communal fields in their fallow (non-arable) years, where manures and night-soil were used as fertiliser.

The whole interwoven system of grazing management, hay production and soil improvement is perfectly summed up in a 1719 document from the bailiff of Brampton Bryan, describing the farming of the land of Sir Robert Harley. He reported that numbers of working oxen had increased in the past year from six to ten, with two more being fattened. No working horses were explicitly mentioned. A 30-acre field sown with clover had been mowed and the aftermath grazed off, but smaller fields of clover were grazed direct, by oxen and some horses. The grass meadows produced 121 waggon-loads of hay, and large volumes of lime and muck had been carted to arable fields prior to sowing.[3]

Enclosures

Grasslands could be managed more efficiently after enclosure, because the grazing animals could be more closely managed. In this respect, Herefordshire had the great advantage that it was not fundamentally a place of nucleated villages and the 'standard' medieval three-field system typical of the East Midlands. In some parishes, such as Ullingswick, Ashperton and Luston, there were indeed probably three medieval open fields, but in many more, notably Whitbourne, Stoke Edith, Marden and Hope under Dinmore, there were multiple irregular-sized communal fields. In Middleton in 1608–09 there were as many as 40 field names used, forming an unknown but clearly large number of fields. Partly this was because the county was dotted with numerous small hamlets and townships, which in turn made them less readily controlled by the lord of the manor and more likely to develop over time into communities of independent-minded yeoman farmers.

One consequence of this complex land-division system was that piecemeal enclosures could occur earlier than in larger-scale and more regulated landscapes, if the local occupants so wished. There is fragmentary evidence for this taking place from at least Tudor times onwards: when Leland rode across the county between 1534 and 1543, he commented on the high-quality grazing at Bromyard and Hereford, and noted the presence of enclosed fields for arable and pasture in Archenfield at Ewyas Harold, between Hereford and Dinmore Hill, from Hampton to Leominster, and from Croft to Richards Castle. Although the evidence is sparse, there seems to have been less opposition to enclosures in Herefordshire than in many other counties, perhaps because the initiative came from a wider communal base. Forced rural depopulation in Tudor times was less severe here, and also the small size of individual open fields meant that fewer families held land in each one, so agreeing to an enclosure was easier.[4]

Most parishes in Herefordshire probably enclosed much of their open field land during the seventeenth century. By the time of Ogilby's road map of 1675, the great majority of land alongside the through-roads appears to have been turned into small fields.

The infamous enclosures period of the late eighteenth and early nineteenth centuries, which deprived many of the rural poor of their common rights, was consequently less traumatic in Herefordshire. The 73 enclosures carried out here by Act of Parliament were much smaller-scale than those in other counties, with many covering under 100 acres. The average was only 150 acres, skewed by a few large ones, notably 1,000 acres in Much Marcle in 1795, 1,380 acres in the Yarkhill and Stoke Edith area in 1799 and 2,000 acres in Bodenham in 1802. It seems that the great majority of land in the county was enclosed more or less with the consent of those who held rights in any given open field or common, and mostly before the nineteenth century. But this same spirit of independence and private decision-making also meant that many parishes still had some residual corners of strip farming in their old open fields at the time of the 1840 Tithe Apportionments. By the time of the official government survey of remaining open fields in 1874, however, it was estimated that only 2,000 acres remained in open fields, and some 10,000 acres of commons.[5]

Sowing or sward?

Once a given area of land had been withdrawn from the open fields and reallocated to a specific farmer, they were free to improve and use it as they saw fit – within any constraints of their lease if they were leaseholders. The principal decision must always relate to the proportion of grassland on the holding, whether this was river-side meadow, upland hill pasture or the large areas of undulating lowland between, be it permanent or ley (grass as part of an arable crop sequence). The county had for many centuries been a district of mixed farming, corn and cattle country as it used to be called, but with an above-average acreage of grass and a surplus of corn for export.

This characteristic mixture is in marked contrast to some other counties, and has broadly persisted down the generations. At the tithe surveys of about 1840, when detailed and quite accurate information for almost every parish is first available, pasture and meadow together made up 40–60% of most of central and western Herefordshire, while arable ranged from 60% in the extreme south of the county to a minimum of 20–30% along the western and northern borders. During the rest of the nineteenth century there was a move away from arable and towards more pastoral farming, partly as a consequence of competition from cheap grain imports and partly due to the beginnings of a stumbling rise in wages for farm labourers. Between 1870 and 1899, arable acreage in central Herefordshire (on land below 500 feet) fell by about 10%, with most of the decline being in wheat and barley. In this, the county followed the broad trend across England, although differences between counties persisted. In 1871, permanent pasture in Herefordshire covered 41% of the acreage, compared with just 23% in Lincolnshire.[6]

Mixed Herefordshire farm land

Manure

It is perhaps no surprise that a range of new techniques started to be used at precisely the time that the open fields were giving way to enclosed privately-managed plots. But nevertheless, the oldest soil improvement method of all, the application of farmyard and domestic manure, clearly remained a key element in the county. This operated in two ways, enriching pastures by direct deposition of manure from grazing animals, especially if many of these were sheep, and carting out muck onto arable lands before ploughing. These farmers would not have known that this was a major source of nitrogen and many other plant nutrients, but the beneficial effects on crops were plain to see.

The Herefordshire probate records sampled for this book show beyond doubt the enthusiasm with which our farmers mucked their land. One of the earliest detailed farming wills surviving in the county is that of William Lovett of Ashperton,

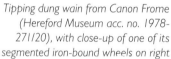

Tipping dung wain from Canon Frome (Hereford Museum acc. no. 1978-271/20), with close-up of one of its segmented iron-bound wheels on right

written in 1557, whose first personal bequest was to a kinsman to whom he left one iron-bound wain (with metal wheel-rims), one dung wain, two oxen, two bullocks and the ox yokes and traces. Such specific mentions of dung wains crop up regularly in wills and inventories over the next 200 years, so that, for example, in 1675 John Streete of Brampton Abbotts had one old corn wain, one dung wain and an assortment of other husbandry implements, together valued at £3 5s., out of total inventory of £88; and in 1750 Rachel Penn of Bull's Hill, Walford, left a dung cart and its tack, valued at £1 10s. – 10% of the total of her inventory.

More surprising perhaps is the continuing valuation of the muck heaps themselves. John Howell of Knighton, for example, whose inventory totalled £175 in 1675 – including 147 sheep (£36) and 26 cattle of all sorts (£70) – had an item for 'muck in the fold', £1. Similarly, Mary Norgrove of Ivington near Leominster left 'grain of all sorts in the barn, hay and other fodder, muck and compost' together valued at £21. In 1725, the inventory of gentleman farmer Richard Nicholson of Leominster totalled £404, but still included £1 10s. worth of 'compost for the land', and in the same year William Bubb of Kingsland's much more modest estate gives additional detail, specifying that he left four loads of dung in the fold valued at 4s.

From the limited information available, it seems that this close attention to their manure was a characteristic of Herefordshire farmers. It was a requirement for inventory-making, but in fact seldom included in some regions. A sample of about 250 inventories from two Essex parishes between 1635 and 1749 found no mention of any manure until 1729, and then only five times in total, in spite of the substantial numbers of livestock on these farms.[7] The Board of Agriculture reports seem to reveal a similar enthusiasm for farm manure here.

Manuring practices in Marches and Somerset Board of Agriculture reports

County	Main manures and fertilisers used	Distinctive features of county farming	Authors and dates of reports
Cheshire	Marl; foul salt; raw lime mixed with ditch scourings or manure; sand. Beginning to pay more attention to manure.	Large numbers of dairy farms	Thomas Wedge, 1794 Henry Holland, 1808
Shropshire	Farm yard manure; lime; marl		J. Bishton, 1794 Joseph Plymley, 1803
Herefordshire	Farm yard manure in large quantities; lime; still using night soil from towns, ditch cleanings etc.		John Clark, 1794 John Duncumb, 1805
Worcestershire	Droitwich foul salt, and others	Many heavy horses, mainly arable.	William Pomeroy, 1794
Gloucestershire	Manure, but not enough cattle to eat straw, because insufficient pasture; burnt lime used west of Severn, at 2 or 3 loads an acre; marl has gone out of fashion.		George Turner, 1794 Thomas Rudge, 1807
N. Somerset	Burnt lime; some marl.		John Billingsley, 1798

The volume of muck that might be carted onto fields before arable crops were sown is shown in the Brampton Bryan bailiff's report mentioned above. He recorded that in addition to two loads of lime for a three-acre field where barley was to be grown, and ten loads of lime onto an eight-acre field, they had carted 62 loads of muck for ten acres of wheat and 36 loads onto three acres (in the Commonfield) for rye. By the eighteenth century, lime was regularly being used on the most acidic land to improve its fertility. Since this account specifies that '17 tun of cole' had also been carted with the ox-teams, it was presumably burnt or kiln-made lime, prepared locally, that they were spreading, not the raw crushed stone that was sometimes used. John Clarke's *General View of Herefordshire Agriculture* (1794) opines that lime could usefully be spread on the poorest land at a rate of up to a load and a half per acre. Meanwhile, John Duncumb, writing in 1805, noted that soils in the Ryelands and Archenfield district had been dramatically improved recently by the generous application of lime. Indeed, John Webb in 1879 claimed that by the outbreak of the Civil War 'they had learned the use of lime as manure, from which the hundred of Wormelow and part of Greytree derived great advantage'.[8]

Muck-spreading from a tipping cart. (BDLHS Picture Archive)

Meadows

Since the earliest accounts of its agriculture, Herefordshire has been famous for being a 'well-watered' county. The Wye, Arrow, Lugg, Frome and a dozen other rivers and scores of brooks and streams, have many areas of adjacent seasonally-flooding meadows. When Leland visited Leominster (between 1534 and 1543), he bemoaned the fact that 'below Ivington the land is low lying, and although there is much good meadowland it is so often inundated that scarcely once in six years can the grass be saved.'[9] Yet, as Leland probably knew, the 46 acres of Encheneye meadow at Ivington was listed in a fourteenth-century survey as the most prized of all the extensive Leominster holdings.[10]

The problem, of course, was that these meadows, which could produce two good crops of hay per year as well as aftermath grazing, were susceptible to the damaging effects of a long, deep flood in a wet winter, and even more so to a shorter summer flood, both of which were liable to kill the grass. But even so their importance was recognised. The largest single block of meadow in the county was, and remains, the Lugg Meadows near Hereford. As far back as Domesday large parts of them were owned and managed by the Crown, and most of the rest belonged to the bishop, Hereford Cathedral or St Guthlac's Priory, indicating their high value. The Red Book (c.1280) records that Bishop Swinfield then held about 120 acres of these meadows.

Other major areas of meadow in the county are located along the middle River Arrow, in the lower Frome valley and above Ledbury, but most parishes had some useable meadow, small or large. Those which had insufficient often had hay-making rights in other parishes, as Ullingswick and Preston Wynne did in Sutton's Lugg Meadows.[11]

Medieval farmers knew (as the ancient Egyptians did long before them) that meadows which flooded could produce richer and greater volumes of hay and other crops. Only recently have the reasons for this been understood, especially in the fertilising benefits of the flood silts replacing depleted phosphorus, but the meadow grazing was nonetheless carefully managed to optimise yields, and it was acknowledged in much higher rents compared with ordinary pasture. As we have seen in Chapter 8, fifteenth-century meadows were valued at over a shilling an acre, while pasture averaged only 2½d. Meadows are sometimes specifically mentioned in Tudor and early Stuart wills. In 1563, Thomas ap Howel of Birley left 'all his messuage, lands, house, meadows, leasowes [catch-all term for grassland] and pastures' to his son Roger, as well as three acres of rye (in two specified plots) and ten acres of oats, one cow and a heifer; in 1574, John Watt of Ledbury left to his wife, among other family bequests, a house and land called Baymores 'with a meadow belonging to it'; and in 1609 Richard Cupper of Ashford Bowdler (on the county boundary in Shropshire) left a house, lands, meadows and pastures to his wife for life, and thereafter 'all the freehold lands called Harmer Ground' were to go to William Cupper.

At about the time these three wills were written, people were beginning to think critically about how meadows could be improved. Population levels were rising, and hay and grazing were at a premium as well as arable crops. Several Elizabethan books made suggestions about how this could be done, and more than one land-owning gentleman was probably looking with interest at the innovations of the old sheep-farming abbeys. Here in Herefordshire, one person above all others put it all together and crucially published an account of his system of 'drowning of meadow' in 1610: Rowland Vaughan of Newcourt, Poston and Turnastone in the Golden Valley. Walter Blith, writing 40 years later, summed up both the problem and cure of low meadow productivity:

> Another cause [of barrenness] is the standing of the winter water upon the
> land, or the rain of Heaven ... the standing, soaking water breeds the Rush and
> fowlness, and likewise gnawes out the heart and strength of it, like the worm at

the stomack, and devoureth the strength of it, as experience will shew in many parts of the land, where ... a great part of that land lieth as it were drowned a great part of the year....

Under great Rivers, which run more dead and slow ... little Opportunity will be gained of bringing but little Land to so great an advance ... But under your lesser Brooks may your greatest quantities of Land be gained, and your water most easily and with small charge be brought over greater parcels than upon greater Rivers.

My advice shall be, never cover thy Land with a standing Water, unless for a day or two ... and so with all speed run off into some drayning Trench again.[12]

In Herefordshire there were of course some extensive meadows, where the major rivers ran 'more dead and slow', but there were also countless smaller areas beside the lesser streams, brooks and rivulets, ideally suited to improvements. As both Vaughan and Blith understood, if you could draw off some water upstream in the steeper valleys, in the same way as leats feeding mills had been constructed for centuries, this could be used downstream to actually increase the area of meadow land, using a carefully managed system of ditches, canals and sluices. Vaughan also realised that a gentle watering early in the season could warm the ground and promote early growth. Since in a good year one could achieve up to a three-fold increase in yield from 'watered' meadows, in hay harvests and in grazing, this was obviously beneficial.

Left: The remains of a drain on the Little Arrow meadows near Ivington
Right: A surviving sluice on part of the Ivington meadow system

Vaughan dug out two long lengths of 'Trench Royal' as he called them, effectively creating a parallel second channel cross-linked to the River Dore from Peterchurch down to Bacton (over 6 km, nearly 4 miles), beyond which there were surviving leats and channels from the Cistercian water works of Dore Abbey. Much of the low-lying land to either side, and along the Slough Brook just south of Turnastone, was also supplied with a system of smaller canals, some of which were in place before Vaughan began his project.[13]

For all his undoubted influence on subsequent farming, however, it would be wrong to see Vaughan as designing a prototype which fitted every parish and all brook-side meadows. At the opposite extreme, Smallham meadow in Whitbourne in the far north-east of the county is less than two acres in extent although it was larger before recent bank erosion. It seems to have been developed to manage flood water from the adjacent River Teme but also storm flow from the precipitous Rook Hill coppices behind. Here, it appears that the preferred solution was to feed flood water to a main ditch (still surviving to 0.5 metres depth) at the foot of Rook Hill, and from there run it over the meadow and back into the Teme via a secondary ditch and a series of angled sluiced channels. The main ditch was connected to the secondary one by at least half a dozen short drains, so that sudden hill run-off could be stored and then released in a controlled way.[14]

Aerial view of Smallham Meadow, Whitbourne, showing the River Teme in spate and the meadow's small size relative to those on the eastern (Worcestershire) bank (© Archie Roberts)

After these meadow improvements were popularised, an interesting Weobley will of 1675 includes a valuation of a meadow lease. Edward Shore, a glover, had a small amount of land in addition to his house, garden and orchard in the town, so that at his death in March he had a little corn, 5s. worth of 'hay and wood', and 'two

Top: Smallham's secondary drain flooded
Above: Smallham Meadow's vestigial outflow point back to the river

parcels of meadow land' with an outstanding annual rent of £2 due from George and Anne Jenkins who were leasing it for 21 years; the meadow was valued at £16. Since Edward's inventory totalled just under £70, this rent was probably a significant part of his domestic economy.

Two Leominster wills proved in 1675 also show the ongoing value of the meadows surrounding the town. In May 1674, John Norgrove of Ivington left two loads of hay which together were worth £1 10s. And the following March, Miles Scull of Wharton also had some hay, but in his case it was valued together with 'all the fodder' remaining at the end of winter, at just £1. He also left 'my part of Beggar's Meadow' (a name which survives today) to his wife for her life and then to his nephew William Scull, son of Barnaby, provided William paid £20 to his relation Henry Hill. If he did not pay this substantial sum, the will stipulates that Henry was to have the use of the meadow for six years before it passed to William.

Clover

The last major turning point in this era of land improvement was the realisation from the late sixteenth century that it was possible to introduce new species to increase the value and volume of grazing and hay. By the turn of the eighteenth century, farmers were beginning to use these techniques to such good effect that the location of their land in the parish was no longer of primary concern, and much of the rationale for the old strip farming was removed.

This transformation was initiated by a series of books, beginning with Master Fitzherbert in 1523, who commented on the various grades of grassland but gave no practical advice on improvements. In 1568, William Turner described several 'clavers' that were grown on the Continent and some were brought here experimentally, but it was another 70 years before Sir Richard Weston, who was exiled to the Low Countries in 1640, wrote a tract recommending various 'clover grasses' to improve the output of poor land. Weston saw these leguminous species as part of a rotation, and suggested leaving clover down for five years before sowing wheat. He understood that you could take hay crops from clover and also harvest the seed, and that it helped to improve the ground. It would be many more years before the means by which these plants captured nitrogen and so fertilized the soil began to be discovered, but the effect was already obvious to some. Andrew Yarranton (1619–84), who was born in Worcestershire, wrote (perhaps a little optimistically) in 1677 that not only, in his estimation, could clover feed as many cattle on six acres as grass could on 30, but that:

> For Herefordshire ... all Urchinfield is now under a great improvement by
> Clover, which improvement I sent into them parts, by sending the seed
> with Books fully directing the Husbandry; and all persons first had liberty
> to receive Seed from Mr Belamy of Ross, and Books of Directions: if the
> Husbandry did take, and the profits made, as in the Book was prescribed,
> then they were to pay Seven-pence a pound for Seed; if not, nothing: By this
> way the Seed was put into the Husbandman's hand, and no venture to him ...
> and at present, certainly Urchinfield is doubled in the value of their Lands by
> the Clover Husbandry.[15]

By 1685, Edward Fuller, a London seed merchant in The Strand, was advertising 'clover, hop-clover, St Foin, lucerne, rye grass, French furze and Dantzick-Flax' as seeds that could be sown to improve land. But there was much confusion about the taxonomy and identification of the various plants, with many overlapping names used. It is most likely that four species were available and suitable for hay and grazing in Herefordshire at this stage, as listed in the Table overleaf.

Leguminous plants available from the seventeenth century

Species	Life-span	height	use	Preferred soil type
Lucerne *Medicago sativa*	Perennial, up to 30 years	30–90 cm	Hay and grazing	From sandy loams to heavy clays
Sainfoin *Onobrychis vicilifolia*	Perennial, up to 20 years	30–60 cm	Hay and grazing	Drained loams and some clays, dry and freely-draining
Red clover *Trifolium pratense*	Biennial to perennial	50–60 cm	Hay and grazing	Good, well-drained soils, may need lime
White clover *Trifolium repens*	Perennial but quite short-lived	5–50 cm	Grazing and some hay	Lighter soils, or clays if drained

Lucerne needed a rich soil, and tended to be a gentleman farmer's crop; sainfoin was most suited to dry chalk downland and also became popular in the Cotswolds; the clovers and to a lesser extent lucerne were often associated with an increase in dairying, especially for cheese as was occurring at this time in Cheshire, Dorset, Wiltshire and some parts of Gloucestershire and Shropshire.[16] On their Cheshire estate, the Tatton family encouraged the early adoption of clover, urging their tenants to sow mixed clover and grass leys at the beginning and end of their tenancies, to enrich the soil. The earliest mention of clover in that area seems to be in the 1701 inventory of an Altrincham merchant, as part of his stock for sale to farmers.[17]

Despite the claims of Andrew Yarranton, Herefordshire does not appear to have embraced clover growing very swiftly, nor did Webtree, Ewyas Lacy and Wormilow (the hundreds covering most of old Archenfield) quickly abandon rye. In the inventory samples used here, there was no clover listed at all in 1675, and only on one farm in 1700: this solitary example was in the diocese, but just over the county boundary at Monmouth, where 64 pounds of clover seed had been sown the previous spring, enough for about three acres. Only in 1725 does clover begin to appear more frequently, with three farmers growing it in Webtree, (Mr Powell at Vowchurch, Mr Parry at Peterchurch and Phillip Pritchard, yeoman, at Callow), as well as one other up on the Worcestershire border at Kyre Wyard. It is probably significant that all but one of these were gentleman farmers with high value inventories, and all but the Kyre one had their own working oxen. They were, in other words, both rich enough to experiment and also needed good quality hay. Early growers of clovers often suffered from supply problems, and in some instances had to send a servant over to the Low Countries to buy seed direct, which no doubt partly explains why it began as a 'gentleman's crop'.

Red clover above, with the shorter white clover below

The last sample of inventories, for 1750, is smaller, but it includes another Mr Parry, gentleman farmer at Garway, who had a large number of oxen and was growing clover in his hay, with additional clover seed worth £4. And over into Radnorshire at Michaelchurch-on-Arrow a yeoman's widow also had a hay-with-clover mix. In Ewyas Lacy, later inventories survive in greater numbers than in 'English' areas of the county, and have already been analysed, showing the pattern seems to have been similar.[18] The earliest evidence is for a Mr John Roberts of Longtown, who was growing £5-worth of clover in 1730.

However, the new crop was still slow to catch on. It is not recorded again until 1769, when Lewis Watkin of Longtown had 'a small quantity'. The following year, David Parry of Clodock had seven acres newly-mown, and in 1781 William Gwillim, also in Clodock, had part of a clover rick. A little later, the Crasswall inventory of Hannah Gilbert in 1794 and that of Rachel Jones of Longtown in 1805 both mention a clover crop as well as some seed.

In 1781 the *Hereford Journal* began publication and straight away there is evidence that, on large farms at least, clover was by then an established part of the scene. One farm to let in June 1781 had 'a large quantity of hay and clover now growing on the premises'; while Treworgan Farm at Llangarren, advertised in February 1783, had '42 acres tillage, meadow, clover, hop-ground and pasture', suggesting that here the clover was a separate crop.

One difficulty these pioneers had to overcome was extracting the clover seeds, which needed prolonged threshing. Before long it was discovered that drying the hay thoroughly (sometimes in hop kilns or malt houses) made extraction easier. Purpose-designed clover-threshing mills were patented from the turn of the nineteenth century, and one still survives in the Arrow valley.

Whether the early clover growers were using it as a ley monoculture and benefitting from the residual seed in the soil, or whether they were deliberately mixing the grass and clover at some point is not always clear, but in some cases hay was listed together with the clovers. Phillip Pritchard's 1725 inventory was worth under £50, but of this the 'hay and clover in the barn' was together valued at £1 10s. We should perhaps think of an initial use as part of an arable rotation or in a ley, with the clover gradually spreading into the hay meadows as they were grazed and as livestock moved around the farm.

The Age of Land Improvers

This period, from about 1550 to 1800, was a time when the gentleman and yeoman farmers undertook far-reaching improvements to their land. Initially, this was achieved by enclosure, which in Herefordshire was largely done piecemeal and by consent. Often complex and representing a very significant social restructuring, it enabled all the subsequent efforts to bear fruit. Thereafter, improvements to the arable, meadows and swards were able to follow, as best suited the individual farming families.

NINE

Yeoman farmers

T HE earliest yeomen to appear centre stage may be the Knight's Yeoman in Chaucer's *Prologue* and the Canon's Yeoman who told one of the *Tales*, but it is clear that these are servants, not men who work the land. From a meaning akin to a valet, through a late-medieval obsession with everyone knowing their place in a hierarchical society, the word took on its agricultural meaning in the sixteenth century. By then, it referred to people who were farmers, like Augustine Horner of Tedstone Delamere, *yeoman*, whose bequests in 1591 included cattle and wheat.

A major characteristic of the yeomanry was their rising literacy. An increasing number of documents were signed by farming people through the Tudor and Stuart periods, and books were written and apparently read on many agricultural topics, from the wide-ranging and unashamedly political Walter Blith, who dedicated his treatise of 1653 to Oliver Cromwell, to specialist books on orchards, water meadows and more. All of these epitomise the Renaissance belief in mankind's boundless potential for improvement and innovation.[1]

In Herefordshire and many other English counties, the yeomanry came to dominate the middling ranks of rural life, with a few achieving entry to the minor landed gentry. But whereas in large parts of the country most of the rural population was overtaken by external economic and political factors such that they were soon forced into the swelling numbers of the poorer labouring classes, in Herefordshire and a few other counties yeoman farming persisted until well into the nineteenth century.

To illustrate the lives and fortunes of these people, there follows an exploration of four yeomanry families, based on new research into primary sources. These families and thousands like them flourished during a period of great agricultural change, with a developing market-based economy and increasing government intervention to promote novel crops such as hemp (in huge demand for equipping the Royal Navy) or madder (for dyes and paint, because Dutch supplies were unreliable). Supply chains also evolved even in this county of notoriously poor transport links, to encourage the growing of hops or cider orchards. Set against this, as population levels increased and the number of potential heirs rose, many yeomen fell into the trap of subdividing their land, leaving unsustainable small-holdings as the economic climate continued to change.

Even though Herefordshire is so far inland, it was significantly affected by the Napoleonic Wars, which continued on and off for 22 years. These drew in an eighth of the male workforce, directly or indirectly, all of whom had to be fed and clothed. Unsurprisingly, wheat prices in Hereford rose to twice the peace-time average, occasionally even tripling. The Navy needed beef and pork in huge quantities, and was not too fussy about quality, so new methods of pig-rearing swiftly developed. Both Navy and Army also demanded large quantities of leather, which in turn required tanning and so needed oak bark from coppices. All this encouraged the more affluent farmers and merchants to build, extend and in many cases to mortgage. Then, after Waterloo, it all came to an abrupt end, with a third of a million service and support personnel laid off, leaving the yeomen with a multitude of new farm buildings and debts. The problems were compounded by a sequence of bad harvests in 1816–20.

Meanwhile, Herefordshire had come to the notice of the new industrialists as an ideal county to found a family estate. One of the first of these was Richard Arkwright junior, the cotton manufacturer, who in 1809 paid £250,000 for Hampton Court and its 6,000 acres. These men then used their financial muscle to buy out their small traditional neighbours, who were reduced to the status of tenantry or else opted to migrate to the cities. It should perhaps be noted that many of these new landlords were themselves increasingly hit by the arrival of cheap imports, notably of American grain once the railway and port systems were operational, and many of them sold up within a century.

THE CHURCHMANS OF BALLINGHAM, 1692–1825

This family appear in the records in 1692 when a Thomas Churchman, yeoman of Ballingham, paid £6 to Alice, widow of William Chynn, gentleman of Trepenkennett, St Weonards, for a piece of land. In the same year, Thomas' wife Jane and their daughter Elizabeth both died. Thomas remarried soon afterwards and had two further children, Thomas and Martha. There is no certain evidence of where this first Thomas had come from (although there is a marriage of an earlier Thomas Churchman in Pencombe in 1559), but he must have been respected in the parish because he was churchwarden from 1708. This was a significant commitment with many religious and social responsibilities beyond the modern remit of the job, including collaborating with other local officials on parish road-maintenance, poor-relief and the maintenance of law and order.

The first detailed information about the family's farming is contained in Thomas's inventory of March 1718. He appears to have lived in a two-bay house with one upper room, and there is no mention of

The Church of St Dubricius, Ballingham

any ready money. This is reflected in his will, which leaves a shilling to each of four children (who must already have been adults) to buy mourning gloves, and £5 to the youngest, Martha. There was, however, a separate cider house and of an estate valued at a substantial £106, £9 was for five hogsheads of cider and perry, empty hogsheads and a cider press and its cloths. Arable crops were flax and 'all sorts of corn in the house and barn' (£7), and 13 acres of autumn-sown rye and wheat at £9 15s. But Thomas was clearly specialising in stock, with a focus on sheep. This part of the inventory specifies:

50 sheep	£9
4 cows	£15 10s
1 3-year-old heifer, 1 bull, 3 2-year-olds	£10
3 small yearling cattle	£4
11 store pigs and 2 sows	£5 10s
poultry of all sorts	5s

Several things stand out here. At this time, it was unusual for Herefordshire farms to have more than a dozen sheep, and even allowing for the occasional large flock, the county average was still only about 35. Thomas's cattle were also apparently high quality; those specifically described as cows were more usually valued at about £2. He was presumably breeding his own, rather than buying in the services of a neighbour's bull, which was a more usual (and cheaper) method. Even if all six surviving children were living at home, the family were unlikely to be expecting to slaughter all 11 store pigs for domestic use, so this, too, seems to represent a cash enterprise.

An additional noteworthy feature of the inventory is that, while there are no oxen, there are four horses, valued at £10 10s., together with a mention of horse harness. Thomas seems to have opted for the 'modern' and innovative use of horses on the farm, including for pulling his corn cart and dung cart when needed.

Apart from the shilling for his gloves, there is no mention of Thomas's elder son John (I) in this will. Perhaps he already had a farm of his own. Instead, the 'family' farm, with all the buildings and stock, went to his son Thomas (II) by his second wife. This Thomas briefly took over his father's role as churchwarden, but although he remained in or near Ballingham and he and his wife baptised at least seven children there before his early death aged 47, this branch of the family does not seem to have prospered. It is most likely that the family holding was taken over by John (I) when Thomas (II) died. It would be nice to think that John took in his brother's widow and her five surviving children, the eldest of whom were Mary and another Thomas (III), aged 14 and 12, but there is no certain proof.

John outlived his younger brother by 12 years, by which time he was running two farms, one at Broad Oak Green (possibly now Ballingham Court), the other his principal residence in the hamlet of Cary, near the brook. Both went to his widow Alice for the remainder of her life, then Cary was left to his younger son Thomas (IV) and Broad Oak Green went to the older son, John (II), 'except for one outhouse near to Cary Brook' which the brothers were to share. Smaller items in his will give a hint of John (I)'s family life: his 'entirely beloved' sons were 'earnestly requested' to lend their mother a horse or mare 'whenever she wants one'; Anne Churchman, then 16 years old, the daughter of his late half-brother Thomas (II), was given five shillings; and John Powell, soon to become a family in-law, was given five shillings for a bible.

The inventory of John (I) shows that he was living in a three-bay dwelling, perhaps having extended Cary (or maybe his parents' original two-bay house was the one at Broad Oak and Cary had always been three-bay). Upstairs, the

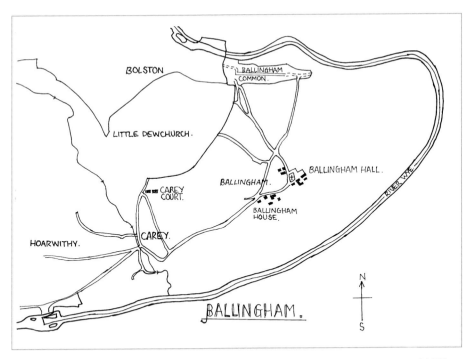

Map of Ballingham, based on the 1839 Tithe Map and the Scudamore estate map of 1695

inventory proudly states that there were 'three rooms joining'. No outbuildings or cider house are mentioned specifically, except the barn by the brook, but there is over £5-worth of cider and barrels. The only arable crop mentioned is wheat.

As for stock and implements, John was clearly following in his father's footsteps. Again there are four horses, now valued more highly at £15, as well as two colts; again '6 biggish pigs and 4 weaners'. There may be more emphasis on cattle than before, with three cows and a further 11 beasts, together worth £49 (over a third of the total valuation). There is a hint that maybe John had some bullocks able to draw carts, since among his waggon, corn wain and two dung wains there were also several yokes. But the stand-out feature is the flock of sheep, with 88 adults and 28 lambs. Of these, 40 are wethers, and a clue to why they were kept in such numbers may lie in the note that in the kitchen there was a spinning wheel. The flock in total was highly valued, at £24.

As far as the evidence goes, it looks as if Alice remained at Cary with her son Thomas (IV) to the end of her life, sharing the farm kitchen with her daughter-in-law, who seems to have been childless. Certainly, Alice describes herself as 'of Cary' in her will, and Thomas was made her sole heir and executor. It is noteworthy that all these three early Churchman wills demonstrate that the family was literate: even Thomas (I) who died aged 80 after a lifetime of farm work still signed his will, and his daughter-in-law Alice, who must have been at least 67, managed to trace out a respectable A. This fits well with this branch of the family becoming more rooted in the parish and acquiring more land. In 1764, the year after his own marriage, Thomas (IV) was churchwarden for a year, and again a decade later when he took over from his brother John on his sudden death.

John (II) died intestate in April 1773, and his brother and brother-in-law drew up his inventory. The brothers had exchanged houses in the interval, and John is described as 'of Cary' in the burial register. This is reasonable since John and his wife had at least three children, while Thomas (IV) remained childless and his mother had by now died. Even if he did have resident servants or dependent poor relations, there would still have been a lot of space in a six-room house, by the standards of the times. John's estate was worth about half that of his father's, only relating to one of the two farms. Again it followed the same broad trends, with almost all the value in the farm stock and implements, although it seems to have been drawn up in less detail:

His wearing apparel and money	£3 10s
bedding and other things in rooms upstairs	£2 10s
In the kitchen and lower rooms	£3
vessels and cider	£4 10s
waggon, carts, plough and harrows	£5 10s
horned cattle	£10
5 horses	£12 10s
sheep and pigs	£10
wheat and other grain	£5
TOTAL	£56 10s

Without any valuations for the land or buildings (which were not normally included in inventories), it is not possible to draw full comparisons with the necessary investment in a modern farm. But there is an interesting contrast between the identical value of the 'waggons, carts, ploughs and harrows' belonging to John (II) and his domestic goods, compared with these two categories today.

The pinnacle of the Churchman family in Ballingham was achieved by Thomas IV (1729–98). A table tomb, rather unusual for a yeomanry family, commemorates his life (and, predictably perhaps, those of two other Thomases), while his grandfather Thomas (I) is remembered on a headstone close by.

The Churchman family table-tomb at Ballingham

Thomas (IV) had been a widower for 20 years when he died, and was back living in the more spacious house at Cary. Significantly, he chose to style himself *gentleman* in his will. His estate had been built up to four farms: Cary, Nicholas Farm in Hentland and Haynes's, both with tenants, and an unnamed recently-purchased property in Little Dewchurch. Being childless, Thomas left all this to his nephew and niece, Alice and Thomas, children of his late brother

John (II). Nicholas Farm was for Alice Probert, married to a Hereford victualler, and the rest was for Thomas (V) Churchman. In the unlikely event that both Thomas and Alice died without heirs, the whole estate was destined for the eldest surviving son of the junior branch of the family, Andrew Churchman, who had abandoned work on the land and was a weaver. His side of the family were barely scraping by: his father and an uncle both died in receipt of poor relief and were registered as paupers, and he himself had been unable to afford the baptism tax of 3d. for one of his children.

The last male Churchman to farm these lands was this Thomas (V), nephew of Thomas (IV), and he too seems to have been childless even though he was married for 18 years. He reverted to the title yeoman, and although he retained five parcels of land in Ballingham, Hentland and Little Dewchurch, at least one was mortgaged and his estate was valued at under £40 at his death in 1825. His sister Alice Probert's two daughters and their heirs were his chief beneficiaries. One of these married a butcher called Amos Jones, of Hoarwithy, and by the time he in turn died in 1836 he had consolidated much of the Churchman lands by buying out the rest of his wife's family. He let these properties, and others in Tetbury, Gloucestershire, for a cash return rather than farming them himself, apparently concentrating on his butchers' business to the end of his life.[2]

By the time of the Tithe Apportionment for Ballingham (1842), Cary farm had been bought up by the Holme Lacy estate, and only small portions of the rest remained in the hands of Amos Jones' children.

THE GODWINS OF ALMELEY

This family from the north-west of the county have a rather different history to the Churchmans, apparently favouring contrasting farm enterprises on their land. By chance, more detail about their farming survives, but over a shorter timespan; one Godwin's life story may well have developed along a radically different path.

Abraham Godwin, son of Henry, first appears in Almeley in 1662, when the Parish Books begin and the Anglican registers recommence after the Puritan Commonwealth period. The registers are poorly preserved and quite patchy, but the parish books supply useful additional information. In 1662, Abraham and his wife Elizabeth baptised their daughter Mary, and Abraham was then working at least part-time as a tiler, presumably making and fitting clay tiles to replace older stone ones or upgrading thatched roofs. However, he also held land called 'Parcors Lands' in Wootton hamlet, for which he was charged 3s. 2d. in church rate (for church repairs). Although this field name does not survive today, it may refer to the man who owned it 60 years earlier. In 1603, the archives show that John Parcker of Wootton in Almeley, yeoman, sold '2 acres of arable land with the customary way belonging thereto, lying in a close called Over Hoppeley,' to a man called Thomas Ball.[3] If this identification is correct, this small plot was the nucleus of Abraham's Almeley lands.

By 1690, when his brother Jacob made his will, Abraham was styled yeoman; his father Henry owned freehold property at Lyonshall, and was also a yeoman. Jacob was training for a profession in Leominster at the time of his death, and not farming. Meanwhile Abraham's wife Elizabeth died quite young, and he went on to have two more wives, but apparently no more children.

Although these three generations can be reconstructed, with the names Abraham, Isaac, Jacob, Henry and Joseph all recurring, the picture then becomes more confusing. However, other Godwins do appear in parish documents for another century and more. Abraham was periodically either churchwarden or overseer of the poor between 1688 and 1703; an Isaac Godwin was parish constable in 1702; and later, a Joseph Godwin (or perhaps two different men of this name) fulfilled these roles between 1726 and 1755. By the 1770s, the family was slipping down the social scale, with two girls placed out at parish expense as apprentices (usually meaning they would learn relevant farming or indoor domestic skills, hopefully saving the parish from paying later poor relief costs). Later still, the 1839–40 Tithe Apportionment shows one small cottage at Meer Common, close to Wootton and Hopley's Green, belonged to a Joseph Godwin. In the 1841 census this was occupied by James Godwin, an agricultural labourer aged about 80, together with a lodger on parish assistance, presumably giving James some much-needed additional income. Interestingly, this woman and her nephew were both born in Almeley, but her younger sister was originally from Lyonshall, an indication of the continuing fluidity of movement between these two parishes.

This is the background against which we can place Abraham Godwin's life as a yeoman farmer between about 1660 and 1704.

A series of documents and scraps of paper surviving with the Foley papers in the county archives show how the land that Abraham farmed was accumulated. In 1719, just a few years after his death, the property passed to the Foley family of ironmasters, who were building up their estates to supply charcoal to their

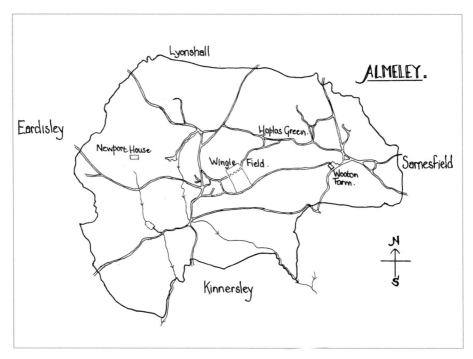

Map of Almeley, based on the 1840 Tithe Map

foundries. A full description of the Almeley lands, running to six pages, was then produced, including some measurements in acres of the individual plots.[4] The house in Lyonshall belonging to Abraham's father Henry, seems to have been owned outright by the Godwins, but the Almeley holding had originally been built up during the 1590s and early 1600s by Thomas Ball, as a tenant of the Pember family of Newport House, and Abraham eventually became subtenant of part of it. The paperwork details the plots bought by Ball on each occasion, for instance: '1 acre of arable land in Jennins Field, with Hopleys Green Common on the south, bought in 1631 ... for 44s.'

After Ball's death in 1647, his entire land-holding passed to his brother-in-law in Yorkshire and thence eventually to Paul Foley when he bought the Pember estate. Ball's holding ran to some 136 acres, with five houses. Three of these were probably small cottages with tenants, while two were sizeable farmsteads – at Stockes and Hopley's Green, hamlets in the east of the parish. The plots are listed as a mixture of arable land (probably mostly still in open fields), pasture, meadow, coppice and wood-ground, together with six orchards. Many of the field names continued in use up to the Tithe Apportionment and beyond. Thus, in 1595 Ball took 'Le Tenement at Hopples Green', with arable including '3 acres in a field called Windle'; in 1719 Foley acquired 'Land ... in a certain field called Windell field ... two acres of Arable land more or less'; and in 1840 the 'Wingle Field' was all arable, partially enclosed but still with some open strips. Ball's Hopleys Green House had a garden and orchard: in 1719 two plots there were described as 'the back Orchard ... and the Great orchard', and in 1840, there were still two orchards next to the house, one known as The Long Orchard.

There is no proof how much of Ball's land was held by Abraham Godwin, but he did eventually succeed him as churchwarden, and such appointments sometimes followed land-holdings and certainly indicated some status in the community. The surviving evidence does show that he was tenant of this same Hopley's Green House. The first reference to Abraham occupying it is a note on the back of another estate document, from Francis Pember Esq, which includes details of the rental agreement and fertilising regime.[5]

Memorandum that I have let Abraham Godwin all my farme at Hopples Green for 3 years. At ye Rate of sixteen pounds per annum & that I give him foure pounds twards ye payment of Taxes. & that I have let him have 9 Acres of lent corne[6] at XI s. an Acre. & that he is to plow an acre of fallow upon heges of it to leave all his manure ... ... and ye hopyards drest & as much [this last line added smaller, up the LH margin]

Lent corne viz 9 Acres same. & that my rent day is upon ye first of May 1669 and for every year. & ye accounts is in my Cozen William Colliers keeping who lives at hoples Green.

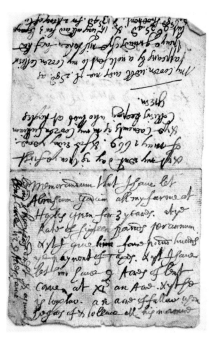

Image of the first rental agreement for Abraham Godwin, with transcription left (Herefordshire Archive Service)

Three shorter notes from the 1690s record ongoing payments of rent for pieces of land and suggest that the tenancy was retained for over 30 years.[7] It seems, therefore, that Abraham Godwin arrived in the parish in or about 1662, renting a small acreage in addition to working as a tiler, but within a few years he was tenant of some or all of Hopley's Green farm, which he kept for the rest of his life.

At his death in 1704, Abraham was able to give each of his four daughters £20, as well as bequeathing his late father's Lyonshall house and garden, then let out, to the eldest and her heirs. The farm and household goods at Almeley were left to his widow.

Abraham's inventory, taken in late June and with a total value of almost £200, is very different from the Churchman ones. Firstly, he had £85 in money, and domestic goods indicating a comfortable and modish lifestyle (including a warming pan, clock and 13 pairs of expensive sheets). It also specifies that he had a resident farm servant with his own room but with a bed worth just five shillings compared with the £2 for the principal bed with feather mattress, curtains and so on. For a few years at least, this farm servant was his relative Henry Godwin.[8]

Like the Churchmans, Abraham had several horses but his seem to have been for riding, with saddles and other tack worth 10s. Instead of farm horses, Abraham had four oxen, valued at four pounds each, and their yokes are included along with the wains, ploughs and harrows. The area of arable can be guessed from the eight acres of barley worth £4 and at least as much peas and oats (£3 10s.), most or all of which could have been for stock-feed. It seems that the winter's hay was all used up, but there was an estimate of £4 10s. for hay 'growing on the ground'. In addition, there was a store of corn and malt, and in the cellar were plenty of barrels and brewing equipment; no mention of cider, but by June it could already have been consumed, and apples on trees were not usually included in inventories, being considered a natural gift of God and not a managed crop.

Abraham was not a sheep farmer. His flock was worth a quarter of Thomas (I) Churchman's 50 sheep a decade later. Instead he was concentrating on cattle, with his four oxen, nine younger stock and four calves (some of which were surely destined for farm work), and seven cows. He also kept his own bull. In all, this herd was valued at a very healthy £51, over a quarter of his total assessed wealth.[9]

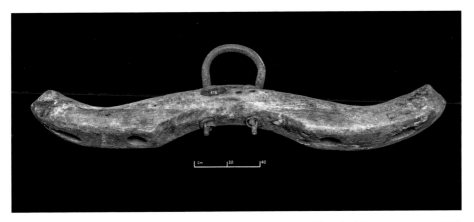

Ox yoke, used until the early nineteenth century in Foy, nr Ross (Hereford Museum acc. no. 578)

Although there is no definite proof of a connection, it is quite likely that one of the half-dozen other men from Almeley called Abraham Godwin was among the early settlers in New England. This was a very unusual name yet it recurs, along with Henry, in an emigrant family whose American history was recorded by the third generation. There were many connections between prosperous Herefordshire families and the New World, so such a migration is entirely possible. To name but two, several of the Quakers of Almeley emigrated to Pennsylvania, and their Meeting paid for other, poorer, Friends who wished to join them. Meanwhile, Jacob Godwin, brother of Abraham of Hopley's Green, was a close friend of Fitzwilliam Conningsby, whose cousin had links to both Maine and Barbados.

The first Abraham Godwin in America settled in the New York area (then still very rural) in about 1720, and had two sons, Henry and Abraham. Abraham junior (1724–77) became a master carpenter, then moved to New Jersey in about 1755 and created an estate at the heart of a new settlement. The 1771 advertisement for the sale of his land shows what he had achieved, and has certain echoes of the aspirations of Herefordshire yeomanry:

> ... I the subscriber ... intend to move [back] ... on my plantation ... and intend
> to sell or let out the House and Farm I now live on ... it is a very pleasant
> Place for a Gentleman's Country Seat, as there is plenty of Gentleman's
> Exercise, as hunting and fishing; there is on the Premises, a large Stone
> House, containing nine Rooms and nine Fireplaces, Cellars through the

whole house; there is also a fine new Shingle Roof Barn on the Place, a fine young Orchard containing 150 Apple Trees; the Farm contains near a hundred Acres of Land half-cleared, can mow 35 loads of English Hay every Year. Whoever inclines to buy or hire, may apply to the Subscriber ... who will give an indisputable Title for the same. This place lies at the Foot of a large Bridge, near Passaick Falls. ABRAHAM GODWIN.[10]

CONTRASTING FORTUNES IN ONE PARISH:
THE CLARKE AND COLLINS FAMILIES OF WHITBOURNE
These two families, both stoutly maintaining their yeoman status, appear in the parish records at very different levels in the farming hierarchy in the 1500s and 1600s. Yet by the mid-Victorian period, as with so many rural people, they had subsided to the same point on the social scale.

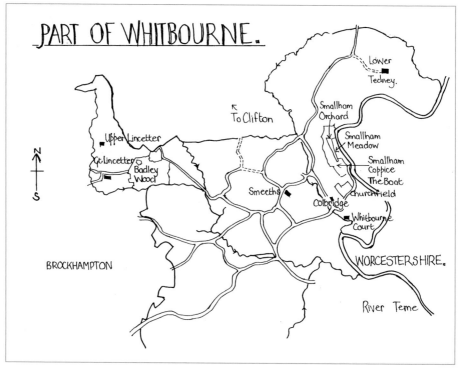

Map of part of Whitbourne in 1838, showing Badley Wood and the vicinity of the parish church

THE CLARKES OF BADLEY WOOD COMMON

The two Whitbourne commons were extensively assarted at times of high population pressure, and this is ultimately the origin of most or all of the Clarke land-holdings, at a place called Lincetter. In the Bishop's Red Book (*c.*1280), some assarts are geographically located, so we know that Alice of Lincestre had three acres, while Walter of Lincestre had six and a quarter. A few years earlier, a Whitbourne deed was witnessed by Nicholas de Lynsete between 1240 and 1268, and this may refer to the same place.[11] There are no Whitbourne Clarkes in Swithin Butterfield's late sixteenth-century survey, but a John Whitinge held a virgate (approximately 30 acres) at Lyncestre. At some time in the next century, the central part of this holding was acquired by a Thomas Clarke. This may be the Thomas who was buried in 1594, or his grandson, also Thomas, who was born in 1609 and married his first wife in 1630.

The names of the various farms and smallholdings are very confusing and rather fluid, but it is likely that Thomas originally held Old (alias Upper) Lincetter, with some or all of this 30 acres. Great Lincetter to the south, which at its peak included 80 acres, was probably never part of the Clarke land, nor was The Combe to the north: both these were for a long time held by the Arden family.

It is certain that in 1645, the grandson Thomas (I) gifted small plots of land to two of his sons, Richard (aged five) and James, and sold a house and more land adjacent to his own farm to his eldest son and heir, Thomas (II). This latter property became known as Tibb Hill. Dividing the land to provide for all his sons meant that no one holding was large enough to prosper. Within a century, Tibb Hill and the smallholdings previously held by Richard and James had all passed through their respective female lines. By the mid nineteenth century, all these outlying properties had been bought up by neighbouring landowners: the Barneby estate at Brockhampton or the newly-formed Evans one at Whitbourne Hall.

This process left the small central area of Lincetter with about 15 acres, which would have been enough to support one family. By the time he made his will in January 1697, Richard (II), (probably the youngest son of Thomas (II)), owned Lincetter and he specified that he 'had it from my father Thomas Clarke, deceased.' He left half the property to his wife Anne for life, and the remainder to his heir Richard (III), but interestingly he specified that mother and son must co-operate in:

manuring and tilling the said lands and in all other improvements ... and contributing to the gathering and bringing in of the profits into the house or barn. And my will is that neither my wife nor my son Richard shall fell or dispose of any of the wood or timber being or growing upon the said premises, without they both of them agree ...

Was there some tension between the generations? At any rate, the inventory of Richard (II) fits with this impression of an arable-focussed farm, but it also indicates its small scale. There were three rooms in the house, a hall and main bedroom downstairs and a chamber above. Out of a total value of just over £19, the farm goods comprised:

2 small swine	15s. 4d.
1 cow, 1 heifer, 1 mare	£6
corn and grain in the ground	£6
TOTAL FARM VALUE	£12 15s. 4d.

When his mother died in 1717, Richard (III) took over the whole holding, but at his own death in 1739 it was divided again, between his two young sons. Since the inventory value had by this time fallen to just £7 8s., with only one old horse (£1 5s.) and two pairs of harrows and a cart (together worth 22s.), it is perhaps as well for the viability of Lincetter that the elder son died without heirs, aged 23, and the property passed intact to the younger, John. There was one indication in his father's inventory of some new hope, however, in the mention of eight hogsheads and two smaller vessels, valued at nearly £2. Perhaps the old horse was also kept on to help with cider making. Literacy is first visible in the Clarke family at this point, too. Although Richard (III) and John (then 11 years old) both made a cross on the 1739 will, the older boy managed an elegant signature.

John Clarke took over the Upper Lincetter holding in 1747 when his older brother died. Even though he had barely 15 acres, he was clear that he was a yeoman, as were his three sons who continued farming in the locality. A small part of the land above Lincetter was hived off for a house called Batchfield for John's second son when he married; however, the rest, reduced to about 11 acres, passed eventually to the youngest son, Richard (IV) (1770–1839). This Richard had six children, of whom the eldest son abandoned farming and became a carpenter in Kidderminster. The youngest, Mark, remained in Whitbourne, but although he styled himself *farmer*, the Tithe Apportionment shows that he was only farming nine acres shortly before his early death in 1844.

This left Job Clarke, the middle son, and his wife Susannah with Lincetter, but in about 1822 it had been sold by either his father or uncle, so Job (1799–1873) was reduced to being a tenant. At the 1840 Tithe Apportionment, he was farming a mixture of arable orchard, grass orchard, coppice, a segment of woodland, one field of pure arable and a small hopyard. Job and Susannah remained at Lincetter for the rest of their lives and had seven children, all but one of whom continued working on the land. The eldest son, another Mark, was given a head-start by his maternal relations: Susannah's sister had married a wealthy local farmer, and at the 1851 census Mark and his sister Eliza were both listed as living with them, he as the farm bailiff. Soon after this, he married the daughter of another very substantial farming family, who then had 200 acres and five resident farm servants. In 1871, Mark himself farmed 260 acres, employing six men and two boys outdoors, but then in 1875 he died suddenly aged 56 and his family's prosperity collapsed as dramatically as he had risen. Job's four youngest children either ended up as agricultural labourers themselves, or married someone who was, and most were probably on a daily or weekly wage for much of their working lives, although one daughter married a man who briefly styled himself *farmer* and had 100 acres.

Job's second son, John (1823–1905), moved a few miles into Worcestershire, to Leigh where he and his own oldest two sons worked as brickyard labourers until he came back to take over Lincetter and support Job. The 1881 census describes John as a 'farmer of twelve acres at Lincettor 2', and he too remained there until he died, at which point the remnant of the property was occupied by other tenants.

Meanwhile, Job and Susannah's eldest daughter, Jane, was the exception. She opted for the route of domestic service and went up to Merseyside, to the home of a Yorkshire-born silk mercer. It was an eclectic household with two other servants, from London and Cumberland. But after a few years in service, Jane returned to Whitbourne and married John Collins, from another yeomanry family. They turned their backs on farming and instead ran the village pub, until first Jane and then John died young, leaving his second wife to run the business until her step-son took it over in the 1880s.

The Collins family of Colbridge and Smallham

The family of John Collins the publican was unlike the three described above, in that it was deeply rooted in the parish. A John Collins had his will proved in 1527, and his widow Eleanor was still paying taxes there in the 1540s, together with three other Collinses.[12] Soon after this, another John Collins of Whitbourne, husbandman, left the bulk of his goods to Margery Combey, 'except for one cow which I give to Thomas Combey her son.' Then, in 1582, a Percival Combey (also described as a husbandman), gave bequests of £1 to the two sons of a Robert Collins.

Swithin Butterfield's survey (1577) gives more information about the early Collins holdings. Robert Collins farmed 24 acres at *Smythesland*, the modern Smeethes up near Rosemore. Gregory Collins had 27 acres at *Pittland*, now Lower Tedney or Pithouse, where the Collins family continued until 1719. Lastly, Thomas Collins held 31 acres at *Hillands*, now Hillhouse. The latter two are in Tedney, a cul-de-sac valley running up to the River Teme in the north-east of the parish; both were bought by Richard Chambers for his Whitbourne Court Estate in the late eighteenth century. In addition to these, Butterfield mentions a newly-built house called Colbridge, and a piece of land at Smallham, which soon came into the Collins portfolio.

Of these interrelated families, it seems to be Thomas of Hillhouse (died 1614) whose holding can most clearly be traced. Thomas's second son, Richard (1592–1666) had several children, but they and his wife all predeceased him and he left his estate to his nephew Robert (1615–1700). The farm consisted of the house called Colbridge, with an acre of garden, orchard and hemp-plot, together with a 'parcel of pasture or woodground' of two acres at Smallham Hill, which he had recently bought, and an additional small house, also in Whitbourne. Richard's will may not detail much land for a yeoman, but he made bequests totalling £117, including £20 to his sister, the wife of a yeoman at Stretton (probably Grandison), £5 to a niece and £4 to a brother-in-law. There were also gifts of £5 to his female farm apprentice and £2 to his maid servant. He had debts totalling nearly £135 that he expected to be repaid. It is clear from this, and from clues in his inventory, that Richard must have held a good deal of land over and above Colbridge and Smallham Hill, and was perhaps acting as the family banker. He was one of the last surviving males in his generation and he was literate, as evidenced by his attempt to sign his will.

Richard's inventory suggests that, at this stage, Colbridge was three-bay but as yet lacking the upper floors it is known to have acquired soon afterwards, with just a hall, chamber and buttery.[13] If the ceilings and upper rooms had already been added, there was no furniture of any worth there. The valuations of the farm goods and stock, meanwhile, seem to reflect a curious mixture of subsistence farming and an operation that was part of a wider cooperative venture:

A small parcel of wool and hemp	10s.
12 old hogsheads, 3 half hogsheads, 3 barrels malting and cheese making equipment, etc.	£2
1 perry mill	£1 10s.
1 load of hay in the barn and the hemp in the yard	£1
3 acres of white corn growing on the ground	£2 6s. 8d.
one acre and a half of pulses	10s.
3 cows and 2 heifers	£9
1 bay mare	£2 10s.
nine old sheep and four lambs	£2
4 store swine and the poultry	£1
Implements of husbandry	10s.
total in whole inventory	£69 10s. 4d.

Of immediate interest is the mare; not an old work horse, but one for riding. In this, Richard was absolutely typical for his generation of Herefordshire yeomen farmers. Nearly half of them had a single mare, sometimes with a colt, with just a few having more than one, and their average inventory valuation was almost exactly £2. 10s. By contrast, there are no working animals, carts or ploughs listed here. Perhaps these had been gifted away shortly before his death, but other parish wills mention oxen and these could have been loaned to work Richard's land. In the next generation of his family, a John Collins of Tedney was in the reverse situation in the early 1700s, with six oxen and bullocks (£20) and only 'one old mare' (£1 13s. 4d.).

The most interesting feature of this inventory is perhaps what it reveals about drink. Even at Colbridge, which is only a few yards from the relatively clean Whitbourne Brook and may by this time also have had its well in operation, ale, perry and possibly some cider were being made and presumably consumed. With hogsheads of between 52 and 66 gallons, the capacity available equates to between two and two and a half gallons a day for the household, in addition to small but regular brewings of ale.

By the time of the death of Richard's heir, Robert, in 1700, the parcel of land at Smallham was assessed as four acres, presumably because more had been bought. The Colbridge farm was described in more detail, as having 'outhouses, gardens, orchards, free land and ground'. No inventory survives for Robert's estate, which apart from some modest bequests (mainly of empty hogsheads) passed to his daughter-in-law Winifred, both his elder sons having predeceased him. Winifred, neé Norgrove, was the daughter of another yeoman family from the neighbouring farm, now called Brook Cottage but then known simply as Norgroves. In a nice touch, Robert left his four-year-old grandson Thomas his 'great bible and all the rest of my books'.

The next generation of the family suffered even more young deaths, so that the only child to outlive her mother was the youngest, another Winifred, aged just one when her father and grandfather both died in 1700. Winifred junior was married while still a minor, in 1719 (11 days before her mother's burial), to a cousin called John Collins who began his adult life as a tailor, but is later styled farmer or yeoman.

John and Winifred represent the high point of this branch of the Collins family, through most of the eighteenth century. Within six months of their marriage, they took over the one-acre Marion Close to the north of Colbridge. To the north-east, between Colbridge and Smallham, Church Field was still an open field, and on the other side of the lane leading to Smallham, Horsham Bridge Meadow had recently been planted up as a hop ground. In 1724 they were involved with further property transfers, for four farms and a cottage, five barns, six orchards and a total of 190 acres of other land, in Whitbourne and a neighbouring parish. Winifred lived to be 71 and John to over 80, and most of their extensive tenancies and freeholds were disposed of in later life, to pay off mortgages, but at some time they had built a new house called The Scar, at the edge of Smallham Meadow, which John retained together with Colbridge.[14]

Out of their 11 children, five were still alive in 1780 when John died, as well as several grandchildren. This was the new reality for many families even of the better-off yeomanry, who struggled to provide for more descendants at a time of increasingly stretched financial resources. Colbridge (now alias The Brook House) went to the eldest son, Robert, with the proviso that he must raise a £50 mortgage to share between his four surviving siblings and two orphaned nephews. A middle brother was a tailor as his father had been, well-established in nearby Lulsley. The youngest son, however, died three years before his father;

his widow and infant son, another John (1775–1852), were then living at The Scar, and they retained it, with a proviso that 'the ash saplings and trees now growing on the said premises called The Scar shall not be fallen before my grandson John attains the age of 21 years.' With The Scar came £40, the interest from which the widow had for John's minority, after which it was his.

Robert retained both Colbridge and the adjacent Marion Close (by now described as a hopyard planted with some fruit trees), but he soon had to raise a mortgage on it. In 1796 it was confirmed that all the mortgages were paid off, and both Robert and his nephew John (by now turned 21) had free possession of their respective houses and land. Three years later, Robert died and his elder son, yet another John, a yeoman farmer in Alfrick, Worcestershire, inherited Colbridge, while the younger, who most probably was working in London as a porter, got only a silver watch. This John's only direct heir also moved to London, and Colbridge was inherited by a nephew, Joseph (1787–1874). Like so many members of the yeomanry in his generation, Joseph had needed to find work elsewhere and had been for a while the toll collector on the Stourport bridge until he inherited Colbridge in 1835, with some additional leasehold land and a much-needed sum of £116. He cannot have hesitated long, since his son William was baptised in Whitbourne in March 1836, presumably named after the king. At the Tithe Apportionment four years later, Joseph owned both Colbridge and Marion Close, which was now described as grass-orchard. In 1844 he sold Marion Close, 'formerly a hopyard planted with fruit trees but now an orchard and meadow' for £60, leaving just the house and garden of less than an acre.

The descriptions of Joseph in the census returns perfectly illustrate the difficulties faced by a smallholder with a sizeable family, trying to keep his head above water in these times. When he first took over Colbridge, he was listed as Independent, but by 1851 whoever provided the information labelled him Agricultural Labourer, even though he was also then running a business as a carrier to and from Worcester. In 1861 he had slipped still further, being designated Lath Cleaver, and finally in 1871 aged 83 he was again called Agricultural Labourer.

Of his eight children, his eldest son John married Jane Clarke of Lincetter and ran the village pub until he died in 1872. When Joseph made his will the year before, John is mentioned as already being unwell. The only other surviving son was William, who was by this time a master pork butcher in Birmingham. His mother had Colbridge for life, but as required in Joseph's will William and

Colbridge, shortly after it was sold to the Harington estate

his brother-in-law John Green (a police constable) then sold it, for £225, to Sir Richard Harington who had recently bought the Whitbourne Court Estate. The money was split equally between the four surviving siblings, which may explain why by the 1881 census both William and his sister Mary Ann had given up their jobs and Mary Ann's husband had started his own grocer's business.

At The Scar, meanwhile, the house now stood in a quarter acre of garden and orchard, and the rest of the land was three further small grass orchards and a quarter of an acre of arable, with half an acre of hopyard beyond as well as two acres of coppiced woodland.[15] The property stood at a ferry and fording point over the River Teme, and in later life John ran it as The Boathouse Inn (part of a cider mill found on the site may date from this period). Most of John's sons became carpenters or coopers, but the eldest, Joseph (1807–93), eventually took over the property. This Joseph's son and heir, who had lived with his parents and worked as an agricultural engine driver, predeceased him. Twelve years later, Joseph seems to have given up the unequal struggle and sold up to the newly-forming Evans estate of Whitbourne Hall. An agreement of April 1876 with the agent for Mr Evans arranges the sale of

> All those two freehold messuages or tenements gardens lands hereditaments and premises ... called ... The Boat House containing by estimation six acres or thereabouts now in the occupation of Joseph Collins and his tenant James Bond together with all timber saplings growing hop poles underwood brush and other trees of every description growing thereon and also the cider mill and cast-metal rack in the kitchen fire place – the hop poles in the Hopyard to be taken at a valuation by the purchaser in the usual manner. £950.[16]

The last reference to the house built by John and Winifred Collins in the eighteenth century is a note in the 1901 census: 'Boat House Pulled Down'.

THE AGE OF THE YEOMEN

The period between about 1600 and 1850, when so many Herefordshire yeomanry families like these flourished, was a time of change, opportunity and then, for an increasing number of them, of difficulty and hardship. This cycle affected individual families at different times and in varying ways, depending on their personal circumstances and traditions, but sooner or later it caught up with almost all, so that by the late nineteenth century there were far fewer smallholders, yeomen or resident farm servants on annual contracts left in the county, and instead most of the agricultural population had joined the ranks of the day- or week-labourers, scraping by on an 'economy of makeshifts'.

Sheep

Sheep farming has changed a great deal over the last thousand years. While these versatile animals have always had multiple uses, the product for which they were chiefly valued has changed dramatically over time, giving them a unique place in farming history.

In Domesday Book, sheep were kept primarily for dairying. Over the next five centuries the value of English wool and then woollen cloth stimulated industries of international importance, which became the mainstay of the national economy, while cows replaced sheep as dairy animals. Sheep were also greatly valued for their dung, with their 'golden hooves' that did minimal damage to pasture, and optimal methods of folding them both indoors and out were devised. At the same time, the fall in population following the fourteenth-century pestilences and famine encouraged a move from arable to stock-keeping, and in particular to sheep. They required less management, since one shepherd could tend a flock of 100 or more, and the only high-input times were at washing and shearing. Only more recently has meat production come to dominate, and sheep have been adapted again to new markets and new demands.

Dairying

Walter of Henley, writing at the end of the thirteenth century, considered that one cow could produce as much milk as ten sheep, but he did not therefore assume that cows were preferable. He was at pains to encourage keeping at least part of the flock under shelter in stone or wooden cotes from 11 November (Martinmas) until Easter, and urged the adding of marl and fresh straw to the floor every fortnight, to improve the quality of manure for the fields. Unfortunately, it is not known what part of England he was writing for, although some have speculated that he may have been based in or near Gloucestershire.

There is a range of evidence from medieval prices and yields for big flocks in south-east England, Devon and Northamptonshire, which shows that sheep continued to be milked on a large scale well into the fourteenth century. They produced between seven and 12 gallons a head, comparable with the

French sheep-cote in February, based on an image in Les Très Riches Heures, *produced c.1412–16 in northern France, for Prince John, Duke of Berry*

modern figure of 11 to 17, while the cows were only managing between 120 and 150 gallons, a tenth of the modern lactation rate. The inquest into the lands of the Knights Templar, taken in 1185, includes the duties of the tenants, and in some places dairying is specifically mentioned. For example, at the downland estate of Rockley near Marlborough, every villein who held over five acres had to send a woman each day to milk the ewes, in exchange for which she got half the whey.[1] On the Templar manor of Garway in 1308, there was a master shepherd with seven assistants, and four women were paid to milk the 370 fertile ewes throughout the season. The 16 breeding cows were also milked in early summer, and 203 one-pound cheeses were made in all, costing 30s. 6d. for pots, cloths, salt and presses for the dairy, plus candles for the cattle-shed, dairy and sheepfold.[2]

What scant evidence there is, does suggest that the desired product was cheese, with whey butter very much a by-product. It also seems likely that the small peasant flocks were together producing a huge volume of milk. The poor widow in Chaucer's *Nun's Priest's Tale*, with her three sows, three cows, some poultry and a ewe called Moll, surely had fewer sheep than most. In the Oxfordshire hamlet of Swyncombe in 1275, for example, there were 21 peasant families, and by chance a record survives which shows that ten of these were smallholders with eight acres of arable. These ten families were each allowed to graze one horse, six oxen and 50 sheep on the common pasture. Even if this were all the peasant livestock in the hamlet, the tenants could have had up to 500 sheep. By this time, there are some signs that the national flock was getting larger, but there is insufficient evidence to be sure whether this was caused by increased demand for food, or by the embryonic wool trade.

Some sheep milking in the Cotswolds continued into the sixteenth century, and even later on the Radnorshire border, and it has been suggested that in these areas the bigger and more robust sheep-cotes may have been built for milking and winter fodder storage, with shelter for the animals a secondary concern.[3]

Medieval dairy women, based on an illustration in the Luttrell Psalter, probably illustrated in East Anglia. British Library Add MS 42130 fol. 163v c.1320–40

The Herefordshire Wool Trade

Some quite early sources show that sheep were beginning to be kept for their wool as well as for dairying. In about 1130, Henry of Huntingdon, who was based in Lincoln diocese but travelled widely in central England, was moved to praise the 'flocks without number' and their 'most precious wool'. Fifty years later, restocking lists for some of the manors in the king's hands more prosaically give the prices of farm animals. In 1195, for example, at Deddington in Oxfordshire there were 54 oxen, six draught horses, 12 cows and three bulls each worth 4s., three boars and 24 sows each valued at 1s., and 249 sheep at 6d. This is in line with the standard prices introduced the year before, which crucially distinguished between coarse-woolled sheep (6d.) and fine-woolled ones (10d.), suggesting that wool quality was now a major consideration. In Herefordshire, the royal manors of Stanford Regis and Dilwyn had purchased a small amount of stock: oxen and horses at Stanford and pigs at Dilwyn, all at regulation prices, but neither had bought any sheep. In fact, only one of the royal manors listed had bought fine-woolled sheep that year, and that was in Cumberland.[4]

At the other end of the social scale, by the mid-1200s as more peasants escaped from the manors to which they were legally bound, records were sometimes kept of the stock and implements they had abandoned. These can occasionally go into useful detail. So, for example a tenant of Crawley in Hampshire, who fled in 1252, left behind two carthorses, five adult cattle and a calf, five pigs and some piglets and poultry, 39 ewes, 27 wethers, 11 yearling sheep and 26 lambs. Keeping wethers in such numbers is a clear sign that wool was a desirable product, since male sheep usually produce heavier fleeces that are less likely to develop breakages in the wool than those of ewes. The high numbers of yearlings retained is also to be expected, as ewes were still barely producing one lamb a year, and subsequent losses were inevitable. For most peasant farmers, a regular additional income from the wool clip would have been a significant benefit.[5]

The first evidence for regulation of the wool trade is actually as far back as the tenth century, when King Edgar fixed the price of a 'wey' weight of wool at ten shillings. (See weights and measures, p. *xiii*) Certainly by the 1250s fortunes could be made from wool, and the wealthiest of the early traders were Nicholas de Ludlow and his son Laurence. Laurence was based in Shrewsbury and London, and was probably concentrating on the most expensive wool then available, the fine produce of the Herefordshire and south Shropshire sheep. By 1281 he had made enough money to buy Stokesay manor, and he invested huge sums rebuilding the main house.

Enough evidence for Laurence's mercantile and banking activities survives to show that many of his Herefordshire contacts had interests in wool. William Rondolf, the lord of Woodcote (Shropshire) and Eye, for example, owed him for '11 sacks of good wool' – about 2,800 fleeces – in 1288.[6] By 1294 he had been King Edward I's chief adviser on the wool trade for several years, and at his urging the tax levied on exports was trebled to a huge 40s. per sack: the so-called maltote, the 'evil tax'. Later that year, Laurence and his brother John sailed with a wool fleet for Flanders, but they ran into a storm and were both drowned. The chronicler of

Stokesay Castle, built from profits from the wool trade c.1290

Dunstable Priory probably expressed the common feeling among wool growers and traders when he wrote:

> He it was who induced the merchants of England to grant the king 40s. for
> each sack of wool ... and because he sinned against the wool mongers he was
> swallowed by the waves in a ship laden with wool.

The Garway Templars' Inquisition of 1308 gives a snapshot of one Herefordshire farming community as it changed from religious to royal control. The livestock included 60 oxen, a bull and 16 cows, but 480 breeding ewes of which 103 were sterile that year, 105 yearling ewes, 352 wethers and 189 yearling wethers, making a flock of over 1,100 adult sheep. From these, the wool clip filled three and a half standard sacks, and was worth the huge sum of £23 6s. 8d.

The short but exceedingly fine wool of southern Marches' sheep, and of the Ryelands breed in particular, was much the most sought after, so that in Pego-lotti's Italian merchants' handbook (c.1340) the list of wool values from various English monasteries has Tintern, Dore and Stanfield in Lindsey at the top, worth 28 marks per sack in the Flemish markets (the cheapest English wool fetched only seven marks). These price differentials continued throughout the English wool era, although transport costs to the ports affected the prices that were paid at the farm gate and gave producers in the south-east a marginal advantage. A later list of standard prices payable at Calais had 35 grades, again topped by Marches wool, and in a late fifteenth-century list of prices for buyers in England, Leominster wool was valued at 19½ marks, Shropshire and the 'Leominster Marches' wool at 14 marks, while Kent, Surrey, Middlesex and Yorkshire were only 4½ marks and Cornish wool was not deemed suitable for export, being too coarse and known as Cornish hair.[7]

By no means all Ryelands wool was grown in the Leominster area, but Leominster, Ross and Ludlow rose to early prominence as markets and export centres. Dore Abbey had by far the largest flock in the county, with 2,790 recorded in 1291, but similar fine short-fleeced sheep thrived on the lighter soils around Ross, the thin sheep-and-barley land of Woolhope and Dinmore, the higher pastures near Bromyard and the less productive north-west of Here-fordshire, the Black Mountains and the Radnor fringe. Beyond the county, there seem to have been similar 'Ross' flocks in western Worcestershire, the Cluns of Shropshire and some 'Heath' flocks in Staffordshire. The Dore and Tintern supply, however, was the one that first made a reputation for quality and reliabil-ity – so much so that in 1275, only 30

Modern Ryelands sheep; the Ryemeadows flock, Birtsmorton, Worcestershire (© Katie James)

years after Dore Abbey was founded, its wool was already used as the gold standard. Darnhall Abbey in Cheshire made a contract that year to supply 'twelve sacks of Herefordshire wool of as good quality as the better Dore wool'.

For several centuries, the great majority of English wool was exported, some to northern Italy but mostly to the weaving towns of Flanders where stable government and high population levels had led to an early dependence on industrial production. Their abundance of fullers' earth soils and variety of dye crops, combined with good trade routes, made an ideal cloth-making region. The first formal arrangement was with Ghent in 1081, then Douai, Bruges and Ypres. For a while, these Flemish towns were allowed to arrange their own trade through London, but by the thirteenth century it was more organised and export licences were required. These show that in 1273 English merchants were carrying a third of the wool, and the rest was shared between a diverse range from Spaniards and Italians to citizens of the German states. By the fifteenth century, English merchants carried four-fifths of the wool, and the remainder was almost entirely handled by Italians. By then, the English state monopoly was so tight that Herefordshire and Cotswold wool had to pass through London on its way to the coast, unless it was covered by exemptions granted to Italian merchants who undertook to sail direct to their home ports.

Edward I's maltote tax was so unpopular it did not last long, but later kings found similar ways to milk the wool trade to fund their interminable wars with France. This resulted in price regulation, export monopolies and restricted membership of the oligarchy which profited most from the trade. The biggest sellers – especially Cistercian monasteries like Dore and Tintern – handled their own wool clip. They made a deal with a merchant, a member of the London Fellowship of the Staple or one of his suppliers, at the start of the year or even several years ahead, and received in advance about a third of the estimated final price. The abbey had to bear the cost of washing the sheep, then clipping, sorting, packing and transporting the wool to an agreed rendevous at a market town. There the woolsacks, each weighing 364lb, were wrapped into sarplers, two or three sacks at a time, for which a standard 12 yards of Arras canvas had to be purchased, weighing a further 28lb. The wool was then loaded on to carts for the five-day journey to London, which in the late fifteenth century cost around 18s. 9d. for two sarplers sharing a cart.

The wool of small growers was managed in a similar way. Broggers, the local woolmen, either went round the fairs and markets buying up individual clips, which was more popular with the townspeople who then took a cut of the profits, or they entered into advance contracts and visited the farms in person. All packing

Sheepwash at Cutsdean, Gloucestershire, rebuilt in the nineteenth century and recently restored; the water-level was controlled by sluices

was supposed to be done in the county of origin, by a specialist member of the independent London Guild of Packers, each sack being overseen by the merchant's official and marked with the unique merchant mark and a record of the place of origin. After being weighed again, the sarplers were stamped with the merchant's and dealer's marks and an indication of the source, quality and batch reference for each consignment of wool. The Merchant of the Staple then exported his wool, divided among several ships in a wool fleet for security, often accompanied by the packer to Calais where it was sold through dealers who after 1429 became incorporated as the Company of the Staple.[8]

If the staple merchants were the ones who grew outstandingly rich, and in some cases entered the ranks of the aristocracy, the middlemen merchants also rose in importance and sometimes in their turn became Staplers. Others looked to their supply chain, and grazed their own flocks. For instance, John Heritage of Moreton-in-Marsh, a wool merchant who bought at Cotswold fairs and markets, sold in London and also acted as middleman for other graziers, had several flocks of his own in September 1510, with 25 rams, 595 ewes, 548 lambs, 217 wethers and a further 677 unspecified others – 2,062 in all.[9] The year before, Heritage had kept a note of the weight of his fleeces, which had averaged under two pounds, compared with the optimal weight for a medieval flock of long-woolled Cotswold sheep of about ten fleeces per todd (28lb). By the late eighteenth century a Cotswold farmer hoped for four to the todd, and in the modern breed a ewe produces a fleece of 16lb. The comparison with Ryelands is interesting. The medieval fleece weighed not much more than one pound, which more than doubled by the eighteenth century and is now about 3lb for a ewe, although even today it is recognised as one of the finest wools in the world. This great increase in fleece weight is partly due to improved diet, but mostly attributable to the effects of breeding for increased body size.

Cotswold wool was always significantly less valuable than the premium Herefordshire type, but although coarser it was longer, the sheep were bigger and there were far more of them, so the Cotswolds became synonymous with good quality, profitable wool. For this reason, the memorial brasses of the richest merchants and middlemen are in the Cotswold churches, and some gave with conspicuous generosity towards embellishing their parish church.

Any of these merchants might have dealt in Ryelands wool as well as the cheaper Cotswold wool which so far outweighed it by volume. One merchant who is quite likely to have done so is John Comber, merchant of Worcester. He specified in his will that he wished his 'body to be buried within that holy churche in which parishe it shall so time me to disease.' He left to the place of his burial 100s. for repair work on the fabric. Perhaps this was because his own church of St Andrew's Worcester had recently undergone an extensive rebuilding programme. In any event, Comber died and was buried in Sevenhampton near Cheltenham in 1497, perhaps while travelling on wool business.[10]

Part of the memorial brass of John Taylour, wool merchant (died 1509), in Northleach which was a major wool town. The sheep stands on a woolsack with Taylour's mark, above a shepherd's crook. (© Julia Owen, Northleach)

A combination of factors both at home and abroad, social and political, meant that export levels of English wool began to decline from the mid fourteenth century, from a peak of about 35,000 sacks a year in 1315, to 18,000 in 1385 and just 5,000 by 1545. But demand for Herefordshire and Cotswold wool remained high, because this fall was matched by an increasing trade overseas in English woollen cloth, more than reversing an earlier small volume of imported foreign cloth.

The Cloth Trade

By the mid thirteenth century, English cloth-making was beginning to recover, after a period dominated

Memorial brass to John Comber of Worcester (died 1497), in Sevenhampton Church, Gloucestershire

by the export of raw wool. Even as early as 1160–1240, the citizens of Hereford included at least two felters, four dyers, six tailors and seven mercers, hinting perhaps at the existence of ongoing or resurgent production.[11] Prominent among the new cloth-making counties were Worcestershire, Herefordshire and Gloucestershire, with Ludlow and Cotswolds cloths appearing alongside the better-known Lincolns and Lindseys. However this was mostly aimed at the home market and only after the 1350s did exports begin in earnest.

The short wool of the Ryelands and southern chalk downlands made a stout cloth after fulling to thicken and clean it, while the longer wools of the Lincolns, Leicesters and Cotswolds came to be used for lighter cloths which were not always fulled. Cloth towns like Worcester and to some extent Hereford flourished, but weaving and finishing of cloth also took place in rural areas, so it was much freer from central control than the wool trade. Exports grew from a minimal quantity in 1350 to 40,000 standard cloths in 1400 and peaked at over 100,000 in 1520, by which time an estimated 160,000 cloths were also used in the domestic market. These exports were taxed when they were traced, but lacking the monopolistic control of the Staple Merchants, the rate was only 2% compared with the wool export tax of about 33%, and many cargoes may have evaded all duty. Exports were also helped by a slight fall in the price of wool in England, possibly due to over-supply, so the finished cloth was sold at competitive prices in Europe, while maintaining its reputation for high quality. Only Spanish Merino wool came near our finest grades.

Michael Drayton, a Warwickshire man, published his *Poly-Olbion* describing the counties of Britain in 1622. He clearly knew the Cotswolds well, extolling their sheep in a famous stanza:

> though famous for her flocks,
> Yet hardly doth [Salisbury] tithe our Cotswolds wealthy locks.
> Though Lemster him exceed for fineness of her ore,
> Yet quite he puts her down for his abundant store ...
>   ... Cotswold wisely fills
> Her with the whitest kind: whose brows so woolly be
> As men in her faire sheep no emptiness should see.

Yet he conceded that fine Herefordshire wool was far superior, even to the mythical Golden Fleece:

> At Lemster, for her wooll whose Staple doth excell,
> And seems to over-match the golden Phrygian Fell.
> Had this our Colchos been unto the Ancients knowne,
> When Honor was her selfe, and in her glorie showne,

He then that did commaund the Infantry of Greece,
Had onely to our Ile adventur'd for this Fleece.
Where lives the man so dull, on Britains farthest shore,
To whom did never sound the name of Lemster Ore?
That with the Silke-wormes web for smalness doth compare:
Wherein, the Winder showes his workmanship so rare.[12]

The heavy and immensely popular broadcloth made locally may have been free from the red tape that fettered the wool trade, but its size was still stipulated by law. For many years, each cloth had to be 7 quarters wide (1.6 m), 26–28 yards long (24–25.6 m) and weigh 44 lb (20 kg), so the fabric was comparable to modern overcoat material. This was the famous English broadcloth which sold so well at home and abroad.

Once woven, the cloth was fulled, at first manually, treading it with fuller's earth to absorb most of the lanolin and to increase its thickness. Later, fulling was done by beating within specially-designed water mills fitted with paddles. The earliest one known in this region was built by the Templars at Temple Guiting in 1185. In Welsh-speaking areas, fulling mills were known as 'pandy', for example Pandy on the Monnow near Grosmont. References to early fulling mills in Herefordshire are now scarce, although they must have been quite numerous. The Knights Hospitaller at Dinmore certainly had one by the 1330s, with an annual value of 50s., compared with their corn mill which was worth a more modest 36s. 8d.[13] The earls of March owned several fulling mills, one at Kingsland by 1389, and others in Knighton and Pembridge soon afterwards. In 1613 there was one on the River Arrow at Maye Hoame Meadow in Lyonshall, with an adjacent house lived in by the fuller Hugh Payne but owned by Richard Eastopp, a dyer of Kington. Fifty years later, a second fulling mill had been built at the site and the owners had prospered sufficiently for the current Mr Eastopp to style himself Gent.[14] Worcester cloth was fulled in mills on the small rivers just upstream, notably the Salwarpe, where one site in Dodderhill parish is still known as Walkmill.[15] After fulling, the cloth was brought back by river to the tentering grounds north of the Worcester city walls, to be stretched. One must assume that Herefordshire cloth was handled in a similar way, using pack horses when water transport was not feasible.

Where the cloth trade flourished, towns in particular often had plenty of associated craftspeople, from weavers and fullers (also known as walkers or tuckers), to drapers and sometimes chaloners (who made blankets). A rare survival of a document which almost certainly relates to the 1377 and 1381 Worcester Poll Taxes has recently come to light, and this enables the occupants' crafts to be explored. Over a fifth of the tax payers (everyone over 14 or 15 years old) were involved in the textiles business even then. There were weavers, fullers (mostly called walkers), dyers, drapers and mercers, the richest of whom were the drapers and mercers, but 11% of tax payers were tailors.[16] A further clue to the booming cloth trade was the rapid increase in imports of dyes, some of them very costly and from far-flung regions of the world, to the Severn ports.

At the Reformation, control of the biggest flocks and the fulling mills came into lay hands and increasingly the clothiers became establishment figures as the wool merchants had been before them. Worcester rose to national prominence as a major cloth town at this time. An Act of Henry VIII had tried to limit cloth-making in Worcestershire to Worcester, Evesham, Kidderminster, Bromsgrove and Droitwich, to control unregulated rural producers and boost urban industry, and major rebuilding programmes at this time do point to the city's prosperity.[17] Leland thought Worcester produced more cloth than anywhere else, and of the finest quality, which may point to the use of Herefordshire wool. Firm evidence for this is lacking, although the author of *A Cheap and Good Husbandry, In A Way to get Wealth* (1675) notes that:

> If you desire to have sheep of a curious fine staple of wooll, from where
> you may draw a thread as fine as silk, you shall see such in Herefordshire,
> about Lempster side, and other special parts of that County; in that part of
> Worcestershire joyning upon Shropshire, and many such like places.[18]

In Herefordshire, Kington, Ledbury and Hereford were for a while significant cloth towns, and among the notable mercers were William Maylord and William Price. By the eighteenth century, however, most of the wool was being sent elsewhere for manufacture.

Even after cloth-making in the county passed its peak, sheep continued to be kept for their wool. Before 1600, a third of Herefordshire wills made personal bequests of sheep, often including lambs for young people such as godchildren. In 1548, for example, Hugh Weaver the Elder of Presteigne left his daughter Katherine six cattle and some other stock, to his daughter Margaret 20 sheep and other stock, and a sum of money to a third daughter. His wife and son were still alive so we must presume that Hugh's flock was significantly larger than 20. An interesting will from 1591 is that of William Weston of Docklow, yeoman, who left his son James some cattle, two horses and 'thirteen English Sheep'. Quite what he meant by that is unclear, but he was perhaps anxious that even if not 'Ryelands' stock, they should not be recent Welsh mountain imports. (In a much later inventory, Phillip Gilbert of Walterstone in 1796 had six 'Welsh ewes' listed, which clearly were not the fine-woolled breed).[19]

Returning to the early wills, in 1577 the Reverend John Higgens of Bridstow made the following bequests of livestock:

to his wife, sixty of his best wether sheep, ten of his best ewes and ten
of his best lambs
to Thomas Higgens his brother, five oxen, ten ewes and ten lambs
to Ales Philpott, six lambs
to Eleanor Higgens, six lambs

So, at the absolute minimum, if he was distributing his entire flock, Higgens must have been keeping 92 sheep, partly or mainly for their wool. On the second page of his will, among his debts due to others, there is support for this in a note recording that he owed an unspecified sum 'to Thomas Maylord the younger, gent, for 4 stones of wool' (perhaps 30 fleeces). This Thomas might perhaps have been the one baptised at St Nicholas, Hereford in 1556, the son of Thomas and Ales, although the Henrican tax lists do not include Thomas the elder as one of the richer inhabitants of Herefordshire. He could also have been a relation of the Maylord family who were Tudor and Stuart city councillors. At least one later member of this family was mayor of Hereford, and John Maylord of Hereford, gentleman, who died in 1657, owned several properties in and near Hereford. It was probably this John's son William who was described as a mercer of Hereford in the same year.[20]

In 1675, about two-thirds of Herefordshire's farming families were keeping sheep, with an average flock size of 30. Some had only a handful, but there were some sizeable flocks, and the animals varied greatly in value. For example, Thomas Parsons of Little Birch had 80, valued in October at only £8. By contrast, William Powel of The Highwood, Yarpole, had a flock of 88 worth £18, and William Hill of Colwall had 48 valued at £10, with four stone of wool 'of all sorts' worth £1 10s., still awaiting sale in November.

Fifty years later, two-thirds of farms still had sheep, and if anything the average flock size had increased slightly. One of the largest flocks among the Herefordshire inventories made in 1725 was at Tretire, where Thomas Tyler had 145 ewes, 24 fat sheep, 59 lambs and three stone of wool on the farm, worth £2 5s. The sheep were valued at nearly £68 in all.

The relative values of the components of the flock belonging to John Churchman at Ballingham in May 1753 are quite revealing. He had over 100 head of sheep, with 40 wethers which must have been kept for wool, 28 couples of ewes and young lambs and 20 yearlings. The table compares their values then with a typical price-range today, showing how the market has changed from a focus on wool to breeding ewes.

Comparison of the eighteenth-century sheep market with today

stock	Estimated value May 1753	Estimated value summer 2020
Ewe with lamb at foot	6s.	£150–180
Yearling	3s. 7d.	£100 (for old season lamb)
Wether	6s.	£50–80

Coming Full Circle: Rearing Sheep for Meat

Even while wool was the primary focus of sheep farmers, most families would have also eaten mutton. There is little evidence for a big autumn cull of stock, but some animals must have been selected for autumn fattening, for market or domestic use.

The transition to commercial meat production began in the seventeenth century, as urban population levels rose and demand for cheap meat increased. At the same time, wool prices began to fall relative to other agricultural products, partly as a result of an ill-fated government attempt to support the cloth trade by banning export of wool. This benefitted the cloth merchants at the expense of wool producers, and ultimately encouraged a move towards mutton and lamb.

Herefordshire was one of the areas which developed early droving of sheep, ultimately to Smithfield. Even in late Tudor times, in Dorset the sheep were capable of early breeding, lambing in October for sale on the London market from Christmas. But the Cotswolds and Welsh borders were not far behind, perhaps because of strong pre-existing trade links. The estate manager at Nibley, Gloucestershire, was sending regular summer consignments to Smithfield through the 1620s: in 1622, 183 lambs, a ram, 31 ewes and 25 wethers; in 1623, 207 lambs, 62 ewes and 18 wethers. The first book devoted exclusively to improving sheep production was written in 1749 by William Ellis, a Hertfordshire gentleman farmer, but unfortunately his publications were known to diverge somewhat from his practice and his farm followed few of his own recommendations 'how to fat them in the quickest and cheapest Manner and to cause them to have a sweeter Flesh, while they are fattening on Turnips or Rape, contrary to the Nature of those Rank plants.'[21]

By the late eighteenth century, most wool for cloth was coming from longwools, because a balance had to be found between rising urban demand for mutton, the far greater carcass weight of longwool sheep and their much heavier fleeces, as the Table below illustrates.

Sample fleece values in 1779

breed	Average fleece weight	Price per lb of wool	typical fleece price
Ryeland	2 lb	30d.	60d.
Lincoln longwool	10 lb	5d.	50d.

Although interrupted during the Napoleonic Wars, when fine Merino wool could not be imported and Ryelands temporarily regained some status, this led to an increasing tendency to cross pure-bred Ryelands with larger breeds. Many such crosses were tried during the early nineteenth century, and many people settled on Leicesters, which gave a leaner mutton than from the pure Leicester then grown quickly and cheaply for the mass market. But this was at the expense of the fine, short wool and sweet meat of the grass-fed Ryelands. The Ryelands-cross mutton was even poorer if the sheep were fed on turnips, as they usually were at this time. In the long run, this meant that Herefordshire lost its long-held status as a prime sheep county, acquiring instead a maze of 'mongrel' sheep flocks of uncertain ancestry.[22]

Only a few more-or-less pure-bred Ryelands were left, and although they benefitted greatly from the early twentieth-century establishment of a breed society, they later suffered a further decline and have only recently been brought back from the edge of extinction as a recognisable breed. Perhaps ironically considering their former pre-eminence in the international wool trade, many are now primarily smallholders' grass cutters or pets. Meanwhile the county is benefitting from the modern specialist demand for leaner, higher quality, grass-fed native lamb, and is again home to many prime flocks.

Organic, grass-fed Lleyn ewe with her Hampshire Down cross lamb, Whitbourne

Cider

Cider may epitomise Herefordshire produce, but it was not always so. Pre-Conquest, the most valued beverages were ale and mead, although there is some evidence from other parts of England that wild crab apples were sometimes used to make an alcoholic drink. Since then, fruit growing and cider and perry have fallen in and out of fashion down the centuries, for a host of reasons. Many would agree that we are fortunate to live in a time when they are enjoying a renaissance.

The Early Years

It is certain that the Romans had access to apples in Britain, whether for cider or dessert use. Pips have been found at several archaeological sites, and the so-called Vindolanda tablet 302, from Hadrian's Wall, asks for 100 nice apples for the commanding officer's supplies (together with eggs and other perishable goods), so the fruit (and not just wild crabs) must have been grown in northern Britain by the second century.[1] The troops stationed on the Wall at the time came from a region of Spain where the Roman author Pliny describes alcoholic drinks being made from apples and pears, so this may be the route by which the first improved varieties came to this country.

Domesday Book is seldom concerned with orchards, but in Nottingham it notes a royal gift of ten acres for the specific purpose of making a new orchard. There are also references to them at Exeter, and at Orchard, in Church Knowle, Dorset.[2] There were no doubt many more places where apples and pears were grown by the millennium, but there are no references to them in Herefordshire. Nor is it clear whether the fruit was used for making drink, or whether it was by then palatable for eating or cooking.

Medieval Orchards and Cider

Cider production in something akin to its modern form was probably introduced to England from Normandy. Several houses of the religious Order of the Knights Templar had supplies of cider recorded in inventories taken when the houses were forcibly suppressed in October 1307. For example, while the preceptory at Baugy, near Bayeux, mostly had wine with a small quantity of beer for the servants, Bretteville south of Caen had wine and cider, and Corval had a barrel of cider 'of which a good deal has been drunk', some new cider for guests and also some wine.[3] Far from being the secretive organisation their enemies portrayed, the Templars', through their small rural houses, had a dual role of farming to raise funds to support the Order's work in the Middle East, and giving hospitality to travellers. The Knights Hospitaller, who received most of the Templar lands in the 1330s, also inherited this obligation, and here at Garway they specifically complained about their numerous Welsh visitors.[4]

Garway's previously-detached tower survives from the old Templar church

Where vineyards were struggling, home-made cider was an obvious choice of drink for such guests, but the Hospitallers seem to have preferred making beer, from oats.

The 2,000-acre Templar estate centred on Garway, given to them in 1187, was their largest property in Herefordshire and one of the larger ones in England. They also held small acreages at Upleadon (on or near Temple Farm, Bosbury), Welsh Newton, Rowlestone and Harewood. Both Garway and Upleadon had areas tended by a 'keeper of the garden', which may well have included fruit trees. In 1308, when the estates were newly taken into royal administration, the report for Garway notes that the produce of the dovecote (which was derelict) and the garden together only amounted to 3s. 8d., but at Upleadon the garden produce alone was sold for 6s., which should have been more but the harvest had been poor.[5] The detailed 1308 accounts for five English Templar properties definitely mention cider, see table overleaf.

Cider Production on English Templar estates, 1308

location	quantity of cider	value	amount sold	income	press or mill?	notes
Upleadon, Herefords.	5 tuns*	25 s.	4 tuns	20s.	–	
Swanton, Beds	1 cask**	4 s.	0	0	press (3d.)	consumed on site?
Royton, Essex	–	–	–	–	press and mill§	Account completed in February – had all the cider been drunk?
Bullstrode, Bucks	–	–	50 gallons	3s. 4d.	–	'produce of the garden'
Keele, Staffs	–	–	1 tun of cider	5s.	–	And 6s. income from sale of apples from the garden

* a tun = a large medieval barrel, probably with a capacity of 256 gallons at this time
** a cask = perhaps a general term for a barrel
§ specifically mentions cider-making: *pressor cum molend ad ciseram faciend*[6]

Cider-making was certainly well-established in parts of southern England by the start of the fourteenth century; many places in Surrey had specialist fruit growers and all Merton College's manors there had cider-presses.[7]

The bailiff's accounts for Kingsland manor in 1389–90 provide the earliest detailed reference to Herefordshire orchard management. Here, the total income for renting out the pastures and meadows was £26 7s., of which the grass in Old-orchard Pasture contributed 18s. and the grass and fruit of Mordenhale Orchard brought in £1. Among the expenses there is 3d. for propping up and pruning 'various fruit-bearing trees'. Here, then, is a glimpse of a long-established tradition of orchards, at least one of which was currently a pasture orchard, and of keeping some of the crop in hand while letting other parts out.[8]

In the early 1400s, orchards were found across much of England and Wales, from Newcastle-upon-Tyne to Swansea, Devon to Kent, although they were not yet common. Most were in the south and west, and many were only an acre or two, often linked to the gardens around manorial buildings. Occasionally, the fruit itself is valued, not just the pasture beneath the trees; for instance, in a 1421 Inquisition Post Mortem (IPM) for Brentwood, Essex, the manor buildings were all ruinous but the site, grass, apples and pears were worth 3s. per year. In Rock parish, west Worcestershire, in 1425 there was a house and a virgate of land called 'Orchard'. In

Kidderminster the following year, there was a 'proof of age enquiry' in which a man named Robert Whateley testified that he remembered the baptismal day of the disputed heir, because an oak tree growing in his orchard had been 'totally blown to the ground by a strong wind'.

Cider was sufficiently widespread by this time for one of the followers of John Wycliffe the Bible translator (d.1384) to use it instead of 'strong drink' in a later version of their text. A copy of this 'cider Bible' is now in Hereford Cathedral Library. It is not known when the manuscript was copied or by whom, but it seems to be all in one expert hand dating to the early years of the fifteenth century. One possible translator is Nicholas of Hereford, an Oxford theologian who was excommunicated in 1382 for his Wycliffite views; he later recanted and was from 1397 to 1417 the Treasurer of Hereford Cathedral. The book found its way into the collection of Robert Bennet, bishop of Hereford from 1602, and he donated it to the library.[9]

Proverbs 31 v. 6: 'gyve ye / sidur to them that moornen: & wiyn to them that be /
of bittir soule' (lines 6–8) (© Hereford Cathedral Library, O.7.1)

Only two Herefordshire orchards were mentioned in early fifteenth-century IPMs: Eaton Tregoes in Foy on the Wye had one and a half acres of orchard valued at 6d. in 1420; and an orchard at 'Ashton' (probably much bigger) was worth 6s. 8d. in 1446.[10] But from other sources we know that in 1413, a house and land in Pencombe, including Pole Orchard, was leased to Walter Wilke and his wife for life, and Kings Orchard in Hereford is also known from 1413; the rent roll for Dorstone for 1428 lists a perry orchard and a field called Castle Orchard; and the Eton Tregoes bailiff's accounts for 1445–65 refer to pressed fruit worth 5s. sold from the manor garden (such a large quantity is almost certain to be for cider or perry). Firm evidence for more widespread production is scarce until mechanical cider-mills became more widespread, since their high value makes them more visible in the archives. One of the earliest local references is dated to between 1475 and 1485, when there is mention of a cider-mill at Rodley, Gloucestershire. But, as ever, it is the court cases that provide most colour. The Court Rolls for Holme Lacy for 1400 include a case of suspected theft of bread and cider at the house of Agathe Fulfodys.[11]

The tomb slab of Andrew and Elizabeth Jones, in Hereford Cathedral

Special mention should also be made of Andrew Jones, who died in 1497 and is buried with his wife Elizabeth in Hereford Cathedral. His image shows him resting his feet on a small barrel, apparently mimicking the wool merchants' brasses. Was he an early cider baron, grown rich from his orchards and so able to make a handsome donation for his burial place?

The Great Improvers

John Beale, writing during the Civil War, claimed that 'very few of our cottagers ... or our wealthiest yeomen, drink anything else' than cider, but he may have been a little ahead of himself. He was the son of a Yarkhill gentleman farmer, travelled on the Continent in the late 1630s and then became a parish priest in Somerset, so would have seen the potential of orchard crops in many different contexts. But although small orchards were by then increasingly common in Herefordshire rental agreements, it seems unlikely that he was familiar with the relative costs, convenience and availability of beer compared with cider and perry, for most of the population. As late as 1725, after all, the innkeeper Alice Coundley of Tenbury Wells (on the county boundary) was offering a choice of ale or beer but no cider.[12] A significant factor must have been the expense of setting up an orchard and then preparing the fruit. Malt was made from oats, barley or wheat, and brewing could be done in small batches. By contrast an orchard was costly to establish, took several years to begin production, and the cider maker also had to invest in milling equipment and storage space for large barrels, or share these facilities with someone else.

One of the earliest Herefordshire wills to refer to a cider mill is that of Margaret Taylor of Townsend Farm, Brampton Abbotts. In 1610 she left all her farm equipment, oxen, and a 'cider mill or must mill', as well as a quern malt mill, to her eldest son John, and several barrels and pipe casks shared between her sons Henry (a clergyman at Eye) and John, and her son-in-law Thomas Walker. Mrs Taylor was clearly comfortably off, with a substantial house and plenty of furniture and furnishings as well as the cider-mill.

Once inventories appear on a regular basis, it becomes possible to estimate frequency of cider production and consumption. Thus, in 1675 20% of inventories mention cider or perry, and only 4% beer, (although this may be because a brewing of beer was too cheap to be recorded separately, since 15% list malt). Similarly, 14% had a fruit mill, one of which was specifically for perry, and these were typically worth one or two pounds, while 8% list a malt mill. Interestingly, the cider and perry is (with one exception) listed in the middle to high value inventories, while the malt is almost always confined to the middle-value ones. It seems, therefore, that beer persisted longer in Herefordshire, and cider took longer to find its way into the hearts of the population, than Beale gave credit for. Beer must always have been a fall-back as long as cider was locally made, just because the supply of apples varied between seasons and so the volume produced was unreliable and might not last the year. Small batches of malt could be brewed as needed as a supplement.

Hand-operated domestic malt mill, c.1715, from Newton (Hereford Museum acc. no. 9297, Trustees of the Coningsby Hospital)

There was undoubtedly, however, a push to establish cider as a more mainstream drink from the mid-1600s. The driving force behind this was perhaps initially Sir John Scudamore, whose family had been at Holme Lacy since the fifteenth century. John was created first Viscount Scudamore in 1628 and became Ambassador to France, where he is thought to have been so impressed by the Normandy 'redstreak' apples that he brought some cuttings home with him and devoted much of his time to developing cider orchards and grafting methods on his estate. Even before his posting to France, Scudamore was experimenting with cider-making in the early 1630s, including some of the earliest attempts to store and transport it in bottles.[13] John Beale, who was a relative of the Scudamores, was moved to write:

> For as no culture or graffs will exalt the French wines to compare with the wines of Greece ... so neither will the cider of Bromyard and Ledbury equal that of Ham Lacy and Kings Capell in the same small county of Hereford. Yes the choice of Graff or fruit hath so much of prevalency, that the red strake cider will everywhere excell common cider.

A major impetus to plant fruit trees arose from the Civil Wars, when the Parliamentary armies spent many months in Herefordshire and neighbouring parts of Worcestershire and Gloucestershire, and saw the local orchards. A concern had arisen that malting would burn so much wood that timber supplies might be depleted, which cider and perry of course circumvented. Also, the ground beneath standard fruit trees could be used for arable crops or pasture, so they produced a bonus crop as well as saving all the acreage for malting grains. Thirdly, French and German wines became less accessible under the policies of the Commonwealth. During the wars, the earl of Southampton is reputed to have planted 15,000 apple trees near Portsmouth, with the intention of making cider. Walter Blith then included a section on 'The great Advance of Land by diverse Orchards and Garden Fruits' in his book of agricultural improvements, which he dedicated to the Commonwealth leaders in 1653. Not only, he said, did the grass in these counties scarcely suffer from the addition of apples, pears and cherries, but 'some question whether with their shadinesse in Summer, and Warmnesse in Winter, they better not the land farre more', so they produced earlier grass and carried more livestock per acre.

Geese grazing in an apple orchard, Humber

Blith's book inaugurated a wave of discussion, publishing and attempts at legislation, greatly helped by John Evelyn's *Sylva*, which he carefully dedicated to Charles II in 1663, with chapters entitled Pomona, dedicated to the same earl of Southampton, and Aphorisms concerning Cider by his friend Beale. Evelyn's section on cider trees in the Pomona highlighted the regional differences already emerging. Gloucestershire, he noted, 'affects the Bromsbury Crab, [which] affords a smart, winy Liquor' but it is not 'fit to be ground for Cider till Christmas, lying so long in heaps'. 'About London, and the more Southern Tracts, the Pepin and especially the Golden, is esteemed . . .' But:

> the Redstrake then amongst these accurate Tasters hath obtained the absolute
> praeminence of all other Cider-fruit, especially in Herefordshire, as being
> the richest and most vinous Liquor, and now with the more earnestness
> commended to our practice, for its celerity in becoming an Orchard, being
> ordinarily as full of fruit at ten years growth as other Trees are at twenty.

Among the proposed legislation intended to encourage cider and perry, was an unsuccessful attempt to persuade tenant farmers to plant orchards by promising them free picking of the fruit until they had recouped all their costs. In Ombersley, west Worcestershire, the manorial court tackled the issue in reverse, by introducing an obligation to plant four new orchard trees for every one cut down, but how successful this was is unclear. Certainly the Royal Society began promoting agricultural improvement soon after its foundation in 1660, beginning with cider fruit. The royalists John Scudamore and John Beale were both invited to take part.

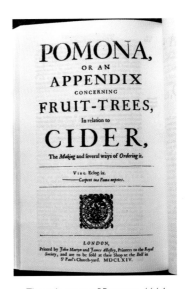

The title page of Pomona, 1664

Over the century to 1750, there was a major national shift in drinking habits, with the share of the market in beer falling by a third, to be taken up by cider, English gin, renewed wine imports and tea and coffee for the richest. Perry was regionally important, but not on a national scale.[14]

These changes were conspicuous in Herefordshire, judging by the evidence from our sample of probate inventories.

Evidence for drinks or their manufacture, from probate sample

year	No. in sample	Cider or perry (%)	Fruit mill (%)	Value of fruit mill	Beer (%)	Malt (%)	Malt mill (%)	Mention of orchard (%)
1675	75	20	14	£1–2	4	15	8	0
1700	68	22	25	£1–2	3	18	13	1
1725	75	43	23	£1–3	3	5	5	7
1750	31	25	31	£1–3	3	3	12	3

Even by 1700, cider seems to have worked some way down the social scale, so that for instance Thomas Rawlins of Much Cowarne, whose total inventory was worth £19 15s., left 10s. of cider when he died in March, together with several empty hogsheads; he also had a mill in a separate cider house. Another yeoman, Morgan Watkin of Ayton in Lucton, had a three-acre garden and orchard around his house, and a further two acres of arable orchard in Bowbery field, with 'the Trees growing in the Nursery', although he only had an old must-mill screw and £3 4s. of cider and empty hogsheads when he died in November.

At the other extreme, Mr Richard Fisher Collins of Foy, gentleman, who died in 1750 leaving an inventory worth the huge sum of £505, had a brew house with copper brewing utensils as well as a kiln house, but not apparently any beer. Nor did he have a cider-mill, but he had 21 hogsheads of perry and nine of cider, 80 empty hogsheads, and 15 dozen bottles awaiting filling.

The design of cider-mills varied across the country, but had to incorporate the two basic stages of fruit preparation: chopping up or crushing, then squeezing to release the juice. In some regions, a stone was run up and down in a deep wooden trough to crush the fruit. Where the bed rock was too soft or alkaline, scratters, often made from apple wood and resembling toothed wheels, ran back and forth powered by a bigger wheel usually propelled by man-power. In Herefordshire, as in the Channel Islands, parts of Normandy and the West Country, a semi-automated system was used. The fruit was often fed from an overhead chute into the circular hard-stone trough and crushed with a rotating stone moved by an axle. Many inventories include 'one old mare' or 'a blind horse', which would in all likelihood have been kept for this purpose.

However the fruit was crushed, it was then scooped out and the resulting pulp had to be squeezed dry. This was typically done using a must-mill or press. Layers of coarse cloth or straw alternating with fruit pulp were built up into a tower and then screwed down from above. In normal conditions, a ton of this must-cheese would produce about 150 gallons (roughly three hogsheads) of cider or perry. These mills and presses now adorn the approaches to many Herefordshire settlements and pubs, a memory of their past ubiquity.

Clockwise from above: Crushing fruit with horse-power, Norton by Bromyard (BDLHS Picture Archive); Restored cider-mill; Cider press; Cider-making machinery on the approach to Bromyard

After this, the skilful stage really began, with different varieties and blends, yeasts, temperatures (dependent in turn on the buildings used) and a host of other factors determining the final product. As John Worlidge noted in 1676:

> You may make it suite almost with any humourous Drinker: It may be made luscious, by addition of a good quantity of sweet Apples in the first operation; pleasant, being made with Pippins or Gennet-Moyles onely; racy, poignant, oyly, spicy, with the Red streak, and several other sorts of Fruits, even as the Operator pleases.

The Beverage of Choice

Through the eighteenth century, cider became an important but more regional product, eventually becoming largely confined to the counties of Herefordshire,

Worcestershire, Gloucestershire, Somerset and Devon, with Kent also making large volumes but using dessert apples.

The popularity of the drink can be gauged by the interest the Excise took in it. At first, only retail cider and perry were charged duty, beginning in 1643 at 1s. 3d. a hogshead but doubled to 2s. 6d. at the Restoration. In 1763 an attempt was made to include cider made for home consumption (for anyone over eight!), causing widespread protests, notably in Devon and the Forest of Dean, and in Ledbury where a procession through the town on the day the Act became law was led by the servants of cider-makers, merchants, coopers, farmers and an assortment of the town poor, and bells rang muffled all day. The new duty was removed in 1766, but the retail element remained until 1830.[15]

Cider was at its zenith during the Napoleonic Wars, with great demand and many new orchards planted. It was a normal component of farm workers' pay in Herefordshire, generally two to three quarts a day in addition to cash wages or board and lodging. In 1809, meanwhile, *Pomona Herefordiensis* was published by Thomas Knight of Wormsley Grange and Downton. With hand-coloured illustrations of the best fruit, it was the product of 25 years experimenting with fruit production, especially apples and pears. Much of the product in this period was surplus to local needs, mainly exported by river from Hereford and Upton to Bristol and onwards by sea to London, or latterly to the north via the tenuous Herefordshire canal system. There was even a Redstreak Tree Tavern in Maylord's Lane, Hereford, until the 1860s.

After suffering something of a decline in the mid nineteenth century, when many orchards were neglected, the Bath and West Show took a lead in the cider and perry revival. Since the 1890s there have often been prizes at the show for cider. Likewise in 1884 the Woolhope Naturalists' Field Club 'became strongly impressed with the necessity of some great effort to restore Herefordshire to its true fruit-growing supremacy', and published the *Herefordshire Pomona*, a classic of Victorian illustrated natural histories. Revd. Charles Bulmer was an enthusiastic Woolhope member in the early years, and it was his son who founded the family cider business, at a time of renewed orchard planting and cider consumption and export.

And Today

After a century of fluctuating fortunes, cider is now enjoying renewed popularity. Most orchards have for many years been in the central and eastern parishes, and although in places there were significant acreages of damsons and some cherries, which confuse the picture, the table below gives a reasonably accurate picture of apple and pear orchards across the county.

Acres of all Orchards by Parish, from the MAFF Parish Returns
(not available by parish after this date)

parish	Parish acreage	1880	1901	1921	1948	1981
Avenbury	3,140	237	177	64	190	21
Bishops Frome	3,560	460	403	95	439	136
Cradley	6,460	426	435	112	324	138
Stoke Lacy	2,370	182	208	73	126	39
Whitbourne	2,700	375	481	189	441	46
Hampton Bishop*	2,070	114	113	386	73	1,306
Holme Lacy	635	139	136	6	106	43
Llangarren	5,605	146	236	16	234	107
St Weonards	4,536	109	133	137	68	2
Abbey Dore	5,790	60	124	38	110	24
Kentchurch	3,286	15	32	14	26	13
Eardisley	4,460	116	150	55	93	22
Orleton	2,603	212	195	80	182	31
Richards Castle	4,871	73	48	42	98	25
Total acreage in sample parishes, excluding Hampton Bishop		2,550	2,758	921	2,437	647

*Hampton Bishop is atypical, often being ahead of the curve, with very large acreages planted in the 1970s.

Bulmers and Westons, two of the largest British cider makers, are both Herefordshire-based, with Bulmers producing over half of the national total by volume. In addition to these giants, modern cider-making has come full circle, often with a revived interest in old varieties of fruit. Smaller cider and perry producers flourish, with well over 20 commercial businesses in the county, and domestic juice- and cider-making is also increasing. In the last decade alone, over 8,000 acres of cider and perry orchards have been planted in the three counties, and at the heart of many of the Herefordshire orchards are giant perry trees, often centuries old, attesting to the continuity of land-use at their heart. These small orchards are increasingly being managed for wildlife and in collaboration with small-scale bee-keeping, showing a new facet of their versatility.

OVERLEAF: *Ancient perry tree, in a recently-established mixed orchard, Tedstone Delamere (with the author included for scale)*

Hereford Cattle

The stocky forms of tan Hereford cattle, with their white curly faces, are so distinctive and well-known, so admired by their breeders in over 50 countries world-wide, that their story seems scarcely to need retelling. Yet it does bear some investigation, if only to answer the most obvious question: why did this superlative British cattle breed emerge in Herefordshire? Or to put it another way: why and how did this land-locked county produce animals that have been exported all over the world?

Top: The Haven herd, with (centre) bull Haven Wizard. Above: Haven Hereford Dowager 137th and her bull calf Haven Cavalier. (both © E.L. Lewis & Son)

In the Beginning

The 'original' ancestral type of our cattle is lost in the mists of time, and may never be fully recovered. But two main strands have contributed to the stock from which the classic Hereford developed. Firstly, as described earlier, oxen continued to be used for ploughing and other draught work until well into the nineteenth century, requiring strong but placid animals. Secondly, the continuing sales of upland Welsh cattle into the county introduced and enhanced specific attributes, including an ability to mature well on a diet of grass and hay alone.

There is very little evidence for what the foundation stocks of these cattle were like, but if the sole surviving records of an early Leominster Fair, held in 1556, are any guide, they seem to have been very varied in colour but with a preponderance of black and red. The table below divides these cattle by type and also by whether they formed part of the 'Hereford' bloodlines or were from Wales but not sold into this county.

Cattle sold at one Leominster fair in 1556
(omitting steers and runts, which cannot be reliably categorised)

	colour	oxen	bulls	bullocks	cows	heifers	total
From Wales but not sold to buyers in Herefordshire	Black	2	1	3	1	1	8
	Brown	–	1	–	2*	–	3
	Black-brown	–	–	2	–	–	2
	Red	1	–	2	3	3	9
	Valow §	–	–	1	–	–	1
	Brindled	–	–	4	3	–	7
	White	1	–	–	–	–	1
Sold from, into or within Herefordshire	Black	16	1	6	6	1	30
	Brown	4	–	2	1	–	7
	Black-brown	–	–	–	–	–	0
	Red	9**	–	2	6	–	17
	Valow §	5	–	–	2	1	8
	Brindled	–	–	–	1	–	1
	White	–	–	–	–	–	0

§ valow (sometimes falow) – pale or yellowish
*1 brown with white face
**1 red with forehead star

The colours of the stock sold at this market should perhaps be no surprise, dominated as it is by 36 brown or red cattle and 38 black. Today's modern Welsh

Black breed has largely developed from this mixed-colour population and it still occasionally throws up brown individuals; in addition the calves have a reddish coat in their first summer.

Welsh Black cow Lucton Seren 5th with calf at foot, with the Welsh mountains behind (Courtesy of Chris and Meg Thorpe of the Lucton Herd of Pedigree Welsh Black Cattle)

Significantly, all six of the red-coloured cows changing hands within the county at this market were bought by gentleman farmers. One was purchased by Edmund Wigmore (probably a member of the family with several properties between Leintwardine, Lucton and Shobdon). Five red cows and one black were bought by Roger Baughan of Burghill, from William John Lewis of Dorstone. Baughan may, therefore, be one of the earliest examples of a prosperous farmer beginning to specialise in breeding what would later become the Hereford cattle. Certainly at the time of his death 25 years later he had several years left to run on the lease of part of Burghill manor, which he left to his son Simon together with all his other farms, his farming equipment and his stock – apart from two heifers each worth a tidy £1, which were bequeathed to two of his grandchildren. He was without doubt an affluent man. His son John was apprenticed in London and was left 200 marks (£133), his five married daughters and his grandchildren were all left bequests, and he set aside £87 for his unmarried daughter and an annuity for a third son.

This tendency for gentleman farmers to have the largest herds of cattle continued for the next 200 years. People of modest means often managed to keep one or two, for example Davy Tayler of Staunton, who died in 1567 and described himself as a labourer (the bottom tier of the rural workforce), left one red cow and a calf to his daughters and a horse and its saddle to his son, among other smaller bequests. But it was the upper echelons of rural society who were keeping cattle on a bigger scale. Thus, Elizabeth Hill of Hom Farm, near Ross, died in 1563, leaving four bequests of cows: one red, one black and two others of unspecified coat colour. In the early seventeenth century, wills continue to mention named cattle, with half including bequests of oxen or cows, but mentions of red or indeed any colour animals soon tails off and ends; perhaps this was because red was already by then predominant.

Gentleman Farmers

In the century when probate inventories were the norm, between the Civil War and 1750, it becomes clear that a good deal of investment was needed to breed cattle, as the individual animals were so valuable. Consequently only the wealthiest farmers could be seriously involved. Four examples from our sample neatly illustrate this point, one from each corner of the county. In 1675, Mr Thomas Bridgewater of Limebridge, Leinthall Starkes, left cattle worth £57 and an additional £21 in oxen; George Winton of Thornbury, a yeoman, left £52 worth of cattle and a further £18 in oxen. In both cases this comprised a third of the value of their inventory. In 1750, Mr Richard Fisher Collins of Foy left cattle valued at £73 7s. and a further £26 worth of oxen, while William Parry, yeoman of Garway, left cattle worth £48 10s. and £56 of oxen. In these cases, the cattle and oxen were worth between a quarter and a fifth of the inventory total, largely because household furnishings were by then more valuable.

So what cattle were being kept in Herefordshire at this period? The four above are typical of the larger herds.

The table opposite is a reminder that it was oxen that were still much the most valuable part of the herd. They took two years to mature, and then more time to train, but they could work for upwards of six or eight years before being fattened.

The cows were by now a dual-purpose animal, for rearing the next generation of traction animals, but also for small-scale dairying. Many rural households aspired to keep a milk cow, and these richer farmers usually had a designated dairy house, with butter and cheese-making equipment. In Mr Fisher Collins's inventory, for example, the dairy house contains '1 cheese press, 1 cheese cowl, other milk things, wooden bottles, 1 cupboard, 1 salting stone', together worth £1 5s. A small proportion of the butter and cheese might be taken to market, but Herefordshire was never a major dairy producer. By contrast Cheddar was already a national commodity by the Middle Ages; Stilton came into its own in the eighteenth century, and Cheshire and Gloucester cattle were being bred to supply the cheese market by this time, too.

Cattle by type and age in these four inventories

name	parish	year	No. of oxen	Value each	No. of 3 yr olds	Value each	No. of 2 yr olds	Value each
Bridgewater	Leinthall Starkes	1675	5	£4 4s	4	£2	4	£2
Winton	Thornbury	1675	4	£4 10s	4	£2 10s	5	–
Fisher Collins	Foy	1750	6	£4 10s	5	£3	6	£2
Parry	Garway	1750	10	£5 12s	4	£2 15s	5	£2 10s

name	parish	No. of yearlings	Value each	No. of bulls	Value each	No. of cows	Value each	Other cattle value
Bridgewater	Leinthall Starkes	5	£1	0	–	12	£3	–
Winton	Thornbury	5	£1 4s	1	–	8	£3	–
Fisher Collins	Foy	11	£1 5s	1	£2 5s	7	£3	£3 12s
Parry	Garway	0	–	0	–	6	£3	£7

There are, however, occasional examples of eighteenth-century Herefordshire farmers apparently experimenting with dairying, for example Mr Thomas Vale of Kimbolton. He died in 1725, but his son or grandson was still a freeholder in Kimbolton in the 1770s. As well as his seven oxen, Thomas had a herd of about three dozen cattle, eight of which were described as 'milking cows' in his inventory. His dairy house contained a total of 32 cheeses worth 2s. each; perhaps these were merely for domestic use and the cows were mainly a suckler herd, but any surplus would presumably sell at Leominster market.

Another noteworthy feature of the table above is that even these affluent farmers did not all run their own bull, so must have been leasing them from neighbours if they did not want to rely on the village bull. At this period, only about 10% of Herefordshire cattle owners seem to have had their own bull. Since the county was still relatively unenclosed, with wide areas of common grazing, it is quite possible that this was reflected in a tendency to retain the custom of having a village bull and for the poorer farmers to use its services. This worked because the numbers of cattle were strictly controlled by the 'stints' allocated to the land, preventing both over-grazing and over-use of the bull. In counties where enclosure was more often enforced by the richest people in the parish, cow-keeping became impossible for those who could not afford to pay for the hire costs of a bull, and so milk, cheese and replacement stock were lost to them even if they had enough land for grazing a cow.[1]

The Hereford Breed Emerges

A small core of farming families is generally credited with breeding and ultimately defining the bloodlines of the modern Hereford cattle. Like those above, they were either gentleman farmers or yeomen freeholders, able to improve their land and their stock. Their story is well-known, but bears a brief repeating because the cattle they bred were the foundation for what is arguably the most widely-recognised livestock breed in the world.

Foremost among these families were the Tompkins of Kings Pyon, Weobley, Wellington and Canon Pyon. Richard Tompkins and his wife Katharine began breeding cattle in about 1700, and their son Benjamin (1714–79) took over part of the herd, latterly farming from Wellington Court. He and his son, another Benjamin (1745–1815), switched their focus from breeding for the plough and cart to stock which would fatten well and might grow larger. But they did not produce anything approaching a standard colour, with everything from red with a white face and spine to a grey. Some of the many transactions and stock produced are recorded in the standard breed history.[2] Shortly after Benjamin junior's death, much of his stock was sold off, and some fetched quite remarkable prices, with in-calf cows selling for over £200 and a prize bull for over £500.

Many other families were involved in the late eighteenth century, including the Tullys at Huntington, who concentrated on grey-faced stock. But it was the Yeomans of Thinghill and Kenderchurch who were chiefly involved with the transition to the classic modern red with a white face, spine and underbelly. So dominant has this colouration now become, that if an element of Hereford is introduced to any herd, the offspring are almost certain to reveal it in their faces. The Australian Braford breed, for example, a Brahman x Hereford cross, is characterised by its white face.

The Rosemore herd of Herefords, Whitbourne

The development of a breed standard was perhaps delayed by the desire to retain good draught animals which would fatten well after their working life, but also because many farmers were anxious to keep the best strains in the county, so were reluctant to formalise things with a breed society. But the high prices obtained during the Napoleonic Wars, when beef was in huge demand, and even more so in the years of poor grain harvests from 1816 to 1819, when the Hereford's ability to fatten well on grass alone gave it a competitive edge in London, earned it a good reputation which it has never lost.

By the nineteenth century, Hereford cattle were coming to the attention of farmers overseas. A few animals were first exported to Ireland, but it was the opening up of the American market in the 1830s which really triggered change. A breed standard was needed for exports, and so the Herd Book was finally established in 1846, many years after some other breeds had founded their own. Exports all round the world began in earnest, including to Australia, New Zealand, South America, South and East Africa and Canada. The Hereford's hardy nature and fattening ability meant it could tolerate high altitude, poor pastures, drought or cold.

Milk or Beef, Hereford or Another Breed?

In September 1826, William Cobbett visited friends in Herefordshire and famously remarked in his diary:

> Mr Walter Palmer, at Pencoyd ... says that his acre has kept two horses all the summer ... Indeed! A stout horse will eat much more than a fattening ox. This grass will fat any ox or sheep ...
> I am here amongst the finest of cattle, and the finest sheep of the Leicester kind, that I ever saw. My host, Mr Price, is famed as a breeder of cattle and sheep. The cattle are of the Hereford kind, and the sheep surpassing any animals of the kind that I ever saw. The animals seem to be made for the soil, and the soil for them.[3]

Nevertheless, it is unlikely that there ever was a time when all or even most of the cattle in the county resembled Herefords, as the picture opposite, showing mixed-colour cows (not oxen) outside Monmouth, suggests.

Some small Hereford milking herds remained in the county up until the Second World War, but they were essentially by then a beef breed, with Friesians, Ayrshires and other dairy cattle filling this role. Herefordshire might be thought of as primarily a beef county, focussed on suckler herds, but this is not in fact the case. Determining the precise proportions of beef and dairy cattle at any given time is fraught with difficulty, not least because the MAFF statistics have been collected using so many different systems over time. However, in 1938 the county herd was recorded in separate categories according to the intended role of each animal, with 43% dairy

Cattle entering Monmouth, by Sir A.W. Callcott (1779–1844)

and 57% beef. Herefordshire is not one of the top ten dairying counties, but there are a surprising number of milking units. A sample of ten parishes from around the county, in 1938 and 1981, gives an indication of their recent numbers and distribution (*see opposite*). The larger dairying element in parishes near Hereford, combined of course with a big rise in milk yield per head, reflects in part the increasing market in the city, which grew from a population of 118,000 in 1938 to 147,000 by 1981, and in part the greatly improved transport networks which are needed for a modern dairy industry.

These ten parishes are not perfectly representative of the county, having rather less dairying and more beef, but the sample does show that in some districts, such as the Golden Valley area, the cattle are predominantly for beef. Overall, the proportions of the two enterprises remained remarkably consistent. It is unfortunate that the MAFF (DEFRA) data is now presented in such a way that this comparison cannot be brought up closer to the present.

Numbers of cattle in dairy or beef enterprises

parish	1938 dairy	1938 beef	1981 dairy	1981 beef	Notes for 1981
Avenbury	507	490	229	1,047	0 specialist dairy farms
Whitbourne	382	297	111	682	1 specialist dairy farm
Withington	279	514	658	750	2 specialist dairy farms
Burghill	522	533	730	553	6 specialist dairy farms
Llangarren	535	845	1,854	1,397	9 specialist dairy farms + 4 mainly dairy
Much Dewchurch	556	503	204	1,007	1 specialist dairy farm
Longtown	286	910	700	1,619	3 dairy farms, 19 mixed stock
Michaelchurch Escley	74	838	486	1251	1 specialist dairy farm, 13 mixed stock
Dilwyn	565	1,377	1,089	2,235	5 specialist dairy farms
Leintwardine	358	945	685	1,209	0 specialist dairy farms
Total in sample parishes	4,064 (36%)	7,252 (64%)	6,746 (36%)	11,750 (64%)	

Herefordshire, or Hereford?

One might end by noting a curious phenomenon. While many people in England, let alone Britain or Europe, have no idea where Herefordshire is and have been known to confuse it with a similar-sounding county closer to London, the gauchos of South America, cowboys of the west, ringers of Australia and cattle farmers from Canada to New Zealand can probably recognise our most famous export with ease.

Hops

Herefordshire has for centuries been famed as a cider county, because of its deep and (mainly) well-drained soils and its benign climate. So why did it also become known as a hop-growing area, when until 200 years ago it was far removed from any major centre of population? A population which, after all, was needed to manage and harvest this labour-intensive crop, as well as to enjoy its produce.

Hop Growing in England

By the late nineteenth century, hops were grown in two separate areas of England, and Herefordshire was the second most important county for its size, as shown in the table below.

English Hop Growing by County, 1894[1]

county	County acreage	Acreage under hops	% under hops	notes
Kent	972,240	35,520	3.7	
Herefordshire	543,800	7,530	1.4	Not in far west of county
Worcestershire	459,710	3,850	0.8	
Sussex	907,920	7,590	0.8	
Surrey	474,480	1,940	0.4	
Hampshire	1,018,550	2,910	0.3	Only in east of county
Gloucestershire	790,470	40	<0.1	
Shropshire	864,360	140	<0.1	Only on southern border

The concentration of the crop in Kent and to a lesser extent in the Home Counties can partly be explained by the huge market for beer in London, a city which grew from about 100,000 in 1600 to 600,000 by 1700, a million in 1800 and three million by 1850. Between 1850 and 1901, the capital's population doubled to seven million. By 1600, wholesale brewers were becoming established in the city, and a century later a dozen firms dominated London's brewing industry, producing over 40% of its beer.[2]

The presence of a second hop-producing region centred on Herefordshire is less obviously explained, since the conurbation of Birmingham developed much later than local interest in the crop. It only had 5,000 inhabitants in 1650, and 10,000 by 1700. Thereafter it did grow more rapidly, reaching 70,000 in 1800. But it was still only half a million in 1901, barely a twelfth the size of London, although the Black Country industrial towns boosted this number considerably. By then, the conurbation was, it is true, the second most urbanised area in Britain, and Herefordshire

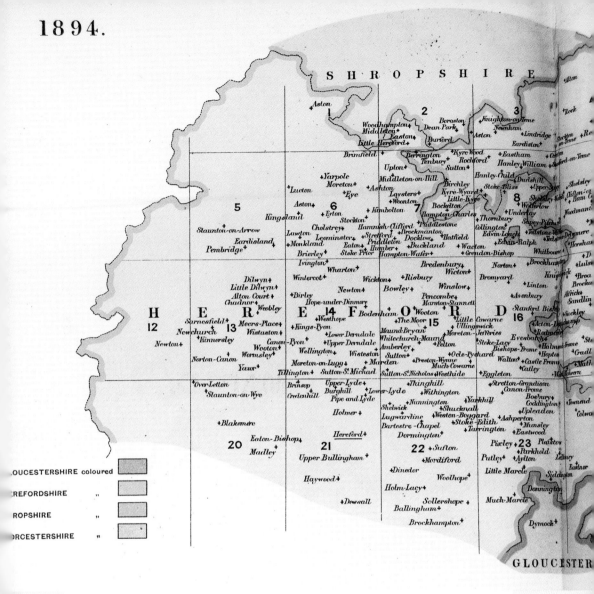

1894.

Map of the hop-growing parishes in Herefordshire at the end of the nineteenth century, produced by Arthur Morris & Co, hop merchants, 1894

was well-placed to meet its demand for ingredients for beer as well as its appetite for cider, but this cannot explain why the crop became established here so early.

An alternative reason for Herefordshire's dominance in this western hop-growing region is that hops are a very hungry crop. As well as thriving in rich deep soils, they benefit from a large input of nitrogen as well as some potash and phosphorous, both at planting and during the growing season; the large numbers of oxen, sheep and later beef and dairy cattle in the county provided an ideal supply of manure.

Herefordshire dung cart with hop poles in wigwams, Stoke Lacy (BDLHS Picture Archive)

Early Evidence for Hop-Growing

Ale has been made for millennia, using barley or other grain. But the malting process makes it sweet, and as far back as records go brewers seem to have aspired to vary the flavour in some way. For this purpose, several herbs and spices were used, many imported from the 'spice islands' of the East, through Palmyra in Syria, or Egyptian Alexandria. In particular, cinnamon, nutmegs and mace were the favourites of the very rich. Pliny (d.79 AD) comments that a Roman pound (about 11 ounces, 0.3 kg) of cinnamon cost 300 denarii, equivalent to between one and four years' wages for a labourer. In the early fourteenth century, the Florentine merchant Pegolotti included in his great *Principles of Commerce* a compendium of 289 spices including nutmeg, black and white pepper, a range of cinnamons, ginger, cloves and mace, all of which might be used in flavoured beer as well as for many other purposes.

The poor, meanwhile, had to content themselves with ale, flavoured only with domestic herbs like juniper, sage, costmary (alias alecost), meadowsweet or perhaps ground ivy (alehoof). Sometimes this ale was brewed at home, otherwise they relied on ale-wives who earned a living (and often a bad reputation, for using short measures) brewing and selling.

It was known in the Middle Ages that hop flowers could also be used for flavouring ale, and indeed the village of Himbleton in Worcestershire probably gets its Anglo-Saxon name, first recorded in 816, from 'hymele tun', a hop-growing place. This is compatible with evidence suggesting that hops were grown in monastic gardens in

An ale-wife with a false measure, being carried off to the Jaws of Hell; misericord in St Laurence's Church, Ludlow (© Jude Harley, CC 4.0 license, reproduced with permission)

Germany and France from the eighth century.[3] But the crop was only re-established in Britain in the sixteenth century, apparently introduced to Kent to supply demand among the immigrant population of Flemish weavers, when the Spanish Netherlands were forbidden from selling hops to England. The first English book on growing hops was written by Reynolde Scot in 1574, and repeatedly reissued. In Herefordshire, hops were already being grown on the bishop's estate by 1577: Swithin Butterfield's survey of the episcopal manors refers to 'A lytle parcell of land called the hoppyard ... containing by estimation 1 rood' in Whitbourne. This plot, just a quarter of an acre, is typical of the way hops were grown for many years, and it is noteworthy that it was the bishop trying out the new crop; it was labour-intensive and the harvest was very variable, so the investment did not always pay off.

Hops on Hills

For many years, hops were grown on little earthed-up mounds up to a maximum of three to four feet, about six feet apart, in small fields with high hedges to give them shelter. These tumps were carefully and generously manured, and three plants, each with a pole, were placed in each. Early writers described the need to earth up the hills, twist and secure the bines around the poles and ensure that the poles were firmly tied together in the late spring. It was recommended that there were no more than 250 hills per rood, and that one man working solely on the hops could only manage two and a half acres. During the winter, the ground must be dug and weeded, tumps manured and coppicing work done to provide new poles. Here Herefordshire had an additional advantage, with many steep slopes covered with woodland after the fourteenth-century population crash, now available to be converted to productive coppice. As the acreage of hops grew, ash beds were also planted along many streams.

The 1623 deeds for Buttas Manor in Canon Pyon and Kings Pyon show this 'hop hills' method in operation, with mention of a kiln house, six malting lofts and a hopyard with 2,000 hills and 6,000 poles.[4] A later example is the 1674 will of Richard Biddle, a yeoman farmer of Bromyard Foreign. Among other enterprises he was producing cider, but not apparently growing hops. However, he left a named meadow to his two eldest daughters and promised that 'if they breake up parte of it to the use of hoppiarde, I do give them the Coppie at Narchard lying by the brook side to manner it with poules'. In aerial photographs taken in the 1950s, part of this meadow still showed traces of residual features that might have been the hop hills established back in the seventeenth century.

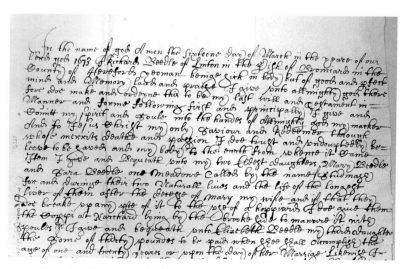

The will of Richard Biddle, 1674, encouraging hop-growing in lines 11–17
(Herefordshire Archive Service)

Hops on Poles

Although most English hops were initially grown in the south-east, the western region soon also came to prominence, so that John Beale claimed in 1656 that the hop growers of Herefordshire 'make haste to be the Hop-masters of England ... having store of coppice-woods, and many provident men.' For many decades, the crop continued to be grown on hills, but then a change was made to planting the bines in earthed-up rows, which significantly reduced the labour required.

In a good year with favourable weather, huge profits could be made from hops. Colonel Birch, who occupied the bishop's manor in Whitbourne for much of the Commonwealth period, must have felt able to plant a very substantial acreage because in some years they 'had been known to produce the value of £700', compared with the £1,348 paid by the previous owner to purchase the whole estate.[5] This level of profits made it worth the expense of investing in coppices, storage and kilns, although for many smaller or more cautious growers the crop remained a gamble only worth taking if balanced by a range of other enterprises.

Large or small, all hop growers needed enormous numbers of poles, since they often rotted after two or three years. In average conditions, between 500 and 1,000 new poles would be needed per acre per year, each 16- to 18-feet long and as straight as possible. So, Elizabeth Caswall of Risbury in Humber parish, who died in February 1700, left hop poles worth £10 and hops to the value of £12, compared to the £18 for her six oxen; in Whitbourne, John Norgroves left 2,400 poles worth £1 4s. in October 1682, while William Jones' 1716 inventory included 'hoppowells in the yards', valued at £10.

The poles came from coppices, cut on a ten- (or more) year cycle depending on the tree species. Oak and sweet chestnut produce timber that is relatively resistant to decay in the ground; hazel and ash grow faster while oak tends to be the slowest-growing of all. In Kent, sweet chestnut was usually preferred for hop poles, and if planted about six feet apart and cut every ten years, the stools grew rapidly to make new poles 16 or more feet long.[6] Today, there is a small amount of chestnut coppice in Herefordshire, grown on the poorer soils which produce stronger timber. A stand might yield approximately 4,000 poles per acre every ten years. So for every acre of hops one would also need roughly two acres of chestnut coppice. At the other extreme, oak grows more slowly and benefits from being started further apart. If the bark was also being used in the tanning industries, oak coppice might be planted at eight-foot spacings and grown on a cycle as long as 24 years, so correspondingly more woodland was needed. Certainly, some now have very large harvesting stools, showing they were coppiced for many generations.

After the later nineteenth century, creosote was widely used to treat the poles against decay, heating it in tanks to increase its efficacy, until safer treatments were found.

The amount of hops grown in the early years is unclear because, like orchard fruit, they were defined as growing naturally rather than as a crop requiring

A half-cut hazel stool in a recently re-opened coppice, Whitbourne

labour, and so they did not have to be included in inventories. But while 10% of inventories mention hops between 1675 and 1700, by 1725 this had increased to about 20%, indicating that they were by then well-established in the county. Nevertheless, the individual hopyards may have remained small. A seventeenth-century example whose details are known was half an acre, in a Vowchurch indenture listed with mixed farming land including meadows, pasture, orchards and arable.[7] This pattern is likely to have persisted well into the eighteenth century, because the uncertain yield and high labour input deterred most people from specialising in the crop. One such farmer might have been William Pearce of Little Hereford, who died in November 1725 leaving livestock totalling £8 2s. (a cow and a heifer, 15 sheep, two pigs and some geese and other poultry) and one bag of hops on the premises, worth £3 5s.

Other, perhaps wealthier, families were already investing more heavily in hops, sometimes using larger plots and rotating the crop. Thus, a 1696 marriage settlement for Thomas Evans of Llangattock Vibon Awell (Avel) to the gentlewoman Alice Clarke, eldest daughter of Richard Clarke of Park Grace Duw, Monmouth, includes among its lands 24 acres of pasture called The Hopyard.[8] Humphrey Lawrence (died 1725) had a 'hopground', orchard and two barns on the east side of South Street in Leominster, which he left to his daughter Ann and her husband Thomas Moore, a maltster. And in March 1750, Mrs Ann Williams' farm in Little Marcle still had six bags of hops and three pockets (the latter perhaps for sale), as well as a mill, kiln and other indicators of prosperity including an astonishing 48 working oxen and five waggons and wains.

Once hop tax records were kept systematically, from 1807 onwards, it is clear that hops had become a significant part of Herefordshire's farming. The total hop acreage in England and Wales in that year was 32,000, increasing to 43,000 in 1850 and peaking at 73,000 acres in 1875. Herefordshire and Worcestershire were together growing 6,000 acres in 1840, and peaked at 10,000 acres in 1890. Whereas in the 1830s hops were still grown in many counties as diverse as Devon and Cornwall, Radnorshire and Lincolnshire, by the end of the century the crop was virtually restricted to the Three Counties, Hampshire and the Home Counties.[9] Some indication of the increasing importance of hops in Herefordshire is that the Fox and Duck tavern in Hereford changed its name between 1755 and 1785 to The Hop Pole. Likewise in Bromyard, an inn called The Hop Pole is first recorded in the late eighteenth century, when the Hawkins family were tenants.[10] It is also apparent from the Tithe Apportionments that by the 1840s the crop was already becoming concentrated in the north-east of this county.

Hops on Wires

While hop-growing relied on lines of poles, imported sisal string was used to stabilise the bines, holding the tops of the poles to each other in the rows and sometimes dropping a string down between each pole and securing the end in the ground. The

Wigwams of treated poles in a winter hopyard at Tarrington (BDLHS Picture Archive)

poles were uprooted for harvesting and then stacked in the hopyards for the winter. In some small yards, this method continued well into the twentieth century.

Herefordshire was also one of the first counties to move away from this old system, instead using far fewer and much stronger posts supporting a network of tensed wires from which the strings were hung for the bines to grow up. As well as eliminating the coppicing part of the work, this new method gave a growing framework which was much longer-lived. Individual sections of wire or posts would have to be replaced during the winter, but the entire structure no longer needed to be dismantled and reassembled annually. Suitable wires became available in the mid nineteenth century, and by the 1870s the biggest growers were already experimenting with wirework. The posts were still sometimes locally-grown oak or sweet chestnut, but more often they were imported softwood, treated to improve its longevity. More recently these have been fir or pine from British plantations, or even metal poles.[11] As before, strings were still needed for the growing bines, held down with steel pegs close to the roots at about 1,800 per acre.

Securing the 'roping wires' at the edge of a hopyard. (BDLHS Picture Archive)

Picking, Processing and Packing

A hopyard will usually produce for 15 to 20 years or more, with replacement poles and wires as appropriate and new strings each year, with a good crop every two or three years on average. Sometimes an orchard was planted in the rows between the hops toward the end of their life, to begin producing as the hops ended, and this is why many orchards on the tithe maps and other early documents are called 'Old Hopyard'. Very occasionally, a yard is kept going much longer by steadily replacing the poorest and oldest bines.

In the early decades of hop growing here, it seems that bines were cut down individually and the hops picked onto sheets or blankets on the ground. But by the late seventeenth century, cribs (known as bins in Kent) begin to appear in inventories, and from then until mechanisation picking into these large hessian troughs was the favoured method.

A family group picking at Ullingswick, early twentieth century. Note the lunch basket and milk can under the rigid crib, and the long-bladed knife stuck in the top of the near left post (BDLHS Picture Archive)

At first, hop-picking offered work for local women and older children, but as the acreages grew an additional workforce was needed for the three or four weeks, and labour came into Herefordshire from South Wales and from the Black Country and Birmingham. This began at least in the eighteenth century. The 1710 Act of

Parliament which imposed the first hop tax also mentions 'many poor and indigent persons commonly employed in the gathering and picking of hops'. Their transport was greatly simplified when the railway finally came through to Hereford (1853) and Bromyard (1877). On one day in late August 1905, for example, a special train service brought 112 pickers for Ullingswick, 70 for Moreton Jeffries, 190 for Bishops Frome and 20 to Leominster, and more trains followed over the next few days.[12]

The pickers were housed in farm buildings or specially built 'barracks' and sometimes tents, and so much labour was needed that the population of some villages swelled to breaking point. Bishops Frome, for example, normally had about 750 inhabitants in the late nineteenth century, but during hop-picking this mushroomed to more like 2,000: good business for the shops and pubs, but hard work for the extra policemen drafted in each year.

The pickers worked as teams on piece-rate, each stage needing to keep up with the others. The poles (or later the bines on strings) were taken down, the bines cut and the flower cones picked into the crib. The fresh green hops were then measured in bushel baskets and thence into a sack. The team's total bushels picked for the day was recorded, traditionally with pairs of matching tally-sticks but later written up by a booker.

Left: *The lady on the left is the booker, while behind a man holds a bushel basket, Avenbury. (BDLHS Picture Archive).* Right: *Bushelling green hops in Whitbourne, c.1950 (BDLHS Picture Archive)*

Once taken to the farm, the green hops were dried. Early authors were insistent that a malting floor would not do, and it was better to spread the hops out in an attic. But kilns (called oast houses or roundels in Kent) were far superior, with the hops dried from below by a charcoal or wood fire. This was soon replaced by coal from the seams in the Wyre Forest, which proved ideal because their high sulphur content improved the colour of the flower cones as they dried. In the eighteenth century this coal began to be replaced by coke, made from the Pensax and Mamble coal mines nearby (these only finally closed in the 1970s). By the 1900s, however, the importation of anthracite from South Wales began, before farms changed to electric driers.

When thoroughly dry, the hops were packed tightly into pockets six-feet long, each weighing about 1½ hundredweight when full. To compress them this much, the empty pocket was suspended through a hole in the floor and one worker, often a boy, fed the dried hops to a man treading them down. It could take up to four hours to fill a pocket, but an expert with plenty of cider or perry to hand to wash down the inevitable dust could do four pockets a day. This method continued until the late nineteenth century, when mechanised presses began taking over. Much more recently a new system has been introduced, eliminating traditional hop pockets entirely. Instead the crop is pressed into a 60 to 80 kg bale and machine-stitched into a protective hessian cloth.

A Madley hop farmer and four workers with their tools, with a filled hop pocket, 1901
(BDLHS Picture Archive)

Loading hop pockets at Felton Court, 1933 (BDLHS Picture Archive)

Modern hydraulic hop-baling (BDLHS Picture Archive)

From Small Yards to Family Farms

The 1840s Tithe Apportionments show that many farms were still growing a small plot of hops. In the 1841 Apportionment for Little Cowarne, for instance, a third of holdings grew some hops, usually five acres or less. But, as had been the case almost from the beginning of hop-growing in Herefordshire, some farmers chose to invest heavily in the crop and to specialise. Bishops Frome is conspicuous as a parish with consistently high hop acreages, almost 300 in 1840 and still 197 acres in 1985, and much of this is down to one family. At least eight generations of Pudges seem to have farmed in and near the parish, with a Thomas Pudge baptised there in 1755 and going on to farm and run a butcher's business locally as a freeholder, with four sons who survived to adulthood. Two generations later, William Farmer Pudge was born in 1851 at New House farm, and it was he who, during his long working life, pioneered moving his farms into specialising in hops. His father was a butcher and ran The Chase Inn as well as farming, but The Chase was taken over by a younger brother, Charles, and their stepmother Elizabeth in the later nineteenth century, while William Farmer Pudge purchased additional land for hops. He temporarily moved into cereal growing during the First World War, but was reputed to have been the largest private hop-grower in England in his old age, with over 200 acres shortly before his death in 1938. Towards the end of his life, he was based at Upper House Farm, and described himself for preference as a farmer and hop-grower.

William Farmer Pudge, 1851–1938 (Pudge family pictures, © Matthew J.F. Pudge)

The hops business was clearly profitable as he was able to build 12 kilns in Bishops Frome, and his only grandchild inherited a substantial part of the estate, leaving her extremely well off. William Farmer's youngest brother, Edwin George, carried on the hopyards at New House Farm, and it is through Edwin's son John Perry Pudge that the present hop-farming family are descended. It is a tribute to the enduring traditions of Herefordshire farming that while hops relied so heavily on seasonal labour, live-in farm servants remained a feature of life even on these large and specialised farms long after the system had been abandoned in almost all other counties of Britain. Only in Yorkshire did the last vestiges also linger. Thus, in 1881 William Farmer Pudge had two live-in farm servants, in 1911 he had one and in 1939 John Perry Pudge had three.[13]

John Perry Pudge, 1892–1977, with his wife Elsie and the next two generations, c.1969 (Pudge family pictures, © Matthew J.F. Pudge

Mechanisation and Marketing

Hop farming epitomises the changes brought about by progressive mechanisation. In particular, harvesting is now done by a team using a small tractor and trailer, altering the optimal height for the wire-work as well as speeding the process up and reducing the labour force needed to a fraction of what it used to be. Removing the cones from the bines is then done in a separate operation away from the field, with a conveyor-belt system, again only using a very few people. The bines are unloaded, hooked on, mechanically plucked clean and then the cones are separated from any leaves or twigs before being taken up to the drying floor. There is some debate about where the first picking machine was made: perhaps in the

The 2020 hop harvest at New House Farm, Bishops Frome

Hop warehouse in Gwynne Street, Hereford, now converted to offices

Worcestershire-Herefordshire area, or perhaps one was imported from America to a Worcester grower just before the Second World War and then improved on locally. Certainly they were widely used here and also being exported by the late 1960s.

The two main markets for Herefordshire hops used to be Hereford itself, with its fairs in September and October and a last annual fair on 2 February, and the bigger Worcester market on 19 September. Indeed, so many of the hops were sold through Worcester that they were collectively known as Worcesters, which annoyed many local eighteenth- and nineteenth-century producers. Some farmers and merchants therefore arranged for their hops to be sold elsewhere, to private buyers in the Black Country and Birmingham or even at the main London distribution centre at Borough Market. In the mid eighteenth century there were several other important regional hop fairs, including Brecknock, Chester, Wrexham, Stow on the Wold, Kingsland, Ledbury, Leominster, Bridgnorth, Ludlow and Shifnal, but all of these ceased as the production area contracted.[14]

Hop acreages in a sample of 12 Herefordshire parishes, 1880 to 1981

Parish	1880	1901	1921	1948	1981
Bishops Frome	216	344	268	301	268
Cradley	234	359	103	185	83
Stoke Lacy	88	141	24	62	27
Holme Lacy	22	20	0	0	0
Eastnor	7	7	8	9	24
Much Marcle	4	28	66	60	70
Dinedor	11	10	0	0	0
Abbey Dore	5	0	0	0	0
Lyonshall	16	0	0	0	0
Richards Castle	7	3	0	0	0
Orleton	0	32	0	0	0
Yarpole	24	13	0	0	0

The reduction in hop acreage in the late twentieth century had three major causes. Popular demand moved towards lighter beers and lagers, requiring different or fewer hops; more were imported from abroad; and the highly infectious fungal disease Verticillium wilt decimated the crops. More recently, however, new varieties have been bred that are resistant to wilt, and hops have staged something of a come-back. So why is this? Why did Herefordshire ever become a hop-growing region, and why is the crop now making a return?

Again, there are multiple factors. As with cider and perry, there were gentleman farmers here in the seventeenth century interested and able to invest heavily in a novel crop. And as with cattle too, the land proved very suitable for all these enterprises. The cattle supplied much-needed manure for the hops, and this was supplemented by waste material from Worcestershire carpet-making. Hereford-shire also has numerous steep hillsides which, at the time when hop-poles were in high demand, had ceased to be used for cereal-growing and were available for coppices to supply the huge numbers of poles the yards required. Then, the pattern of land tenure which developed here meant that there were many independent yeoman farmers, many of them freeholders, able to invest in the infrastructure needed for hops. And finally, the dramatic population explosion in Birmingham and the Black Country from the late eighteenth century provided both a market and a labour supply for Herefordshire's hops.

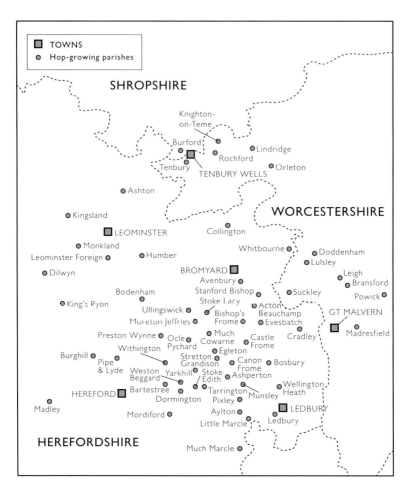

Herefordshire parishes growing hops in 1988 (based on mapping carried out by Morris Hanbury Jackson Le May Ltd. and Alan Meredith of English Hops Ltd., and shown in A Pocketful of Hops, The Bromyard and District History Society, 2007*)*

Postscript

There is always a risk of painting too rosy a picture: despite its fruit trees and well-watered meadows, Herefordshire is not quite the Eden we would like it to be. Farmers through the ages have always had to contend with weather, disease, all kinds of pests from wild boar to woodpigeons, and more recently the occasional ignorance of town-dwellers. To say nothing, of course, of interference from revenue-hungry governments: even at Domesday there were taxes on oxen, sheep, honey and all ale wives within or without Hereford city.

Yet it is a special county whose present-day farmers can boast of major awards for new wine, prime cattle, community service and prize-winning stands of oak, all within a few years. Perhaps this is because, unlike with so many rural counties, industrial development has passed us by to such a very large extent, allowing farmers more of the centre stage.

Farmers epitomise continuity, keeping the most ancient enterprises adaptable and viable yet working ahead of the curve with the return of vineyards, renewed interest in coppicing, orchard plantings, smallholders' specialist interests, organic and slow-grown techniques and new alternative products from crisps to gin.

Herefordshire, it turns out, is not a backwater and out on a limb, but for millennia its farmers have been vitally connected through their suppliers and markets as far back as the evidence extends: to the Lake District and East Anglia for stone tools, to west and east by the droving trades, and now all over the world for our most famous exports.

The diversity of Herefordshire farming is the other unifying theme. Unlike arable districts where:

The Farmer will never be happy again
He carries his heart in his boots.
For either the rain is destroying his grain,
Or the drought is destroying his roots.

Here there are many options and even with global warming seeming to modify rainfall distribution through the year, the climate is still essentially benign. Perhaps we might, after all, end on a rosy and anachronistic note, with words I first learnt on a Herefordshire dairy farm:

Let the wealthy and great roll in splendour and state,
I envy them not I declare it.
I eat my own lamb, my chickens and ham,
I shear my own fleece and I wear it.
I have fields I have bowers, I have trees I have flowers,
The lark is my morning alarmer;
So jolly boys now, here's 'God Speed the Plough',
Good luck and long life to the farmer.

~

BIBLIOGRAPHIC REFERENCES AND NOTES

PRELIMS

1   Ray, Keith, *The Archaeology of Herefordshire: An Exploration* (Logaston Press, Almeley, 2015).

2   The Bromyard and District Local History Society, *A Pocketful of Hops: Hop Growing in the Bromyard Area* (Privately published, 1988).

ONE

1   The Tupsley and Welsh Newton axes: Hereford Museum accession nos. 2004–43 and 1977–150.

TWO

1   Søren Andersen & Tybrind Vig. 'A Preliminary Report on a Submerged Ertebølle Settlement on the West Coast of Fyn', *Journal of Danish Archaeology* 4 (1985), 52–69.

2   Bell, Martin, Caseldine, A. & Neumann, H. *Prehistoric Intertidal Archaeology in the Welsh Severn Estuary*, (Council for British Archaeology Report, 2000).

3   Ray, Keith, *The Archaeology of Herefordshire: An Exploration* (Logaston Press, Almeley, 2015), 26–28.

4   Barton, R.N.E., Berridge, P.J., Walker, M.C. & Bevins, R.E., 'Persistent Places in the Mesolithic Landscape: An Example from the Black Mountain Uplands of South Wales', *Proceedings of the Prehistoric Society* 61 (1995), 81–116.

5   Cunliffe, Barry *Britain Begins* (Oxford University Press, 2012), 108.

6   'Mount Sandel, a Mesolithic Campsite', *Irish Archaeology* (2013.7), http/irisharchaeology.ie/2013/7/mount-sandel-a-mesolithic-campsite/

7   Field, David, 'The Development of an Agricultural Countryside', in Pollard, Joshua (ed.), *Prehistoric Britain, Blackwell Studies in Global Archaeology, no. 11* (Blackwell, 2008), 202–224.

8   Zvelebil, Marek, 'Plant Use in the Mesolithic and its Role in the Transition to Farming', *Proceedings of the Prehistoric Society,* 60 (1994), 35–74.

9   Cunliffe, Barry, *Britain Begins*, . . . , 109.

10 Ibid. 116.

11 Brown, Alex, 'Mesolithic to Neolithic Human Activity at the Severn Estuary Wetland Edge: Studies at Llandevenny, Oldbury Flats, Hills Flats, and Woolaston', in Bell, Martin (ed.), *Prehistoric Coastal Communities: The Mesolithic in Western Britain* (CBA Report 149, 2007).

12 Barnard, Alan, 'From Mesolithic to Neolithic Modes of Thought', in Whittle, Alasdair & Cummings, Vicki (eds), *Going Over: The Mesolithic-Neolithic Transition in North-West Europe* (Proceedings of the British Academy 144, 2007), 5–19.

13 Thomas, Julian, 'The Mesolithic-Neolithic Transition in Britain', in Pollard, Joshua (ed.), *Prehistoric Britain, Blackwell Studies in Global Archaeology no 11* (Blackwell, 2008), 58–89.

THREE

1 Kooijmans, Leendert P. Louwe, 'The gradual transition to farming in the Lower Rhine Basin', in Alasdair Whittle & Vicki Cummings (eds), *Going Over: The Mesolithic-Neolithic Transition in North-West Europe* (Proceedings of the British Academy 144, Oxford University Press, 2007), 287–309.

2 Thomas, Julian, 'The Mesolithic-Neolithic Transition in Britain', in Pollard, Joshua (ed.), *Prehistoric Britain* (Blackwell Studies in Global Archaeology no. 11, Blackwell, Oxford, 2008), 58–89.

3 Tipping, Richard, 'The Case for Climatic Stress Forcing Choice in the Adoption of Agriculture in the British Isles', in Finlayson, Bill, & Warren, Graeme (eds), *Landscapes in Transition* (Oxbow Books, Oxford & Oakville, 2010), 66–76.

4 Jackson, Robin, 'Pits, Pots, Places and People: Approaching the Neolithic at Wellington Quarry', in Garwood, Paul (ed.), *The Undiscovered Country: The Earlier Prehistory of the West Midlands* (Oxford, Oxbow Books, 2007), 109–122; Jackson, Robin & Miller, Darren, *Wellington Quarry, Herefordshire (1986–96) Investigations of a Landscape in the Lower Lugg Valley* (Oxbow Books, Oxford and Oakville, 2011), 38–43.

5 Sheridan, Alison, 'The Neolithization of Britain and Ireland: The Big Picture', in Finlayson, Bill, & Warren, Graeme (eds), *Landscapes in Transition* (Oxbow Books, Oxford & Oakville, 2010), 89–105.

6 Thomas, Julian, 'The Mesolithic-Neolithic Transition in Britain', in Pollard, Joshua (ed.), *Prehistoric Britain* (Blackwell Studies in Global Archaeology no. 11, Blackwell, Oxford, 2008), 58–89.

7 Hey, Gill & Barclay, Alistair, 'The Thames Valley in the late fifth and early fourth millennium cal BC: the appearance of domestication and the evidence for change', in Whittle, Alasdair & Cummings, Vicki (eds), *Going Over: The Mesolithic-Neolithic Transition . . .*, 399–422.

8 Caesar, *De Bello Gallico*, VI, 28. Aurochs are thought to have been hunted to extinction in Britain by about 1,000 BC, but in Poland they survived under royal protection until 1627: Cotton, Jonathan, Elsden, Nicholas, Pipe, Alan et al, 'Taming the Wild: A Final Neolithic/Earlier Bronze Age Aurochs Deposit from West London', in Serjeantson, Dale & Field, David (eds), *Animals in the Neolithic of Britain and Europe* (Oxbow Books, Oxford, 2006), 149–167.

9 Bollongino, Ruth & Burger, Joachim, 'Neolithic cattle domestication as seen from ancient DNA', in Whittle, Alasdair & Cummings, Vicki (eds), *Going Over: The Mesolithic-Neolithic Transition . . .*, 165–187.

10 Field, David, 'The Development of an Agricultural Countryside', in Pollard, Joshua (ed.), *Prehistoric Britain . . .*, 202–224.

11 Brown, Alex, 'Mesolithic to Neolithic Human Activity at the Severn Estuary Wetland Edge: Studies at Llandevenny, Oldbury Flats, Hills Flats, and Woolaston', in: Bell, Martin (ed.), *Prehistoric Coastal Communities: The Mesolithic in Western Britain* (CBA Report 149, 2007).

12 Garwood, Paul, 'Regions, Cultural Identity and Social Change, c.4500–1500 BC: The West Midlands in Context', in Garwood, Paul (ed.), *The Undiscovered Country . . .*, 194–215.

13 Johnston, Robert, 'Later Prehistoric Landscapes and Inhabitation', in Pollard, Joshua (ed.) *Prehistoric Britain . . .* 268–287.

14   Garrow, Duncan, 'The Temporality of Materials: Occupation Practices in Eastern England during the 5th and 4th Millennia BC', in Finlayson, Bill and Warren, Graeme (eds), *Landscapes in Transition* (Oxbow Books, Oxford & Oakville, 2010), 208–218.

15   Fairbairn, Andrew S., 'On the spread of crops across Neolithic Britain, with special reference to southern England', in Fairbairn, Andrew S. (ed.), *Plants in Neolithic Britain and Beyond* (Oxbow Books, Oxford 2000), 107–121.

16   Children, G. & Priestly, S., *Shobdon Mains Refurbishment Scheme Report on the Archaeological Excavation of Engineering Access Pits at Leen Farm Pembridge Herefordshire*, (Border Archaeology, Unpublished Report, 2008).

FOUR

1   Garwood, Paul, 'Regions, Cultural Identity and Social Change, c.4500–1500 BC: The West Midlands in Context', in Garwood, Paul (ed.), *The Undiscovered Country: The Earlier Prehistory of the West Midlands* (Oxbow Books, Oxford, 2007), 194–215.

2   Dorling, Peter, Ray, Keith & White, Paul, 'Herefordshire: From the Middle Bronze Age to the Later Iron Age', in Hurst, Derek (ed.), *Westward on the High-Hilled Plains: The Later Prehistory of the West Midlands* (Oxbow Books, Oxford, 2017), 70–84; Ray, Keith, *The Archaeology of Herefordshire: An Exploration* (Logaston Press, Herefordshire, 2015), 106–7.

3   Yates, David Thomas, *Land, Power and Prestige: Bronze Age Field Systems in Southern England* (Oxbow Books, Oxford, 2007).

4   Dorling, Peter, *The Lugg Valley, Herefordshire: Archaeology, Landscape Change and Conservation* (Herefordshire Archaeology, Hereford, 2007), 35.

5   Ray, Keith, *The Archaeology of Herefordshire . . .* , 119–123.

6   Field, David, 'The Development of an Agricultural Countryside', in Pollard, Joshua (ed.), *Prehistoric Britain. Blackwell Studies in Global Archaeology no 11* (Blackwell, Oxford, 2008), 202–224.

7   Cunliffe, Barry, *Britain Begins* (Oxford University Press, 2012), 203–205.

8   Fitzpatrick, A.P et al, *The Amesbury Archer and the Boscombe Bowmen: Bell Beaker burials at Boscombe Down, Amesbury, Wiltshire* (Wessex Archaeology Report 27. Salisbury, 2011).

9   Jackson, Robin & Miller, Darren, et al, *Wellington Quarry, Herefordshire (1986-96): Investigations of a Landscape in the Lower Lugg Valley* (Oxbow Books, Oxford and Oakville, 2011), 58–63; Ray, Keith, *The Archaeology of Herefordshire . . .* , 74.

10   Cunliffe, Barry, *Britain Begins . . .* 206.

11   Yates, David Thomas, *Land, Power and Prestige . . .*

12   Dorling, Peter, Ray, Keith & White, Paul, 'Herefordshire: From the Middle Bronze Age to the Later Iron Age' . . . in Hurst, Derek (ed.), *Westward on the High-Hilled Plains . . .* , 70–84.

13   Albarella, Umberto, 'The end of the Sheep Age: people and animals in the late Iron Age', in Haselgrove, Colin & Moore, Tom (eds), *The Later Iron Age in Britain and Beyond* (Oxbow, Oxford, 2007), 389–402.

14   Ratkai, Stephanie, in Jackson, Robin, et al, 'Interim Report on Salvage Recording of a Neolithic/ Beaker and Bronze Age Settlement and Landscape at Huntsmans Quarry, Kemerton 1994–6', *Transactions of the Worcestershire Archaeological Society* 16 (1998), 57–68.

15   Serjeantson, Dale, 'Intensification of Animal Husbandry in the Late Bronze Age? The Contribution of Sheep and Pigs', in Haselgrove, Colin & Pope, Rachel (eds), *The Earlier Iron Age in Britain and the Near Continent* (Oxbow Books, Oxford, 2007), 80–93.

16   Gibson, Alex, 'The Neolithic pottery', and Berstan, Robert & Evershed, Richard P., 'Organic residue analysis', in Jackson, Robin & Miller, Darren (eds), *Wellington Quarry, Herefordshire (1986-96) . . .* , 65–72 and 72–78.

17 Whitehouse, Ruth & David, 'The Fauna', in Stanford, S.C., *Croft Ambrey: Excavations carried out for the Woolhope Naturalists' Field Club (Herefordshire), 1960–1966* (Adams and Sons, for the Author, 1974), 215–220.

18 Cunliffe, Barry, *Iron Age Communities in Britain. An Account of England, Scotland and Wales from the Seventh Century BC until the Roman Conquest* (Routledge, London and New York, 2005), 407–445.

19 Johnston, Robert, 'Later Prehistoric Landscapes and Inhabitation', in Pollard, Joshua (ed.), *Prehistoric Britain . . .* , 268–287; Cunliffe, Barry, *Iron Age Communities . . .* , 407–445.

20 Field, David, *The Development of an Agricultural Countryside . . .*; Yates, David Thomas, *Land, Power and Prestige . . .*

21 Cunliffe, Barry, *Iron Age Communities . . .* , 407–445.

22 Cunliffe, Barry, *The Extraordinary Voyage of Pytheas the Greek* (Allen Lane: The Penguin Press, 2001), 108–111.

23 Dineley, Merryn & Graham, 'Neolithic Ale: Barley as a source of malt sugars for fermentation', in Fairbairn, Andrew S. (ed.), *Plants in Neolithic Britain and Beyond* (Oxbow Books, Oxford, 2000), 138–153; Dineley, Merryn, 'The Use of Spent Grain as Cattle Feed in the Neolithic', in Serjeantson, Dale & Field, David (eds.), *Animals in the Neolithic of Britain and Europe* (Oxbow Books, Oxford, 2006), 56–62.

24 Dorling, Peter, Ray, Keith & White, Paul, 'Herefordshire: From the Middle Bronze Age to the Later Iron Age', in Hurst, Derek (ed.), *Westward on the High-Hilled Plains . . .* , 70–84.

25 Stanford, S.C., *Croft Ambrey . . .*

26 Wright, Edward, *The Ferriby Boats: Seacraft of the Bronze Age* (Routledge, 1991); McGrail, Sean, 'North-west European Seagoing Boats before AD 400', in Clark, Peter (ed.), *The Dover Bronze Age Boat in Context. Society and Water Transport in Prehistoric Europe* (Oxbow Books, Oxford, 2004), 51–66.

FIVE

1 More come from professional digs, but the Portable Antiquities Database gives an approximate comparison between counties, reducing bias from regional differences in funding: https//finds.org.uk/database December 2020.

2 Gloucester (Glevum) was one of five cities that were at some point British *coloniae* for army veterans and associated civilians.

3 Mattingley, David, *An Imperial Possession: Britain in the Roman Empire, 54 BC–AD 409* (Penguin Books, London, 2007), chapters 5 & 16.

4 Ibid. 42.

5 Some are very large; reconstruction experiments show they were better suited to malting than drying grain: Russell, Miles & Laycock, Stuart, *Unroman Britain: Exposing the Great Myth of Britannia* (History Press, Stroud, 2010), 129.

6 Mattingley, David, *An Imperial Possession . . .* 220.

7 Wilmott, Tony and Rahtz, Sebastian P.Q., 'An Iron Age and Roman Settlement Outside Kenchester, (Magnis), Herefordshire Excavations 1977–1979', *Transactions of the Woolhope Naturalists' Field Club* 45 (1985), 31–185 esp. 62–74; University of York Rural Economy of Britain Project, https://archaeologydataservice.ac.uk/archives/view/romangl.

8 Mattingley, David, *An Imperial Possession . . .* 353 ff.

9 Ray, Keith, *The Archaeology of Herefordshire: An Exploration* (Logaston Press, Herefordshire, 2015), 186.

10 Ray, Keith, 'Herefordshire in Roman Britain', in White, Roger & Hodder, Mike (eds), *Clash of Cultures? The Romano-British period in the West Midlands* (Oxbow Books, Oxford and Philadelphia, 2018), 83–114; Wilmott, A.R., 'Kenchester (Magnis): A Reconsideration', *Transactions of the Woolhope Naturalists' Field Club* 43 (1980), 116–133.

11 Wilmott, Tony, & Rahtz, Sebastian P.Q., 'An Iron Age and Roman Settlement . . .' 44–53.

12 Ray, Keith, 'Herefordshire in Roman Britain' . . .

13 Rippon, Stephen, Smart, Chris & Pears, Ben, *The Fields of Britannia: Continuity and Change in the Late Roman and Early Medieval Landscape* (Oxford, Oxford University Press, 2015), 62; White, Paul, *The Frome Valley, Herefordshire: Archaeology, Landscape Change and Conservation* (Herefordshire Archaeology, Hereford, 2011), 71–75.

14 Pedanius Dioscorides, *De Materia Medica* I, 88.

15 Ray Keith, *The Archaeology of Herefordshire* . . . 178–179.

16 For example White, Paul, *The Arrow Valley, Herefordshire: Archaeology, Landscape Change and Conservation* (Herefordshire Archaeology, Hereford, 2003), 43–47.

17 Mattingley, David, *An Imperial Possession* . . . 453–470.

18 White, K.D., *Agricultural Implements of the Roman World, volume I* (Cambridge, Cambridge University Press, 1967), 67 and 181–182.

19 Wilmott, Tony, & Rahtz, Sebastian P.Q, 'An Iron Age and Roman Settlement . . .' 129.

SIX

1 The second plague is mentioned in two early British texts: Adomnan of Iona (II. 46) in the 690s, in the Hebrides, and Bede (III. 27) in about 731, on Tyneside. Adomnan writes: 'For I visited my friend King Aldfrith [of Northumbria] while the plague was at its worst and many whole villages on all sides were stricken.'

2 The Life of St Samson was written somewhere between 610 and 820, but is based on earlier sources.

3 Munro, Dana Carleton (trans.), *The Life of St. Columban, by the monk Jonas* (Llanerch Reprints, Felinfach, 1993), chapter 47; Lack, Katherine, *The Eagle and the Dove: The Spirituality of the Celtic Saint Columbanus* (SPCK Triangle, London, 2000), 91–98.

4 Metlake, George (ed. and trans.), *The Life and Writings of St. Columban* (Llanerch Reprints, Felinfach, 1993), 72; Munro, Dana Carleton, *The Life of St. Columban* . . .

5 Jackson, Kenneth H. (ed. and trans.), *A Celtic Miscellany* (Penguin Classics, London, 1971), 280 and 284.

6 Brook, Diane, 'The Early Christian Church East and West of Offa's Dyke', in Edwards, Nancy & Lane, Alan (eds), *The Early Church in Wales and the West* (Oxbow Monographs, Oxford, 1992), 77–89; Finberg, H.P.R., *The Early Charters of the West Midlands* (Leicester University Press, Leicester, 1972).

7 Coplestone-Crow, Bruce, *Herefordshire Place-Names* (Logaston Press, Almeley, 2009); Finberg, H.P.R., *The Early Charters* . . .

8 Waddington, Sheila Kathryn, *The Origins of Anglo-Saxon Herefordshire: A Study in Land-Unit Antiquity* (Unpublished PhD Thesis for the University of Birmingham, 2013), especially 407, fig. 8.3.

9 Coplestone-Crow, Bruce, *Herefordshire Place-Names* . . .

10 Hooke, Della, *Worcestershire Anglo-Saxon Charter-Bounds* (Boydell Press, Woodbridge, 1990).

11 Staunton: Finberg, H.P.R., *The Early Charters* . . . , 418, 141–142; Whitelock, Dorothy, *English Historical Documents vol I* (Routledge, London and New York, second edition 1996), 557–559; Acton Beauchamp: Finberg, H.P.R., *The Early Charters* . . . 406 and 120, 139 and 143; Pratt, C.W.M., 'The Charter Bounds of Acton Beauchamp', *Transactions of the Woolhope Naturalists' Field Club* 49 (1997), 33–46.

12 Finberg, H.P.R., *The Early Charters* . . . , 122, 60, 118, 143 and 149.

13 Ibid., 253 and 270, 103 and 107.

14   Leigh Sinton: Finberg, H.P.R., *The Early Charters . . .* , 201, 87–88; Finberg, H.P.R. (ed.), *The Agrarian History of England and Wales, vol I part ii: A.D. 43–1042* (Cambridge University Press, Cambridge, 1972), 403; Bentley: Finberg, H.P.R., *The Early Charters . . .* , 77, 48 and 104; Whitelock, Dorothy, *English Historical Documents vol I . . .* , 526–527.

15   Hooke, Della, *Worcestershire Anglo-Saxon Charter-Bounds . . .* , 199–203, 208–219.

16   Williams, Ann & Martin, G.H. (eds), *Domesday Book, A Complete Translation* (Penguin Books, London, 1992), 493–4.

SEVEN

1   *Ælfric's Colloquy*, now surviving in a late eleventh-century Canterbury manuscript.

2   Douglas, David C., & Greenaway, George W. (eds), *English Historical Documents II: 1042–1189* (Eyre and Spottiswoode, London, 1968), 813–816; Harvey, P.D.A., 'Rectitudines Singularum Personarum and Gerefa', *The English Historical Review* 426 (1993), 1–22.

3   For more information see the volumes in Darby's Domesday Geography: Darby, H.C., *Domesday England* (Cambridge University Press, 1977); Darby, H.C., & Terrett, I.B. (eds), *The Domesday Geography of Midland England* (Cambridge University Press, 1954); Darby, H.C., & Campbell, Eila M.J. (eds), *The Domesday Geography of South-east England* (Cambridge University Press, 1962); Darby, H.C., *The Domesday Geography of Eastern England* (Cambridge University Press, 1952); Darby, H.C., & Weldon Finn, R. (eds), *The Domesday Geography of South-west England* (Cambridge University Press, 1967).

4   Williams, Ann & Martin, G.H. (eds), *Domesday Book: A Complete Translation* (Penguin Books, London, 2002), 515.

5   The twelfth-century Register for Battle Abbey implies that there, a league was 1½ miles, or twelve furlongs, but local usage probably varied considerably.

6   Williams, Ann & Martin, G.H., *Domesday Book . . .* 496.

7   Ibid. 1189.

8   Chibnall, M. (ed.), *Charters and Custumals of the Abbey of Holy Trinity Caen* (London, Oxford University Press, 1982); Walmsley, John, 'The Twelfth-century Surveys of Holy Trinity, Caen: A Comparative Study of Peasant Conditions', *Agricultural History* 65 (1991), 70–104.

9   Darby, H.C., & Terrett, I.B., *The Domesday Geography of Midland England . . .* 79; Darby, H.C., *Domesday England . . .* 127.

EIGHT

1   Dyer, C., *Lords and Peasants in a Changing Society. The Estates of the Bishop of Worcester 680–1540* (Cambridge University Press, 1980), 85.

2   Harding, Alan, *England in the Thirteenth Century* (Cambridge University Press, 1993), 94–95.

3   *The Red Book of the Bishop of Hereford* is now preserved at the Hereford Archives.

4   Dyer, C., *Lords and Peasants . . .* , 67.

5   Webb, John (ed.), *A Roll of the Household Expenses of Richard de Swinfield, Bishop of Hereford, during part of the years 1289 and 1290. vol 2: Abstract, Illustrations, Glossary and Index* (Camden Society, 1855, Nabu Reprints).

6   Dyer, C., *Lords and Peasants . . .* , 69.

7   Taxatio Ecclesiastica Nicholi.

8   Numbers are not strictly comparable owing to different livestock regimes, but the total English ewe flock in 2019 was about 6 million, and the total sheep population was 10 million: DEFRA Farm Statistics, December 2019.

9   Capes, William W. (ed.), *The Register of Bishop Swinfield* (Cantilupe Society, 1909), f.64a and 147a.

10   Baker, A.R.H., 'Evidence in the "Nonarum Inquisitiones" of Contracting Arable Lands in England During the Early Fourteenth Century', *The Economic History Review* 19 (1966), 518–532; Long, W.H., 'The Low Yields of Corn in Medieval England', *The Economic History Review* 32 (1979), 459–469.

11   Dyer, C., *Lords and Peasants . . .* , 111; Slavin, Philip, 'Market Failure During the Great Famine in England and Wales (1315–1317)', *Past and Present* 222 (2014), 9–49.

12   Slavin, Philip, 'The Great Bovine Pestilence and its Economic and Environmental Consequences in England and Wales, 1318–1350', *The Economic History Review* 65 (2012), 1239–1266; DEFRA, June 2010 Survey of Agriculture Report, 2000 vs 2010 www.defra.gov.uk/statistics/foodfarm/landuselivestock/junesurvey, 1; Connor, Jane, Meat and Livestock Commission, January 2002.

13   Slavin, Philip, The Great Bovine Pestilence . . . , 1249.

14   Jack, R.I., 'Wales and the Marches', in Hallam, H.E. (ed.), *The Agricultural History of England and Wales, vol II, 1042–1350* (Cambridge, Cambridge University Press), 412–497.

15   See for example the *Elegie and Eulogie* by John Troy: *Athenae Oxoniensis. An Exact History of All the Writers and Bishops who have had their education in the University of Oxford, vol 3* (London, 1817), 650–51.

16   Arkell, Tom, 'Illuminations and Distortions: Gregory King's Scheme Calculated for the Year 1688 and the Social Structure of Later Stuart England', *The Economic History Review* 59 (2006), 32–69; Fenwick, Carolyn C. (ed.), *The Poll Taxes of 1377, 1379 and 1381. Part 1: Bedfordshire-Leicestershire* (Oxford University Press, for the British Academy, 1998); Goose, Nigel & Hinde, Andrew, 'Estimating Population Sizes at Fixed Points in Time, Part II: Specific Sources', *Local Population Studies* 78 (2007), 74–88; Whiteman, Anne & Clapinson, Mary (eds), *The Compton Census of 1676: A Critical Edition* (Oxford University Press, for the British Academy, 1986).

17   Broadberry, Stephen, Campbell, Bruce M.S. & van Leeuwen, Bas, 'English Medieval Population: Reconciling Time Series and Cross-sectional Evidence', https://warwick.ac.uk/fac/soc/economics/staff/sbroadberry/wp/medievalpopulation7.pdf 24–25.

18   Field, R.K., 'Migration in the Later Middle Ages: The Case of the Hampton Lovett Villeins', *Midland History* 8 (1983), 29–48.

19   Cole, E.J. (ed. and trans.), 'The Bailiff's Accounts for the Manor of Kingsland, 1389–90', *Transactions of the Woolhope Naturalists' Field Club* 35 (1956), 168–177.

20   Ibid. 135.

21   Data from the on-line IPM project, http://www.inquisitionspostmortem.ac.uk/

DROVING AND MARKETS

1   Aikin, Arthur, *Journal of a Tour through North Wales and part of Shropshire* (1797), 153 and 168.

2   Viner, Sarah, et al, 'Cattle mobility in Prehistoric Britain: Strontium Isotope Analysis of Cattle Teeth from Durrington Walls (Wiltshire, Britain)', *Journal of Archaeological Science* 37 (2010), 2812–2820.

3   White, Roger & Hodder, Mike, 'The Archaeology of the Romano-British West Midlands: Overview and Research Priorities', in White, Roger & Hodder, Mike (eds), *Clash of Cultures? The Romano-British period in the West Midlands.* (Oxbow Books, Oxford and Philadelphia, 2018), 1–14; Bradley, Richard & Yee, Min Gan, 'Multi-isotope evidence for cattle droving at Roman Worcester', *Journal of Archaeological Science Reports* (2018).

4   Hillaby, J. *Ledbury: A Medieval Borough* (Logaston Press, 1997).

5   Thirsk, Joan (ed.), *The Agrarian History of England and Wales, volume 4: 1500–1640* (Cambridge University Press, 1967), 83.

6   Pigot's Directory for 1830, 484 ff.

7   Williams, Phyllis, *Bromyard: Minster, Manor and Town* (Bromyard and District Local History Society, 1987), 46.

8 Foot, Sarah, *Æthelstan: The First King of England*, (Yale University Press, 2011), 137; Pratt, David, 'Written Law and the Communication of Authority', in Rollason, David, Leyser, Conrad & Williams, Hannah (eds), *England and the Continent in the Tenth Century: Studies in Honour of Wilhelm Levison (1876-1947)*, (Brepols, Turnhout, Belgium, 2010), 335–346.

9 Statutes of the Realm, 5 & 6 Ed VI cap 14, 21; 39 Eliz. I cap 12; 39 Chas. II cap. 7; *The Gloucester Journal*, August 4th, 1817; Colyer, Richard, 'Welsh Cattle Drovers, part 3', *National Library of Wales Journal* XIX.1 (1975), available at: www.genuki.org.uk/big/wal/Archives/NLWjournals/ CattleDrovers3

10 Bathurst, J. & Cole, E.J.L., 'Leominster Fair, 1556', *Transactions of the Woolhope Naturalists' Field Club* 42 (1976), 72–88.

11 Emsley, Clive, Hitchcock, Tim & Shoemaker, Robert, 'London History – A Population History of London', *Old Bailey Proceedings Online*, www.oldbaileyonline.org, version 7.0, 08 April 2020.

12 Dickens, Charles, *Oliver Twist* (London, 1837–39), chapter 21; the old market was closed by Acts of Parliament in the 1850s, and a new wholesale meat market was built on Caledonian Road.

13 Blackman, J., 'The cattle trade and agrarian change on the eve of the Railway Age', *The Agricultural History Review* 23 (1975), 48–62.

DRAUGHT ANIMALS

1 Creasey, John S., *The Draught Ox* (University of Reading, Institute of Agricultural History, 1974).

2 Davies, R.H.C. (ed.), *Kalendar of Abbot Samson of Bury St Edmunds* (Camden Series 3, 84), 119 and 127; Hale, W.H. (ed.), *The Domesday of St Pauls* (London, 1858), 13, 86; Trow-Smith, Robert, *A History of British Livestock Husbandry to 1700* (Routledge and Kegan Paul, London, 1957).

3 Dyer, C., *Lords and Peasants in a Changing Society. The Estates of the Bishop of Worcester 680–1540* (Cambridge University Press, 1980), 135.

4 Webb, John (ed.), *A Roll of the Household Expenses of Richard de Swinfield, Bishop of Hereford, during part of the years 1289 and 1290. vol 2: Abstract, Illustrations, Glossary and Index* (Camden Society, 1855).

5 *The Pinchbeck Register* (Rolls Series, London, 1925) I, 475; Power, Eileen, 'On the Need for a New Edition of Walter of Henley', *Transactions of the Royal Historical Society* 17 (1934), 101–116.

6 Nicholson, Helen J. (trans.), 'The Knights Templar Estates in Herefordshire: 1308–13', translated from The National Archives E358/18 roll 2, reproduced with permission.

7 Slavin, Philip, 'The Great Bovine Pestilence and its Economic and Environmental Consequences in England and Wales, 1318–1350', *The Economic History Review* 65 (2012), 1239–1266; Slavin's sample included 14 manors in Cambridgeshire, Essex, Suffolk and Hertfordshire, and 14 in the four counties surrounding Herefordshire.

8 Bathhurst, J. & Cole, E.J.L., 'Leominster Fair, 1556', *Transactions of the Woolhope Naturalists' Field Club* 42 (1976), 72–88.

9 Groves, Jill, *Piggins, Husslements and Desperate Debts: A Social History of North-east Cheshire through Wills and Probate Inventories, 1600–1760* (Northern Writers Advisory Services Publications, 1994); Peachey, Stuart, *Horses and Oxen on the Farm, 1580–1660* (Stuart Press, Bristol, 2003); Owen, Hugh (ed.), *The Diary of Bulkeley of Dronwy, Anglesey, 1630–1636* (1937); Russell, G.E. (ed.), *Robert Loder's Farm Accounts, 1610–1620* (Camden Series 3, 53), 20 ff.

10 Smith, Brian S., 'Wigmore Fairs, 1669–1710' *Transactions of the Woolhope Naturalists' Field Club* 50 (2002), 356–385.

11 Creasey, John S., *The Draught Ox . . .* ; Perkins, J.A., *The Ox, the Horse, and English Farming, 1750–1850. Working Paper in Economic History, 3/1975.* (University of New South Wales, 1975).

12 Shakesheff, Tim, *Rural Conflict, Crime and Protest: Herefordshire, 1800–1860* (Boydell, Woodbridge, 2003).

13   MacDonald, James & Sinclair, James, *History of Hereford Cattle* (Vinton and Co, London, 1909), 123.

14   Eyton, T. C., *The Herd Book of Hereford Cattle, vol. 1* (Longman Co., London, 1846), Appendix, 58.

15   Collins, E.J.T., 'The Latter-day History of the Draught Ox in England, 1770–1964' *The Agricultural History Review* 58 (2010), 191–216; Duckham, J., 'On the Farming of Herefordshire', *Journal of the Bath and West of England Agricultural Society* 13 (1865), 52–3.

IMPROVING THE LAND

1   Thirsk, J. (ed.), *The Agrarian History of England and Wales. vol V.ii, 1640–1750: Agrarian Change* (Cambridge, Cambridge University Press, 1985), Table 13.7.

2   TEMPEST database, https://www.nottingham.ac.uk/geography/extreme-weather/search/ notes from the Calverton Parish Register Book, Nottinghamshire, recorded by Charles Cavendish-Bentinck.

3   Howse, W.H., 'A Harley Miscellany', *Transactions of the Woolhope Naturalists' Field Club* 35 (1957), 299–306.

4   Chandler, John (ed.), *John Leland's Itinerary: Travels in Tudor England* (Sutton Publishing, Stroud, 1993), 222–225.

5   Tate, W.E., 'A Hand List of English Enclosure Acts and Awards. Part 15 – Herefordshire', *Transactions of the Woolhope Naturalists' Field Club* (1941), 183–194.

6   Phillips, A.D.M., 'Agricultural Land Use and the Herefordshire Tithe Surveys, circa 1840', *Transactions of the Woolhope Naturalists' Field Club* 43 (1979), 54–61; Robinson, Guy M., 'Agricultural Depression, 1870–1900', *Transactions of the Woolhope Naturalists' Field Club* 42 (1978), 259–278; The National Parish Agricultural Returns, 1866 onwards: note that these exclude hill pastures (which would double the permanent pasture figure for Radnorshire), leys and grass under orchards.

7   Steer, Francis W. (ed.), *Farm and Cottage Inventories of Mid-Essex, 1635–1749* (Essex County Council, Chelmsford, 1950).

8   Webb, John, *Memorials of the Civil War between King Charles I and the Parliament of England, as it affected Herefordshire and the Adjacent Counties* (London, Longmans 1879), volume 1. 4.

9   Chandler, John, *John Leland's Itinerary: . . .* , 223.

10   Norman, Peter, *pers.com.*; Hillaby, Joe & Caroline, *Leominster Minster, Priory and Borough, c.660–1539* (Friends of Leominster Priory, in association with Logaston Press, Almeley, 2006), 216.

11   Brian, Anthea, *The History and Natural History of Lugg Meadow* (Logaston Press, Almeley, 2002); Brian, Anthea, 'A Tenurial History of Lugg Meadow', *Transactions of the Woolhope Naturalists' Field Club* 52 (2004), 57–96.

12   Blith, Walter, *The English Improver Improved, Or, The Survey of Husbandry Surveyed, Discovering the Improuveableness of All Lands . . .* (London, 1653; reprinted to order by EEBO), 10, 17–18.

13   The Golden Valley Study Group, *The Man Who Drowned the Meadows: Rowland Vaughan, 1558–1627* (Logaston Press, Almeley, 2016), especially 36, 37 and 47.

14   Hoverd, Tim, *Whitbourne: The Archaeology of a Herefordshire Village* (Herefordshire Archaeology Report 197, 2006), 16.

15   Yarranton, Andrew, *England's Improvement by Sea and Land: To Out-do the Dutch Without Fighting . . .* (London, 1677), 156.

16   Lane, Carolina, 'The Development of Pastures and Meadows during the Sixteenth and Seventeenth Centuries.' *Agricultural History Review* 28 (1980), 18–30; Thirsk, Joan, *Alternative Agriculture: A History from the Black Death to the Present Day* (Oxford, Oxford University Press, 1997).

17   Groves, Jill, *Piggins, Husslements and Desperate Debts: A Social History of North-east Cheshire through Wills and Probate Inventories, 1600–1760* (Northern Writers Advisory Services Publications, 1994).

18   Flower-Smith, Priscilla, *The Hidden History of Ewyas Lacy in Herefordshire* (Logaston Press, Almeley, 2013), 64.

NINE

1   Blith, Walter, *The English Improver Improved, or, the Survey of Husbandry Surveyed. Discovering the Improveableness of all Lands some to be under a Double and Treble, others under a Five or Six Fould . . .* (London: Kings Head, Old Bailey, 1653, PTO by Early English Books Online).

2   Amos Jones' will, PCC 1836, piece 1867. Butcher of Hoarwithy, Hentland. www.ancestry.co.uk/interactive

3   HAS 07/54

4   HAS 07/115

5   HAS 07/105

6   Spring-sown wheat already growing in the ground, which if not noted would be a perk.

7   HAS 07/113 and 114

8   According to the *Herefordshire Book of Sufferings*, in 1693 an Almeley Quaker was forcibly deprived of hay, rye, wheat, barley and peas together worth 52s., by Abraham Godwin and his man Henry Godwin (Hereford and Mid-Wales Area Quaker Meeting).

9   The law did not require the inclusion of real estate.

10   17 January, 1771, *The General Advertiser*; family information from *David Godwin's Recollections*; source: Liz Rizzo, *pers comm.*, The Early Godwin Family in New England.

11   Found by Mrs Phyllis Williams, Dean and Chapter archives no. 1403.

12   Faraday, M.A., *Herefordshire Taxes in the Reign on Henry VIII* (Almeley, Logaston Press, 2005), 263, 288 and 355.

13   James, Duncan, *An Analysis of the Historic Fabric of Culbridge Cottage in Whitbourne, Herefordshire* (Presteigne, Insight Research, 2006).

14   This and much of the following documentary detail is in private hands, traced by Mrs Phyllis Williams, BDLHS archives AWe E78/34.

15   1802 deed in private hands; 1840 Tithe Apportionment.

16   BDLHS archives Sb A 78/4 and De A 23/12.

SHEEP

1   Lees, B.A. (ed.), *Records of the Templars in England in the Twelfth Century* (British Academy Records 9, 131, 56); Trow-Smith, Robert, *A History of British Livestock Husbandry to 1700* (Routledge and Kegan Paul, London, 1957).

2   Nicholson, Helen (ed. and trans.), from TNA E358/18, rot. 2., E199/18/4 and E199/18/5, *The Knights Templar in Herefordshire, 1308–1313: The Garway Accounts Jan–Sept 1308*, Wattpad, https://www.wattpad.com/35721413-the-knights-templar-in-Herefordshire-1308-13 .

3   Hurst, Derek, *Sheep in the Cotswolds: The Medieval Wool Trade* (Tempus, Stroud, 2005); Trow-Smith, Robert, *A History of British Livestock Husbandry . . .*

4   Poole, A.L., 'Livestock Prices in the Twelfth Century', *The English Historical Review* 55 (1940), 284–295.

5   Gras, N.S.B. & E.C., *The Economic and Social History of an English Village* (Cambridge, Mass., 1930), 70.

6   Summerson, Henry, '"Most Renowned of Merchants": The Life and Occupations of Laurence of Ludlow (d. 1294)', *Midland History* 30 (2005), 20–36.

7   Power, Eileen, 'The Wool Trade in the Fifteenth Century', in Power, Eileen, & Postan, M.M. (eds), *English Trade in the Fifteenth Century* (Routledge and Sons, London, 1933), 39–90.

8   Lloyd, T.H., *The English Wool Trade in the Middle Ages* (Cambridge University Press, 1977); Power, Eileen, *The Wool Trade in English Medieval History* (Oxford University Press, 1941).

9   Dyer, Christopher, *A Country Merchant, 1495–1520: Trading and Farming at the End of the Middle Ages* (Oxford University Press, 2012).

10   Hurst, Derek, *Sheep in the Cotswolds . . . , 201;* Lack, Katherine, *The Cockleshell Pilgrim: A Medieval Journey to Compostela* (SPCK, London, 2003), 1–10.

11   Barrow, J., 'The Canons and Citizens of Hereford c. 1160–1240', *Midland History* 24 (1999), 1–23.

12   Drayton, Michael, *Poly-Olbion* (1622), song 14 from line 235 and song 7 from line 145.

13   Larking, Lambert, & Kemble, John Mitchell (eds), *The Knights Hospitallers in England: Being the Report of Prior Philip de Thame to the Grand Master Elyan de Villanova for A.D. 1338* (Camden Society, 1857), 30.

14   HAC B33/16, 68, 78, 79.

15   Tucker, Gordon, 'Watermills of the River Salwarpe and its Tributaries: Part 2. The System outside Bromsgrove', *Wind and Watermills* 3 (1982), 2–18.

16   Barron, Caroline, 'The Fourteenth Century Poll Tax Returns for Worcester', *Midland History* 14 (1989), 1–29.

17   Hughes, Pat, 'Property and Prosperity: The Relationship of the Buildings and Fortunes of Worcester, 1500–1660', *Midland History* 17 (1992), 39–58.

18   Markham, G., *Cheap and Good Husbandry, In A Way to get Wealth* (13th edition, London, 1676), 85.

19   Flower-Smith, Priscilla, *The Hidden History of Ewyas Lacy in Herefordshire* (Logaston Press, Almeley, 2013), 57.

20   Griffith, Rhys, *pers comm*; John Maylord 1657 probate PCC; HAS M24/60a; Faraday, M.A., *Herefordshire Taxes in the Reign of Henry VIII* (Woolhope Naturalists' Field Club, Herefordshire, 2005).

21   Thirsk, Joan (ed.), *The Agrarian History of England and Wales, vol IV, 1500–1640* (Cambridge University Press, 1967).

22   Jones, E. L., 'Hereford Cattle and Ryeland Sheep: Economic Aspects of Breed Changes, 1780–1870', *Transactions of the Woolhope Naturalists' Field Club* 38 (1964), 36–48.

CIDER

1   Vindolanda Tablets Online http://vindolanda.csad.ox.ac.uk .

2   Darby, H.C., *Domesday England* (Cambridge University Press, 1977), 9 and 135–6.

3   Barber, Malcolm & Bate, Keith (eds), *The Templars, Selected Sources* (Manchester University Press, 2002), 192–98.

4   Nicholson, Helen J., 'Relations between Houses of the Order of the Temple in Britain and their Local Communities, as indicated during the Trial of the Templars, 1307–1312', in Housley, Norman (ed.), *Knighthoods of Christ: Essays on the History of the Crusades and the Knights Templar, Presented to Malcolm Barber* (Ashgate, Aldershot, 2007), 195–207.

5   Nicholson, Helen (ed. and trans.), from TNA E358/18, rot. 2., E199/18/4 and E199/18/5, *The Knights Templar in Herefordshire, 1308–1313: The Garway Accounts Jan–Sept 1308*, Wattpad, https://www.wattpad.com/35721413-the-knights-templar-in-Herefordshire-1308-13 .

6   Nicholson, Helen, 'Drink and Food', Gawain's Mum, WordPress, posted 10 February 2016, https://gawainsmum.wordpress.com/2016/02/10/drink-and-food/ .

7   Blair, John, *Early Medieval Surrey. Landholding, Church and Settlement before 1300* (Alan Sutton and Surrey Archaeological Society, 1991).

8   Cole, E..J., 'The Bailiff's Accounts for the Manor of Kingsland, 1389–90' *Transactions of the Woolhope Naturalists' Field Club* 35 (1956), 168–177.

9   Hereford Cathedral Library Ms O vii. 1; Mynors, Roger, Thomson, Rodney & Gullick, Michael, *Catalogue of the Manuscripts of Hereford Cathedral Library* (The Dean and Chapter, D.S. Brewer, 1993), 46; Firman, Rosemary, *pers com*.

10   Data from the on-line IPM project, https://www.inquisitionspostmortem.ac.uk/.

11 HAS AF72/10; Roseff, Rebecca, 2007 https://www.archivesofciderpomology.co.uk/Origins_of_
    cider.htm .

12 Hereford Diocesan Probate Inventories.

13 Morgan, F.C. (transcr. and ed.), 'The Steward's accounts of John, first Viscount Scudamore of Sligo
    (1601–1671), for the year 1632', *Transactions of the Woolhope Naturalists' Field Club* 33 (1950),
    155–184; Crowden, James, *Ciderland* (Birlinn Ltd, Edinburgh, 2008), 28–30.

14 Thirsk, J. (ed.), *The Agrarian History of England and Wales. vol V.ii, 1640–1750: Agrarian Change*
    (Cambridge University Press, Cambridge, 1985).

15 Bowyer, Peter R., *A History of Cidermaking in England* (Brighton Polytechnic, 1977).

HEREFORD CATTLE

1 Tan, Elaine S., '"The bull is half the herd": property rights and enclosures in England, 1750–1850',
   Explorations in Economic History 30 (2002), 470–489.

2 MacDonald, James & Sinclair, James, *History of Hereford Cattle, Revised Edition* (London, Vinton
   and Co, 1909).

3 Cobbett, William, *Rural Rides volume 2* (London, J.M. Dent, 1912), 124–125.

HOPS

1 Morris & Co., Arthur, Hop Merchants, *A Series of New Maps of the Hop growing Districts of
   England: Kent, Sussex, Surrey, Hampshire, Worcestershire, Herefordshire, Shropshire and
   Gloucestershire, with an alphabetical list of Parishes and Various Statistical and Descriptive
   Information* (Arthur Morris and Co., London, 1894).

2 Clarke, Peter, *European Cities and Towns 400–2000* (Oxford University Press, Oxford, 2009).

3 Burgess, A.H., *Hops: Botany, Cultivation and Utilization* (World Crop Books, Leonard Hill,
   London 1964); Adalhard of Corbie (*c.* 800); Hildegard of Bingen, *Physica* (1150–1158).

4 Thirsk, Joan (ed.), *The Agrarian History of England and Wales, vol iv, 1500–1640* (Cambridge
   University Press, Cambridge, 1967).

5 Webb, John, *Memorials of the Civil War between King Charles I and the Parliament of England as it
   Affected Herefordshire and the Adjacent Counties, volume 2* (Longmans, Green and Co., London,
   1879), 310.

6 Edlin, Herbert, *Woodland Crafts in Britain* (Country Book Club, Newton Abbot, 1974), 48–49.

7 HAS F94/II/101.

8 HAS E23/5.

9 Lance, Edward, *The Hop Farmer, or A Complete Account of Hop Culture, Embracing its History,
   Culture and Laws* (Ridgeway and Sons, London, 1838); Phillips, A.D.M., 'Agricultural Land Use
   and the Herefordshire Tithe Surveys, Circa 1840', *Transactions of the Woolhope Naturalists' Field
   Club* 43 (1979), 54–61; Thirsk, Joan, *Alternative Agriculture: A History from the Black Death to the
   Present Day* (Oxford University Press, Oxford, 1997), 96–103.

10 HAS BN86/51/1–21; Williams, Phyllis, *Bromyard: Minster, Manor and Town* (Bromyard and
    District Local History Society), 135.

11 John Walker, *pers. com.*

12 Bromyard News & Record, 31 August 1905, data extracted by the Bromyard Local History Society
    Pocketfull of Hops research team.

13 1911 census; 1939 National Register.

14 William Owen's Book of Fairs, 1765, cited in Burgess, A.H., *Hops: Botany, Cultivation and
    Utilization . . .*

INDEX OF PEOPLE

INDEX OF PLACES

GENERAL INDEX

Also from **Logaston Press** (www.logastonpress.co.uk)

The Scratch of the Hop
Hop-farming in Herefordshire, Worcestershire & Shropshire

MARSHA O'MAHONY

Tracing the story of hop-farming in Herefordshire, Worcestershire and Shropshire – through local archives, interviews and a wealth of unseen photographs, from the early days of hand-picking through mechanisation to modern varieties, farming methods and the boom in craft-brewing – this richly-illustrated book celebrates the social history, traditions, culture and magic of hops.

More than 200 colour illus • 288pp • 242 x 171 mm
2021 • ISBN 9781910839447 • PB/ flaps £15

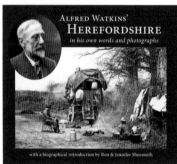

Alfred Watkins' Herefordshire
in his own words and photographs

ALFRED WATKINS, WITH AN INTRODUCTION BY
RON & JENNY SHOESMITH

Extended to contain more than 200 of Watkins' photographs of Herefordshire, this is a fascinating and atmospheric record of the county in the early twentieth century.

210 b&w photographs • 224pp • 210 x 240 mm

Revised Apr 2020 • ISBN 9781910839409 • PB/ flaps £15

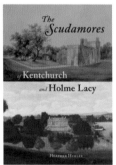

The Scudamores of Kentchurch and Holme Lacy

HEATHER HURLEY

'As a story of two families and their houses, this is a very good read and will probably never be bettered.' – **TWNFC**

Highly illustrated local history that sets the people and places of the two great Herefordshire houses within the wider context of emerging events at Kentchurch, Holme Lacy and beyond, from the eleventh century up to the middle of the twentieth century.

235 colour and b&w illus • 240pp • 242 x 171 mm
2019 • ISBN 9781910839386 • PB £12.95

The Man who Drowned the Meadows
Rowland Vaughan, 1558–1627

GOLDEN VALLEY STUDIES GROUP

Offers rare and often surprising insights into an imaginative but rather litigious family man and his understanding of the benefits of irrigating farmland and managing flood-water in the Golden Valley during the Elizabethan era.

5 colour illus • 160pp • 242 x 171 mm
2016 • ISBN 9781910839003 • PB £12.95 NOW £6